The Physics
of
Phonons

'For do we must what force will have us do'
William Shakespeare, *Richard II*, Act III, Scene III

The Physics

of

Phonons

J. A. REISSLAND

Department of Physics,
University of Essex

A Wiley–Interscience Publication

JOHN WILEY & SONS LTD.

London · New York · Sydney · Toronto

Library of Congress catalog card number
72-8614

ISBN 0 471 71585 9

Printed by J. W. Arrowsmith Ltd., Bristol

Preface

The influence of phonons is felt in almost every aspect of solid-state physics. A single phonon is not a difficult concept. Chapter 1 discusses the equations of motion of a perfect lattice and a normal mode of vibration, which we find can be treated like a particle for many purposes. In Chapter 2, models of solids are found to lead to the idea of a large number of phonons. The practical difficulties in computing the phonon energies from the basic interactions between atoms are faced and a number of approximate solutions to the problem outlined. Since a lattice dynamical calculation must ultimately produce numbers and not abstract theories, part of this chapter and its associated appendices are devoted to the details leading to a numerical result.

Of course, we soon lose interest in phonons *per se* and look wider to their influence on crystalline properties. Chapter 3 describes the occupation-number formalism of phonon states and the use of operators that represent the creation or destruction of particular phonons. It follows naturally that we need to understand the statistical behaviour of phonons, and this gives us expressions from which the thermodynamical properties of the crystal may be predicted. Here we digress again, to consider the calculation of some of these quantities.

The properties of a lattice in an equilibrium state are not given accurately by a model in which phonons are regarded as independent. The interaction between phonons modifies these equilibrium properties but, moreover, is essential to account for certain non-equilibrium properties. Chapter 5 investigates some of the consequences of this interaction. At this stage we realize that our original simple concept has progressed to something requiring quite cumbersome algebraic description. The mathematically disinclined may like to avoid Chapter 6, but it contains an essential technique. The literature on lattice dynamics—and indeed on solid-state physics as a whole—is largely couched in the Green's-function formulation. The survey given is scant and particularized to phonons, but it is hoped that it provides a link between the 'conventional' methods and the high-brow discourses that exploit the full elegance and potentialities of quantum-field theoretical techniques.

Chapter 7 begins the fanning out of interest. Exchanging depth for breadth, we discuss a number of topics in which lattice dynamics play a major role.

Likewise in Chapter 8, depth is sacrificed for the opportunity to put side-by-side the most important of the other crystal excitations with which a phonon interacts. References to fuller descriptions are given in all of these chapters to redress any shortcomings arising from the omission of detail.

Some steps in derivations in early chapters will be quite clear to some readers and not to others. Where explanations of such steps would disrupt the flow of the argument, they have been separated out to appear as 'Chapter notes' at the end of the relevant chapter and are identified thus: [a]. References to existing literature also appear at the end of each chapter and are indicated thus: [1]. Despite the inclusion of over 300 references, I am aware that I may easily have omitted important, perhaps even vital, papers. If this is so, it is unintentional and apologies are sincerely offered. In choosing a reference when the available publications are numerous, the paper originating the technique and a more recent one (if possible a review) that gives a comprehensive list of other work has been selected. In addition, papers reporting outstanding advances are included. It is this last category which is most likely to be incomplete.

Where a choice of units is demanded, S.I. units have been used, but the factors such as $4\pi\varepsilon_0$ have been kept together so that the corresponding equations in other units may be readily extracted. The various specialists within solid-state physics are likely to continue with their own conventions, since these have developed out of convenience and flow easily from the tongue: a spectroscopist will talk of radiation in units of cm^{-1}, a crystallographer will work in Å, and so on. The table of conversion factors following the list of contents relates units that are in current use.

Acknowledgements must go to the authors of the books, reviews and papers that make up the formidably large collection on lattice dynamics—to these, a humble 'thank you'. Finally, I must express very grateful thanks to my wife for patiently and accurately typing from a barely legible handwritten draft, for assembling the references and all the other tedious but essential work in the production of a manuscript.

J. A. Reissland
Lawford
May 1972

Contents

Table of energy-conversion factors

Energy may be expressed in various units and it is often necessary to change from one to another. This table shows eight units in common use and the factors relating them. The table is used by looking **along the row**, labelled by the existing units, to the column corresponding to the required units. This gives the conversion factor; for example, $x\,\mathrm{eV} \equiv x \times 1.5193 \times 10^{15}\,\mathrm{s}^{-1}$, $x\,\mathrm{kg} \equiv x \times 8.9874 \times 10^{16}\,\mathrm{J}$.

	Joules (J) E	Calories (cal) E	Electron volts (eV) Ee^{-1}	Wave number (m^{-1}) $k = E(ch)^{-1}\ddagger$
1 J	1 J	2.3892×10^{-1}	6.2418×10^{18}	5.0346×10^{24}
1 cal	4.1855	1 cal	2.6125×10^{19}	2.1072×10^{25}
1 eV	1.6021×10^{-19}	3.8277×10^{-20}	1 eV	8.0659×10^{5}
1 m^{-1}*	1.9863×10^{-25}	4.7457×10^{-26}	1.2398×10^{-6}	1 m^{-1}
1 s^{-1}†	1.0545×10^{-34}	2.5194×10^{-35}	6.5820×10^{-16}	5.3090×10^{-10}
1 a.m.u.	1.4923×10^{-10}	3.5654×10^{-11}	9.3147×10^{8}	7.5131×10^{14}
1 kg	8.9874×10^{16}	2.1473×10^{16}	5.6098×10^{35}	4.5248×10^{41}
1 K	1.3804×10^{-23}	3.2981×10^{-24}	8.6162×10^{-5}	6.9497×10^{1}

	Angular frequency (s^{-1}) $\omega = E\hbar^{-1}\S$	Atomic mass units (a.m.u.) Dimensionless‖	Mass (kg) Ec^{-2}	Temperature (K) Ek_B^{-1}
1 J	9.4832×10^{33}	6.7011×10^{9}	1.1127×10^{-17}	7.2443×10^{22}
1 cal	3.9692×10^{34}	2.8047×10^{10}	4.6571×10^{-17}	3.0321×10^{23}
1 eV	1.5193×10^{15}	1.0736×10^{-9}	1.7826×10^{-36}	1.1606×10^{4}
1 m^{-1}*	1.8836×10^{9}	1.3310×10^{-15}	2.2101×10^{-42}	1.4389×10^{-2}
1 s^{-1}†	1 s^{-1}	7.0661×10^{-25}	1.1733×10^{-51}	7.6391×10^{-12}
1 a.m.u.	1.4152×10^{24}	1 a.m.u.	1.6604×10^{-27}	1.0811×10^{13}
1 kg	8.5229×10^{50}	6.0226×10^{26}	1 kg	6.5107×10^{39}
1 K	1.3091×10^{11}	9.2498×10^{-14}	1.5359×10^{-40}	1 K

The conversion factors employed are those in the table of general constants below.
* To get conversion of 1 cm^{-1} multiply this row by 100.
† To get conversion of $v = (\omega/2\pi)$ multiply this row by 2π.
‡ To find corresponding k in cm^{-1} multiply this column by 1/100.
§ To find corresponding $v = (\omega/2\pi)$ multiply this column by $1/2\pi$.
‖ Conversion based on carbon 12 isotope = 12 a.m.u.

Values of constants used

h (Planck's constant)	$= 6.6255 \times 10^{-34}\,\mathrm{J\,s}$
$\hbar$ $(h/2\pi)$	$= 1.0545 \times 10^{-34}\,\mathrm{J\,s}$
k_B (Boltzmann's constant)	$= 1.3804 \times 10^{-23}\,\mathrm{J\,K}^{-1}$
N (Avogadro's number per mole)	$= 6.0248 \times 10^{23}\,\mathrm{mol}^{-1}$
e (electronic charge)	$= 1.6021 \times 10^{-19}\,\mathrm{C}$
c (velocity of light in vacuo)	$= 2.9979 \times 10^{8}\,\mathrm{m\,s}^{-1}$

Conversion factors (see also table of conversion of energy units)

$$1\ \text{Newton (N)} = 10^5\ \text{dyn}$$
$$1\,\mathrm{n\,m}^{-2} = 10\ \mathrm{dyn\,cm}^{-2}$$
$$1\,\mathrm{eV} = 1.6021 \times 10^{-19}\,\mathrm{J}$$

1

A Phonon

1.1 Introduction

The atoms of a solid interact with each other by various and complex forces. There are both weak and strong forces present and clearly, since a solid is stable, there are attractive and repulsive forces which act on the atoms and cancel each other at points of stable equilibrium. Sometimes it is possible to simplify analysis by the choice of a suitable function, which is significant for only a limited number of surrounding atoms, to represent the interaction. There are worked examples of this approach in Appendix A. In other solids there may be long-range forces which deny this approximation and necessitate the inclusion of so many atoms that the summations cannot be performed. In these cases alternative methods are devised, but their physical interpretation is often not very clear, their justification being in the results they produce. For the many kinds of real solid in which we may be interested, there are other complications to be included or approximated away. These may be imperfections in the correspondence of the real solid to the theory which is being used, interaction terms that are too complex to manipulate, a lack of sufficient or accurate experimental data to fit the parameters thrown up by the basic theory, critical points leading to structural changes, and so on.

It is in no way surprising that a solid should provide a variety of problems which have no rigorous solution. The close proximity of atoms that contain many electrons inevitably leads to highly complex wave functions. The atoms of each element have distinct electronic structures, and hence there are many different highly complex systems. In addition, most solids of interest contain more than one kind of atom. One could continue to make a case for never attempting to solve the problems of a solid, but, despite this, there have been some remarkably successful theories which are made all the more remarkable by their simplicity. Physics could be described as the art of approximation supported by the scientific techniques of application.

We begin by defining simple models of solids and inventing tests of their validity. The models are caricatures of real solids: the solid is represented in terms of some particular eccentricity which is relevant to the problem in hand. Then, with this simple description, the problem has been converted into a

1

representation which is manageable and we have embarked on the long process of solution and its improvement. The most important of all properties characterizing the solids that we shall consider is space periodicity of the atoms. We shall consider only crystalline solids.

1.2 Order

The atoms of a solid form themselves into a pattern that exhibits a long-range order. This is distinct from a liquid and a gas, which exhibit short-range order and no order, respectively. The 'order' criterion is seen most clearly by reference to a plot of distribution of the atoms (or molecules) against distance from some reference point.

Figure 1.1 shows that the solid continues to have a structure to its distribution function at large distances from the origin, while the liquid reaches a constant average whose value is related to its mean density. The gas reaches a constant even in very short distances from the origin. The abscissa scales are the same—but note the order of magnitude difference in the ordinates for the gas.

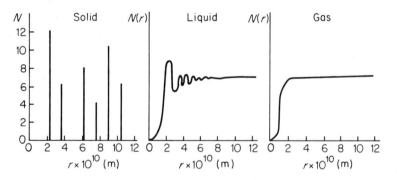

Figure 1.1   Typical number distribution for atoms of a solid, liquid and gas. N for the solid is an absolute number, $N(r)$ for the liquid and gas is a radial distribution function. The ordinate scale for the gas is several orders of magnitude smaller than that for the liquid. The magnitude of the liquid scale corresponds closely with that of the solid

The atoms of a crystalline solid occupy mean positions which are very well approximated by a mathematical lattice. The simplest model of a solid is obvious; a set of atoms located at points in space which form a perfect lattice. Thus we have the basic model. The actual space-group properties of the lattice formed are dependent on the type of atoms making up the solid. Early crystallographic work[1] employed X-ray photography. Structures were classified by interpreting diffraction patterns formed by X-ray beams which had passed through, or been reflected from, the crystal. We shall not discuss crystallography to any extent, but we shall return later to the subject in another connection.

1.3   Atomic motion

The atoms of a solid do not remain stationary but each atom moves in a region of space centred on its lattice point. The atoms are localized in a volume which is unique for each atom at low temperatures, no atom overlapping into the volume occupied by another. (In a quantum-mechanical description, an atom would be represented by a wave function which was finite over a considerable volume. On this simple model, we are considering the atom to be a mathematical point.) The atoms are constrained to remain localized by the strong forces that act on the atom when it is not at its lattice point. The forces are provided by the interaction of the atom with all the other atoms. The lattice points are positions of equilibrium for the atom experiencing these forces—points at which the repulsive and attractive forces cancel. Whenever an atom is displaced, the forces no longer cancel and they act to reduce the displacement. In principle, a given atom has a potential energy of interaction with every other atom in the solid. In practice, beyond a certain separation the interaction energy becomes negligible, and so only atoms within a reasonable distance of the atom under consideration need to be included in the summation of all the interaction energies. However, there is no general rule to say how many of the surrounding atoms must be included to achieve a specified accuracy. The specific form of the interatomic-force law and, in particular, the rate at which it falls off with distance, determines the number of neighbours to be included. Each case must be considered according to its own detail.

Any energy absorbed by our system becomes kinetic energy of the atoms, hence the qualification in the previous paragraph 'at low temperatures'. The greater the kinetic energy of an atom, the further it can move against the forces acting on it. Eventually it attains enough energy to threaten the ordering of the crystal. However, it is for reasons other than a breakdown of ordering that we shall require the atoms to be localized within a small volume. These reasons will become apparent as will the meaning of 'low temperature'. For the moment it is sufficient to understand 'low' to mean at temperatures such that the kinetic energy per atom causes a maximum displacement of an atom from equilibrium that is small compared with the nearest-neighbour separation. It will be clear that the absolute magnitude of the temperature corresponding to a given maximum displacement will depend on the potential-energy function, which equally clearly depends on the particular atoms involved. During the early parts of this book we shall develop enough ideas to enable us to specify temperature ranges of validity of any approximations that may be necessary. We shall defer discussion on the distribution of kinetic energy among the atoms present.

1.4   Mechanics of atomic motions

At this stage we do not wish the discussion to be limited to any specific model, and we shall assume merely that the interactions can be expressed by means of a function $\phi_{ll'}(\mathbf{r})$ where l and l' label the two atoms and $\mathbf{r}$ is their separation. Thus we assume only two-body interaction energies.[a] Finally let us assume that $\phi_{ll'}(\mathbf{r}) = \phi_{ll'}(|\mathbf{r}|)$, i.e. that the energy of interaction does not depend on the orientation of the line joining the two atoms. Forces that satisfy this requirement are called 'central forces'. Non-central forces arise when, for example, interactions between asymmetric molecules or between groups of atoms with an asymmetric configuration are involved.

For example, in Figure 1.2 there is a lattice of diatomic molecules. The interaction between molecule 1 and molecule 2 would be expected to differ

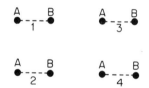

Figure 1.2   Part of a square lattice with asymmetric configuration of atoms at lattice points

from that between molecule 1 and molecule 3, even though they are the same distance apart. The interaction between molecule 1 and molecule 4 would be different again and we would expect an angular dependence as well as a separation dependence. This is a fairly extreme example, but clearly any asymmetry could give rise to an angular dependence of the two-body interaction energy.

Let us now consider the motion of an atom in more detail. It moves in a field of force due to surrounding atoms. The resultant field is the summed effect of two-body forces which have the form shown in Figure 1.3.

If we denote the displacement of the lth atom from the equilibrium position as $\mathbf{u}^l$ and the α component of this as u_α^l (where α is x, y or z in Cartesian coordinates), we can expand the potential energy of the atom in a Taylor series in powers of u_α^l:

$$\Phi = \Phi_0 + \sum_{\substack{l \\ \alpha}} \phi_\alpha^l u_\alpha^l + \tfrac{1}{2} \sum_{\substack{l,l' \\ \alpha\beta}} \phi_{\alpha\beta}^{ll'} u_\alpha^l u_\beta^{l'} + O(u^3). \tag{1.1}$$

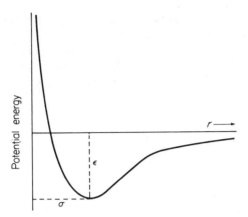

Figure 1.3 The potential energy of inter-action of two atoms; the minimum represents a bound-state equilibrium between the long-range attraction and the short-range re-pulsion (see Chapter 2 and Appendix A for examples)

It should be apparent now why we required the displacements to be small. The neglect of cubic and higher terms has significant consequences, and in later chapters we shall have to reintroduce them. The coefficients ϕ_α^l and $\phi_{\alpha\beta}^{ll'}$ are the derivatives

$$\left(\frac{\partial\phi}{\partial u_\alpha^l}\right)_{u_\alpha^l=0} \quad \text{and} \quad \left(\frac{\partial^2\phi}{\partial u_\alpha^l\,\partial u_\beta^{l'}}\right)_{u_\alpha^l=u_\beta^{l'}=0}$$

Φ_0 is the potential energy of the crystal when $u_\alpha^l = 0$ for all l and α, i.e. the potential energy of the crystal when all the atoms are at their equilibrium positions. Let us consider the interpretation of the terms in equation (1.1). $-\phi_\alpha^l$ is the α component of the force on an atom l in its equilibrium position when all $u_\alpha^l = 0$. Now, since we are considering a model in which atoms are situated at a lattice of points, we can say more about this term. Each lattice point is equivalent. By this we mean that an observer at any lattice point cannot distinguish that lattice point from any other lattice point.[b] Thus the forces acting on each atom must be the same, and we may write $\phi_\alpha^l = \phi_\alpha^0$, where zero labels a particular site. By symmetry, there are as many positive values of u_α^l as negative values (i.e. the average of u_α^l is zero), and the first-order term in equation (1.1) vanishes. We can go further than this; since the force on each particle must be zero when all displacements are zero, $\phi_\alpha^l = \phi_\alpha^0 = 0$. Thus each term of the sum vanishes when the crystal is in equilibrium. The second derivative is the force on one atom due to the displacement of another. The periodicity of the lattice introduces various relations between these second-order force constants. The most significant of these at this stage is that $\phi_{\alpha\beta}^{ll'}$ depends only on the relative positions of the atoms. Since any lattice vector could be added to both $\mathbf{r}^l$ and $\mathbf{r}^{l'}$ without changing $\phi_{\alpha\beta}^{ll'}$, we may write $\phi_{\alpha\beta}^{ll'} = \phi_{\alpha\beta}^{(l-l')} \equiv \phi_{\alpha\beta}^{l}$, where we have written $(l - l') \rightarrow l$, since the difference between two lattice vectors must be a lattice vector itself. Thus we have an expression for the potential energy of a crystal in terms of the displacement of its atoms from equilibrium and the forces of interaction experienced by the atoms.

The kinetic energy of the crystal is the sum of the kinetic energy of each of the unit cells:

$$\text{Kinetic energy} = \sum_{\substack{l \\ \alpha}} \tfrac{1}{2} m^l \dot{u}_\alpha^{l2}. \tag{1.2}$$

It is convenient to apply the Einstein summation convention where all repeated labels in a product imply a summation, e.g.

$$A_{\alpha\beta} B_{\beta\gamma} \equiv \sum_\beta A_{\alpha\beta} B_{\beta\gamma}.$$

Thus the Hamiltonian for our simple model becomes

$$H = \tfrac{1}{2} \phi_{\alpha\beta}^{ll'} u_\alpha^l u_\beta^{l'} + \tfrac{1}{2} m^l \dot{u}_\alpha^l \dot{u}_\alpha^l \tag{1.3}$$

where Φ_0 has been dropped since it only changes the zero of the energy scale.

1.5 Normal modes of vibration

Now we have a Hamiltonian, we are in a position to solve the equations of motion of our set of atoms. However, let us first take a close look at the form of equation (1.3). The kinetic-energy term is simple; it is the sum of energies associated with the motion of each particle. Each term in the sum involves only one point in space. The potential-energy part is not like this, since it involves displacements at two separated points in the crystal. Thus the summation involves many cross terms coupling different points in space. It would effect a substantial simplification if these cross terms could be removed by finding a coordinate system in which they were zero. Making a coordinate transformation to uncouple equations is a standard procedure, and if a system exists in which there are no cross terms, they are called 'normal coordinates'.

We wish to find a set of coordinates to replace the u_α^l. We require that the energy can be expressed in terms of these new coordinates without the cross terms that appear in equation (1.3). Applying the criterion of simplicity, we choose first to try a linear transformation. Suppose the normal coordinates are $q(\mathbf{k}, j)$ (we have to label u_α^l in terms of a vector $\mathbf{r}^l$ and a component α, thus we expect a vector and a label will be required to specify the various normal coordinates), so we write

$$u_\alpha^l = \xi(l\alpha; \mathbf{k}j)q(\mathbf{k}j) \qquad (1.4)$$

where ξ are the transformation coefficients and the Einstein summation convention is still in force. Now we must find a set of coefficients ξ that fulfil the requirements of the transformation. To eliminate the coupled terms when equation (1.4) is substituted into equation (1.3), we must impose restrictions on the form of the ξ

$$\xi^*(l\alpha; \mathbf{k}j)\xi(l'\alpha'; \mathbf{k}j) = K\delta_{ll'}\delta_{\alpha\alpha'} \qquad (1.5a)$$

and

$$\xi^*(l\alpha; \mathbf{k}j)\xi(l\alpha; \mathbf{k}'j') = K\delta_{\mathbf{k}\mathbf{k}'}\delta_{jj'}. \qquad (1.5b)$$

The δ are the usual Kronecker form. It is easy to verify that if the coefficients are defined to satisfy equations (1.5), equation (1.4) performs the required transformation of equation (1.3). We also define a momentum conjugate to q by the relation

$$\dot{u}_\alpha^l = \xi(l\alpha; \mathbf{k}j)p(\mathbf{k}j). \qquad (1.6)$$

Using equations (1.4) and (1.6) to transform the Hamiltonian [equation (1.3)], we obtain an expression for the energy of our solid that does not contain awkward terms coupling different points in space:

$$H = \tfrac{1}{2} \sum_{\mathbf{k}j} [mK^2|p(\mathbf{k}j)|^2 + |q(\mathbf{k}j)|^2\omega^2(\mathbf{k}j)]$$

where we have introduced

$$\omega^2(\mathbf{k}j) = \sum_{\substack{ll'\\\alpha\alpha'}} \Phi_{\alpha\alpha'}^{ll'}\xi^*(l\alpha|\mathbf{k}j)\xi(l'\alpha'|\mathbf{k}'j)\delta_{\mathbf{k}',-\mathbf{k}}$$

If we define $K^2 = m^{-1}$, this becomes

$$H = \tfrac{1}{2} \sum_{\mathbf{k}j} [|p(\mathbf{k}j)|^2 + \omega^2(\mathbf{k}j)|q(\mathbf{k}j)|^2] \qquad (1.7)$$

where the $\omega(\mathbf{k}j)$ are quantities that are determined by the details of the interatomic interactions. We can arrive at this result most easily by noting that u_α^l and $\dot{u}_\alpha^l$ are real quantities, therefore $u_\alpha^l u_\alpha^l \equiv (u_\alpha^l)^* u_\alpha^l$ and similarly for $\dot{u}_\alpha^l$. The normal coordinates and momenta $q(\mathbf{k}j)$ and $p(\mathbf{k}j)$ are complex. We can define real operators that describe the same system, but this is deferred until Chapter 3. The physical significance of $\omega(\mathbf{k}j)$ will be clear shortly. Meanwhile, let us look at equation (1.7). Unlike equation (1.3), equation (1.7) is a summation over an argument evaluated at one point in space. It looks like the total energy for any set of non-interacting entities. The argument of the summation is a 'phonon'. The total expression is the sum of phonon energies, each characterized by a $\mathbf{k}$ and a j. So we see that our first encounter with the term 'phonon' shows it to be a localization of energy at a point defined by $\mathbf{k}, j$. We have not considered the meaning of $\mathbf{k}$ and j, and this is clearly important in an understanding of the properties of this new concept.

The relation between $\omega(\mathbf{k}j)$ and $\phi_{\alpha\beta}^{ll'}$ may be established using the Lagrange equations of motion:

$$\frac{\partial L}{\partial q_i} = \frac{d}{dt}\left(\frac{\partial L}{\partial \dot{q}_i}\right) \tag{1.8}$$

where $L = $ (kinetic energy) $-$ (potential energy). Thus we get

$$\frac{\partial L}{\partial \dot{u}_\alpha^l} = m\dot{u}_\alpha^l$$

$$\frac{\partial L}{\partial u_\alpha^l} = -\phi_{\alpha\beta}^{ll'}u_\beta^{l'}$$

$$m\ddot{u}_\alpha^l = -\phi_{\alpha\beta}^{ll'}u_\beta^{l'}. \tag{1.9}$$

If we now assume that a plane wave may travel through the lattice, it will result in displacements of neighbouring atoms differing by a phase factor which depends on the wave vector $\mathbf{k}$:

$$u_\alpha^l = u_\alpha^0\, e^{-i(\omega t - \mathbf{k}.\mathbf{r}^l)} \tag{1.10}$$

u_α^0 is an amplitude. Substitution of equation (1.10) into the equations of motion [equations (1.9)] yields

$$-m\omega^2 u_\alpha^0\, e^{-i(\omega t - \mathbf{k}.\mathbf{r}^l)} = -\phi_{\alpha\beta}^{ll'}u_\beta^0\, e^{-i(\omega t - \mathbf{k}.\mathbf{r}^l)}$$

or

$$\omega^2 u_\alpha^0 = \frac{1}{m}\phi_{\alpha\beta}^{ll'}\, e^{i\mathbf{k}.(\mathbf{r}^{l'} - \mathbf{r}^l)}u_\beta^0$$

$$= \frac{1}{m}\phi_{\alpha\beta}^l\, e^{-i\mathbf{k}.\mathbf{r}^l}u_\beta^0. \tag{1.11}$$

The last step is justified by earlier arguments. Equation (1.11) is an eigenvalue equation and may be used, together with a knowledge of the interatomic interactions, to evaluate the energies of waves in the crystal corresponding to a given wave vector $\mathbf{k}$. The coefficient of u_β^0 is called the 'dynamical matrix' and is conventionally written

$$D_{\alpha\beta} \equiv \frac{1}{m}\phi_{\alpha\beta}^l\, e^{-i\mathbf{k}.\mathbf{r}^l}. \tag{1.12}$$

Initially the dynamics of our model were described by an infinite set of coupled equations, but this has now been reduced to independent sets of soluble simultaneous equations. If we consider N atoms of an infinite lattice, we have reduced the problem to the solution of N sets of three simultaneous equations. Each of these sets may be solved to find the normal mode frequencies corresponding to a given value of the wave vector $\mathbf{k}$.

$$\omega^2 u_\alpha^0 = D_{\alpha\beta} u_\beta^0 \tag{1.13}$$

The complex motions of the atoms have been resolved into harmonic modes characterized by a wave vector $\mathbf{k}$ and for which there are three eigenvalues ω^2. We shall label these three by j and hence write $\omega(\mathbf{k}j)$. It will now be apparent that there is a correspondence between the eigenvalue equation (1.13) and the Hamiltonian for the system (1.7). The Hamiltonian is the sum of the energies of these modes, and what is there called a phonon is now recognized as the energy of a mode of vibration of the crystal. This energy is distributed throughout the crystal in real space but is localized in the space defined by $\mathbf{k}$ and j. Another correspondence also becomes obvious, namely the connection between the eigenvectors in equation (1.13) and the transformation co-efficients in the relations (1.4) and (1.6). If we write the l dependence of ξ as a phase factor so that

$$\xi(l\alpha ; \mathbf{k}j) = \frac{1}{(mN)^{1/2}} e_\alpha(\mathbf{k}j)\, e^{-i\mathbf{k}.\mathbf{r}^l} \tag{1.14}$$

(no Einstein summation in this expression) we can identify the transformation coefficients e_α with the eigenvectors of the dynamical matrix. These eigenvectors represent the polarization of the mode $\omega(\mathbf{k}j)$, i.e. they describe the orientation of the atomic vibrations corresponding to a particular mode defined by $\mathbf{k}$ and j. We shall not discuss the symmetry or functional properties of e_α until they are required, except to note that for lattices with one atom per unit cell $e_\alpha(\mathbf{k}j)$ is real (as it must be if it is to represent the 'amplitude vector' or the polarization.) These transformations are used again in Section 3.5.

1.6 A phonon

The energy in equation (1.7) has been called a phonon, and we have identified this with the energy of a normal mode of the vibrating system of atoms that forms our model of a solid. The implication that we can think of this energy as a particle, just as a photon is related to an electromagnetic wave, is already apparent. It would not be justified to propose the quantization of a sound wave purely by analogy with an electromagnetic wave. We know that although mathematically similar, physically the two wave motions are very different. We must justify quantization analytically or by its successful application. All the evidence and arguments supporting the usefulness of the concept of a phonon are distributed throughout this book, but a fair summary would seem to be that we **may** (rather than **must**) consider the vibrational energy states of a lattice as particles. In Chapter 2 we consider the values of these energies, and in Chapters 3 and 4 the effects of large numbers of non-interacting phonons are discussed.

1.7   Oscillators

Each atom (or unit cell) is vibrating about a lattice point, and the assumptions we have made in Section 1.5 are equivalent to treating the motions as harmonic oscillations. Let us consider briefly the mechanics of an oscillator. We have the Hamiltonian for a one-dimensional oscillator:

$$H = -\frac{\hbar^2}{2m}\frac{\partial^2}{\partial x^2} + \tfrac{1}{2}m\omega^2 x^2. \tag{1.15}$$

We can solve the Schrödinger equation

$$H\psi(x) = E\psi(x)$$

since it may be transformed into a standard differential equation, namely Hermite's equation. The requirement of physical reality (that all wave functions must possess an integrable square, otherwise normalization is not possible) leads to the energy levels of the oscillator being allowed to take only certain discrete values. This is 'first quantization' or quantization of a particle energy. Alternatively, we may obtain the same result by using the Heisenberg method and showing that the allowed energies differ by integer multiples of $\hbar\omega$ and that $\tfrac{1}{2}\hbar\omega$ is the lowest energy. Instead of either of these, let us find the allowed energies by a simple variational method. The trial wave function of the ground state is chosen by a knowledge of the physics of the system (a paraphrase for common sense or intuition). If we picture an oscillator, symmetry requires that the wave function (or at least its squared modulus) must be equal at positive and negative displacements of the same magnitude. Moreover, since it is localized about an equilibrium point, the wave function must go to zero at plus or minus infinity, i.e. if $\psi(x)$ is the wave function:

$$|\psi_0(x)| = |\psi_0(-x)|$$

or

$$\psi_0^*(x)\psi_0(x) = \psi_0^*(-x)\psi_0(-x)$$

since this is the probability density that the particle executing the oscillation will be found at x and $-x$, and harmonic motion is symmetric about $x = 0$.

$$\psi_0(\infty) = \psi_0(-\infty) = 0$$

since the particle is localized at $x = 0$.

Furthermore, it is not compatible with the motion to have an oscillatory function, since this would yield nodes in the probability density. We require that

$$\psi_0^*(x)\psi_0(x) > 0 \quad \text{for } |x| > 0.$$

A function that satisfies all these requirements is

$$\psi_0(x) = \alpha\, e^{-\beta x^2} \tag{1.16}$$

which has the form shown in Figure 1.4.

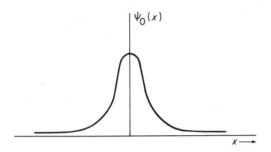

Figure 1.4   Suitable trial wave function for the
ground state of a harmonic oscillator

Using equation (1.16) as a trial wave function, we may employ the variational condition

$$\frac{\partial}{\partial\beta}\int_{-\infty}^{+\infty}\psi_0^*(x)H\psi_0(x)\,\mathrm{d}x = 0 \tag{1.17}$$

where β is regarded as the variational parameter and α is found from the normalization condition

$$\int_{-\infty}^{+\infty}\psi_0^*(x)\psi_0(x)\,\mathrm{d}x = 1 \tag{1.18}$$

to be

$$\alpha = \left(\frac{2\beta}{\pi}\right)^{1/4}.$$

From equations (1.15), (1.16) and (1.17), we have

$$\frac{\partial I_0}{\partial\beta} = 0$$

where

$$I_0 = \int_{-\infty}^{+\infty} \left(\frac{2\beta}{\pi}\right)^{1/2} e^{-2\beta x^2} \left(\beta \frac{\hbar^2}{m} - 2\beta x^2 \frac{\hbar^2}{m} + \tfrac{1}{2}m\omega^2 x^2\right) dx$$

$$= \left(\frac{2\beta}{\pi}\right)^{1/2} \left(\beta \frac{\hbar^2}{m} - \beta \frac{\hbar^2}{2m} + \frac{1}{\beta} \frac{m\omega^2}{8}\right). \tag{1.19}$$

Hence, by differentiating with respect to β

$$\frac{\hbar^2}{2m} - \frac{m\omega^2}{8\beta^2} = 0$$

and thus $\beta = m\omega/2\hbar$ and $\alpha = (m\omega/\hbar\pi)^{1/4}$. Hence the ground state energy, given by

$$E_0 = \int_{-\infty}^{+\infty} \psi_0(x) H \psi_0(x)\, dx = I_0 \tag{1.20}$$

is

$$E_0 = \tfrac{1}{2}\hbar\omega \tag{1.21a}$$

and the wave function of the ground state is

$$\psi_0(x) = \left(\frac{m\omega}{\hbar\pi}\right)^{1/4} e^{-(m\omega/2\hbar)x^2}. \tag{1.21b}$$

We can now look at the first excited state $\psi_1(x)$. The requirements are that this satisfies the same physical conditions as $\psi_0(x)$ and in addition is orthogonal to $\psi_0(x)$. Thus we have

$$\int_{-\infty}^{+\infty} \psi_0^*(x)\psi_1(x) = 0 \tag{1.22a}$$

$$\int_{-\infty}^{+\infty} \psi_1^*(x)\psi_1(x) = 1 \tag{1.22b}$$

$$E_1 = \int_{-\infty}^{+\infty} \psi_1^*(x) H \psi_1(x)\, dx. \tag{1.22c}$$

A function that satisfies these will be odd in x, e.g.

$$\psi_1(x) = \alpha x\, e^{-\beta x^2} \tag{1.23}$$

which has the form shown in Figure 1.5.

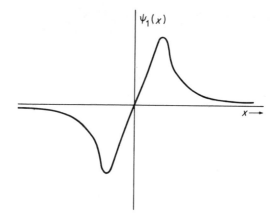

Figure 1.5 Suitable trial wave function for the first excited state of a harmonic oscillator

The condition corresponding to equation (1.19) is

$$\frac{\partial}{\partial \beta}\left(\frac{3\beta}{2}\frac{\hbar^2}{m} + \frac{3}{8}\frac{m\omega^2}{\beta}\right) = 0$$

and hence

$$\beta = \frac{m\omega}{2\hbar} \quad \text{and} \quad \alpha = \left(\frac{4}{\pi}\right)^{1/4}\left(\frac{m\omega}{\hbar}\right)^{3/4}.$$

Therefore

$$E_1 = \tfrac{3}{2}\hbar\omega \tag{1.24a}$$

$$\psi_1(x) = \left(\frac{4}{\pi}\right)^{1/4}\left(\frac{m\omega}{\hbar}\right)^{3/4} x\, e^{-(m\omega/2\hbar)x^2}. \tag{1.24b}$$

The details of the third- and higher-order wave functions may be found by continuing this process. Each successive wave function must be normalized and orthogonal to each of the lower states. Thus the number of conditions increases as higher states are derived, but, in principle, the method may be extended indefinitely. The general solution becomes

$$E_n = (n + \tfrac{1}{2})\hbar\omega \tag{1.25a}$$

$$\psi_n(x) = \left(\frac{m\omega}{\hbar\pi}\right)^{1/4}(n!\,2^n)^{-1/2}H_n\left[x\left(\frac{m\omega}{\hbar}\right)^{1/2}\right]e^{-(m\omega/2\hbar)x^2} \tag{1.25b}$$

where $H_n[x(m\omega/\hbar)^{1/2}]$ are the Hermite polynomials. For sketches of the form of some of the higher states see, for example, Merzbacher.[2]

Thus we see from equation (1.25) that the energy of a harmonic oscillator is an equally spaced set of levels, and the oscillator can take up energy only in units of $\hbar\omega$.

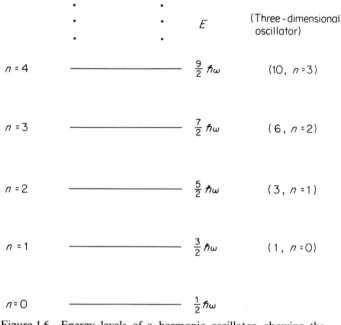

Figure 1.6   Energy levels of a harmonic oscillator, showing the quantum numbers on the left-hand side and the energy (in terms of the angular frequency) on the right-hand side. The numbers in parentheses are the degeneracies and quantum numbers for a three-dimensional oscillator

It is important to remember that at this stage we are discussing a single oscillator, and that the quantization we have derived is the quantization of a particle energy—first quantization. The lowest level $\frac{1}{2}\hbar\omega$ is called the zero point energy of the oscillator, and we shall discuss this further in Chapter 4.

We have been considering the quantum mechanics of a linear harmonic oscillator, but an atom may move in **three** dimensions. We can show that a three dimensional oscillator can be represented as three **linear** harmonic oscillators (see, for example, Dekker[3]). The energy levels of a three-dimensional oscillator are

$$E_n = (n + \tfrac{3}{2})\hbar\omega \tag{1.26a}$$

to be compared with three linear oscillators of the same angular frequency,

$$E_{n_1} + E_{n_2} + E_{n_3} = (n_1 + \tfrac{1}{2})\hbar\omega + (n_2 + \tfrac{1}{2})\hbar\omega + (n_3 + \tfrac{1}{2})\hbar\omega$$

$$= (n_1 + n_2 + n_3 + \tfrac{3}{2})\hbar\omega. \tag{1.26b}$$

We see from these equations that, if the two are to be equivalent

$$n = n_1 + n_2 + n_3$$

and hence that there is more than one way of choosing the three integers n_1, n_2 and n_3 to add up to a given integer n. This means that the levels of the three-dimensional oscillators are degenerate. For example, the first excited state $(n = 1)$ can be $n_1 = 1, n_2 = n_3 = 0$ or $n_2 = 1, n_1 = n_3 = 0$ or $n_3 = 1$, $n_1 = n_2 = 0$. Each of these three are distinguishable states of vibration, corresponding to motion in the x direction, y direction and z direction, respectively, but they have the same energy. Thus the first excited state of a three-dimensional oscillator is three-fold degenerate, and any summation over states must include this as a weighting factor. For higher excited states there are more combinations of three integers which sum to yield a particular level. The general case is easily computed, as the number of ways three positive integers may be chosen to add exactly to a given integer n. There are $n + 1$ ways of choosing the first, say r; the second may be chosen between 0 and $n - r$, thus $n - r + 1$ ways and the third is then determined. Hence the degeneracy of a level with quantum number n is

$$W = \sum_{r=0}^{n} (n - r + 1)$$

$$= \tfrac{1}{2}(n + 1)(n + 2). \tag{1.27}$$

These are shown in Figure 1.6 for the first few levels. We shall usually consider that a crystal of N atoms is $3N$ linear oscillators rather than N three-dimensional oscillators.

1.8 A solid

Let us now return to our collection of atoms. This is a system of many three-dimensional oscillators, which we shall treat as a set of normal modes or as phonons. In our discussions to this point we have avoided becoming involved with details of the lattice structure. We have assumed a set of lattice points and have not looked too closely at the space configuration of them or, for that matter, questioned exactly what is at each of the lattice points. We have slipped in the term 'unit cell' and hence given an indication that there may not be a one-to-one correspondence between lattice points and atoms. This has been adequate for the initial discussions, but the details of the structure introduce important factors which our treatment has so far omitted.

For convenience in diagrammatic representation, let us consider a one-dimensional chain of atoms (Figure 1.7).

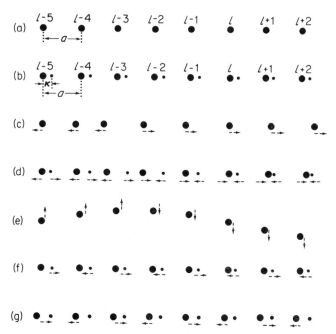

Figure 1.7 One-dimensional lattice: (a) one atom per unit
cell, atoms in their equilibrium positions; (b) two atoms per
unit cell, atoms in equilibrium positions; (c) one atom per unit
cell, atoms displaced owing to a travelling wave—the displacements are exaggerated relative to the atomic spacing
to show the phase differences more clearly—δ is the phase
difference between neighbouring atoms, in this case about
$\pi/5$ radians; (d) two atoms per unit cell, internal vibrations of
the unit cell with $\delta \approx \pi/5$; (e) one atom per unit cell, transverse
vibrations with $\delta \approx \pi/5$; (f) two atoms per unit cell, optical
mode $\delta = \pi$; (g) two atoms per unit cell, acoustic mode $\delta = \pi$

The simplest pattern is an equally spaced set of points as in Figure 1.7(a).
Our model thus associates one atom to each lattice point, and we say that
there is one atom per unit cell. The next simplest possibility is a chain where
pairs of atoms are close but separated from neighbouring pairs. This has two
atoms per unit cell and is shown in Figure 1.7(b). In one dimension, equal
spacings between all the adjacent atoms is more likely to satisfy the equilibrium
conditions, but it serves as a better illustration to assume a structure as in
Figure 1.7(b). In principle we could have three, four or many atoms per unit
cell, and this is determined by the types of atoms present in the crystal.
The structure of each unit cell is identical, and each cell is associated with a
lattice point. Thus the vectors $\mathbf{r}_l$ that have been used in this chapter should be
generalized to $\mathbf{r}_l + \mathbf{r}_\kappa$, where $\mathbf{r}_\kappa$ is the position vector of the atom labelled κ

relative to the lattice point. The effect in the analysis of the earlier sections is to include a label κ wherever there is a label l and to carry out a κ summation as well as an l summation.

The wave [equation (1.10)] in the chain of Figure 1.7(a) is interpreted as causing displacements that differ in phase by an amount δ, which is the same for all adjacent atoms, as shown in Figure 1.7(c). For one atom per unit cell we have just this one degree of freedom. [This is the case if we assume that the atoms can move in only one dimension. However, if the linear chain of Figure 1.7(a) can move in three dimensions, along the line (z axis) and in the perpendicular directions (x and y), we would have three degrees of freedom and we would expect x and y to be degenerate. We shall call these degrees of freedom **branches**.]

Now consider a chain of the type in Figure 1.7(b). In addition to the unit cells (the pairs of atoms) moving with respect to the lattice points, the pair of atoms may vibrate so that, for long waves, the centre of mass of the unit cell is undisplaced. These internal vibrations of the unit cell also have phase relationships with the neighbouring cells as in Figure 1.7(d), and a wave may be propagated by this mode of vibration. The lattice with only one atom per unit cell does not have this degree of freedom. The distinction between these two modes of vibration is most clear for small $\mathbf{k}$ (long waves). Modes involving a displacement of the centre of mass of the unit cell are called **acoustic**; those involving only an internal degree of freedom are called **optic**. Clearly, if there are more atoms in a unit cell, there will be more distinct internal vibrational modes, and hence there can be many optic modes but only one acoustic mode. (We are still in one dimension.) There are general properties which characterize these two types of modes irrespective of the details of the interatomic interactions. In the limiting case of an infinite-wavelength acoustic mode, all the unit cells move in phase and there is no restoring force, since no unit cells have changed their relative positions. Thus we expect this mode to have zero energy associated with it. On the other hand this does not hold for an optic mode where, even if the internal motions of all cells are in phase, the restoring force is provided internally and is non-zero. This is usually the highest-energy mode of vibration. If the two atoms have equal and opposite charges, the long-wave optical mode produces a set of oscillating electric dipoles which may couple to an electromagnetic wave. (In one dimension there are problems about polarization, but in three dimensions it is basically this mechanism which is involved in the interaction with radiation, since the acoustic mode does not have an oscillating dipole at $\mathbf{k}$ values compatible with those of photons.)

As we go to shorter wavelengths we reach the situation shown in Figures 1.7(f) and (g). The two modes are: Figure 1.7(f)—the heavy masses practically stationary (exactly stationary if the equilibrium spacings are all equal), while the light masses oscillate 180° out of phase with the neighbouring light atoms, this being the optic mode; Figure 1.7(g)—the heavy masses oscillating while the light masses remain almost stationary, this being the acoustic mode. The **k** value of these two modes is π/a (since $\lambda = 2a$) and they are degenerate if the two masses are equal (irrespective of the spacing). This is a special value of **k** as we shall see in Section 1.10.

Thus we have seen in one dimension that, for any given wavelength propagating through a chain of diatomic unit cells, there are two associated energies. Each value of **k** has two $\omega(\mathbf{k})$, i.e. $\omega(\mathbf{k}, j = 1)$ and $\omega(\mathbf{k}, j = 2)$ in the notation of Section 1.5. In three dimensions the number of degrees of freedom is increased by a factor of three. Thus for a lattice with two atoms per unit cell, we expect six values of $\omega(\mathbf{k}, j)$ for each **k**, three of which correspond to acoustic modes and three of which correspond to optic modes. The generalization is self apparent; for a crystal with s atoms per unit cell there will be $3s$ modes (three acoustic modes and $3(s - 1)$ optic modes).

A three-dimensional lattice is defined in terms of three basis vectors, say **a**, **b** and **c**. Any lattice point **l** is related to the origin by a vector

$$\mathbf{r}_l = l_1\mathbf{a} + l_2\mathbf{b} + l_3\mathbf{c} \qquad (1.28)$$

where l_1, l_2 and l_3 are integers. A detailed list of different basis vectors used to define crystalline lattice structures is given in References 4 and 5. At each of the lattice points given by equation (1.28) there is a unit cell, and the structure of this is defined by a set of vectors relating each atom to the lattice point for the unit cell of which it is a part.

1.9 Polarization

We shall now consider a linear chain like that in Figure 1.7(a) but which exists in three-dimensional space. Each atom can vibrate along the line of the chain and perpendicularly to it. If we are still dealing with small vibrations, a moment's thought leads us to expect that the frequency of the transverse vibration of Figure 1.7(e) will be smaller than that of the longitudinal vibration of Figure 1.7(c). The force constant to be used in equation (1.11) for the evaluation of this transverse mode is ϕ_{xx}^l, while that for the longitudinal mode is ϕ_{zz}^l. Clearly, by symmetry, $\phi_{xx}^l = \phi_{yy}^l$ and the two transverse modes are degenerate.

The direction of propagation (in this case the z axis, since the wave vector is k_z) is the same for all three modes. The polarization vector [i.e. the eigenvectors of equation (1.11)] is along the direction of propagation for the longitudinal mode, hence

$$\mathbf{e}(k_z, j = 1) = \begin{pmatrix} 0 \\ 0 \\ 1 \end{pmatrix} \qquad (1.29a)$$

for all values of k_z. (j labels the different modes for given k_z; the number of j values is the number of degrees of freedom of the unit cell). For the transverse modes as in Figure 1.7(e), the atoms move perpendicularly to the direction of propagation. These eigenvectors are not unique, since any mutually orthogonal set of three vectors satisfies the requirements and the two transverse vibrations may be in any two mutually perpendicular directions in the $z = 0$ plane. Therefore we may choose one of them to be any vector perpendicular to $\mathbf{e}(k_z, j = 1)$, say

$$\mathbf{e}(k_z, j = 2) = \frac{1}{\sqrt{2}}\begin{pmatrix} 1 \\ 1 \\ 0 \end{pmatrix} \quad \text{or} \quad \begin{pmatrix} 1 \\ 0 \\ 0 \end{pmatrix} \tag{1.29b}$$

and then the polarization vector for the other transverse vibration is specified:

$$\mathbf{e}(k_z, j = 3) = \frac{1}{\sqrt{2}}\begin{pmatrix} -1 \\ 1 \\ 0 \end{pmatrix} \quad \text{or} \quad \begin{pmatrix} 0 \\ 1 \\ 0 \end{pmatrix} \tag{1.29c}$$

Either of the two examples are equally acceptable; therefore we choose the simplest set

$$S = \begin{pmatrix} 0 & 1 & 0 \\ 0 & 0 & 1 \\ 1 & 0 & 0 \end{pmatrix}$$

and from matrix algebra we know that

$$S^{-1}D_{\alpha\beta}S = \omega^2\delta_{\alpha\beta}. \tag{1.30}$$

In this example the diagonalization is trivial, since the dynamical matrix [equation (1.12)] is

$$D_{\alpha\beta} = \begin{pmatrix} D_{xx} & 0 & 0 \\ 0 & D_{yy} & 0 \\ 0 & 0 & D_{zz} \end{pmatrix}. \tag{1.31}$$

The physical assumption implied in this is that the restoring force in the z direction acting on an atom is independent of any atomic displacements in the x or y directions, i.e. we have written

$$D_{xy} = D_{yx} = D_{xz} = D_{zx} = D_{yz} = D_{zy} = 0.$$

From equation (1.31), we see immediately that

$$\omega^2(k_z, j = 1) = D_{zz}$$

$$= \sum_l \frac{1}{m} \phi_{zz}^l \, \mathrm{e}^{-ik_z l a} \tag{1.32}$$

Equation (1.32) may be considerably simplified by pairing positive and negative values of l. Consider, for example, the nearest-neighbour interactions as in Figure 1.8.

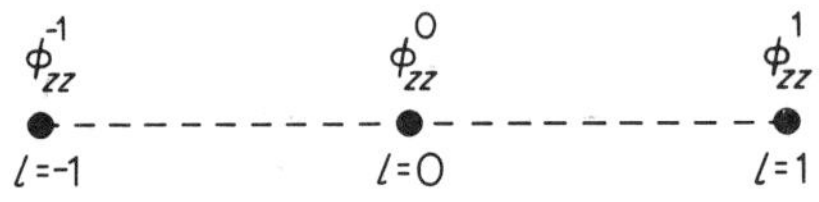

Figure 1.8   Nearest-neighbour force
constants for the longitudinal mode

We know that $\phi_{zz}^{l=-1} = \phi_{zz}^{l=1}$ from the definitions of the coefficients (since the potential energy is the sum of two-body interactions, which depend only on the separation of the atoms involved), and thus an equal displacement of the atom at $l = 1$ and the atom at $l = -1$ causes the same change in the potential energy of interaction with $l = 0$. However, the same displacement of the atom labelled $l = 0$ causes twice this change in interaction energy; therefore

$$\phi_{zz}^0 = -2\phi_{zz}^1.$$

The negative sign arises because a displacement of $l = 1$ or $l = -1$ tends to increase the magnitude of the displacement of the atom $l = 0$, whereas if the atom $l = 0$ is displaced the force experienced is such as to decrease the displacement. The same argument holds for all values of l, and we may thus write equation (1.32) as

$$\omega^2(k_z, j = 1) = \frac{2}{m} \sum_{l>0} \phi_{zz}^l (1 - \cos k_z la)$$

$$= \frac{4}{m} \sum_{l>0} \phi_{zz}^l \sin^2(k_z la/2). \tag{1.33a}$$

Similarly

$$\omega^2(k_z, j = 2) = \omega^2(k_z, j = 3)$$

$$= \frac{2}{m} \sum_{l>0} \phi_{xx}^l (1 - \cos k_z la) \tag{1.33b}$$

This simple example provides a check on the interpretation of the formalism, since we can derive this result in another, and more direct, way. For the three atoms of Figure 1.8, we may write the equation of motion

$$m\ddot{u}_{l=0} = -\alpha(u_{l=0} - u_{l=-1}) - \alpha(u_{l=0} - u_{l=1})$$

$$= -\alpha(2u_{l=0} - u_{l=-1} - u_{l=1}) \tag{1.34}$$

where α is the restoring force for the linear displacements. This has the solution

$$u_l = u_0\, e^{i(kl + \omega t)}.$$

Therefore

$$m\ddot{u}_{l=0} = -\alpha(2 - e^{-ika} - e^{ika})u_{l=0}$$

$$= -2\alpha(1 - \cos ka)u_{l=0}. \qquad (1.35)$$

Equation (1.35) has the same solution as equation (1.33a) with the identification of α and ϕ_{zz}^l.

Extending the above arguments to a three-dimensional lattice, we can have waves with finite k_x and k_y. The expressions become correspondingly more complex. Consider, for example, a cubic lattice and a wave propagating in the direction of a face diagonal, e.g. in [110] direction,[c] so that we have $\mathbf{k} = (k, k, 0)$.

The polarization vector for the longitudinal wave will be

$$\mathbf{e}(\overline{k, k, 0}, j = 1) = \frac{1}{\sqrt{2}}\begin{pmatrix} 1 \\ 1 \\ 0 \end{pmatrix}. \qquad (1.36a)$$

The transverse waves arise from atomic vibrations that are perpendicular to the [110] direction. Choosing one of these to be the z axis:

$$\mathbf{e}(\overline{k, k, 0}, j = 2) = \begin{pmatrix} 0 \\ 0 \\ 1 \end{pmatrix}. \qquad (1.36b)$$

and this fixes the other as

$$\mathbf{e}(\overline{k, k, 0}, j = 3) = \frac{1}{\sqrt{2}}\begin{pmatrix} -1 \\ 1 \\ 0 \end{pmatrix} \qquad (1.36c)$$

i.e.

$$S = \begin{pmatrix} \dfrac{1}{\sqrt{2}} & -\dfrac{1}{\sqrt{2}} & 0 \\ \dfrac{1}{\sqrt{2}} & \dfrac{1}{\sqrt{2}} & 0 \\ 0 & 0 & 1 \end{pmatrix} \quad \text{and} \quad S^{-1} = \begin{pmatrix} \dfrac{1}{\sqrt{2}} & \dfrac{1}{\sqrt{2}} & 0 \\ -\dfrac{1}{\sqrt{2}} & \dfrac{1}{\sqrt{2}} & 0 \\ 0 & 0 & 1 \end{pmatrix}.$$

The dynamical matrix for a wave in this direction is

$$D_{\alpha\beta} = \begin{pmatrix} D_{xx} & D_{xy} & 0 \\ D_{yx} & D_{yy} & 0 \\ 0 & 0 & D_{zz} \end{pmatrix}. \tag{1.37}$$

Using the eigenvalue equation (1.13) and the above expressions for the eigenvectors, we get values for the angular frequencies of the three modes, *viz*

(a) Longitudinal, $j = 1$:

$$D_{\alpha\beta} \begin{pmatrix} \frac{1}{\sqrt{2}} \\ \frac{1}{\sqrt{2}} \\ 0 \end{pmatrix} = \begin{bmatrix} \frac{1}{\sqrt{2}}(D_{xx} + D_{xy}) \\ \frac{1}{\sqrt{2}}(D_{yx} + D_{yy}) \\ 0 \end{bmatrix} = \omega^2 \begin{pmatrix} \frac{1}{\sqrt{2}} \\ \frac{1}{\sqrt{2}} \\ 0 \end{pmatrix}$$

Therefore

$$\omega^2(\overline{k, k, 0}, j = 1) = D_{xx} + D_{xy} \tag{1.38a}$$

since from the cubic symmetry $D_{xx} = D_{yy}$ and $D_{xy} = D_{yx}$.

(b) Transverse 1, $j = 2$:

$$D_{\alpha\beta} \begin{pmatrix} -\frac{1}{\sqrt{2}} \\ \frac{1}{\sqrt{2}} \\ 0 \end{pmatrix} = \begin{pmatrix} -\frac{1}{\sqrt{2}}(D_{xx} - D_{xy}) \\ \frac{1}{\sqrt{2}}(D_{yy} - D_{yx}) \\ 0 \end{pmatrix} = \omega^2 \begin{pmatrix} -\frac{1}{\sqrt{2}} \\ \frac{1}{\sqrt{2}} \\ 0 \end{pmatrix}.$$

Therefore

$$\omega^2(\overline{k, k, 0}, j = 2) = D_{xx} - D_{xy}. \tag{1.38b}$$

(c) Transverse 2, $j = 3$:
Similarly

$$\omega^2(\overline{k, k, 0}, j = 3) = D_{zz} \tag{1.38c}$$

Thus the three eigenvalues are non-degenerate for all values of k except $k = 0$. Obviously we could have found the three values of ω^2 by diagonalizing $D_{\alpha\beta}$ via

$$\{S^{-1}\}\{D_{\alpha\beta}\}\{S\} = \begin{pmatrix} (D_{xx} + D_{xy}) & 0 & 0 \\ 0 & (D_{xx} - D_{yz}) & 0 \\ 0 & 0 & D_{zz} \end{pmatrix}. \tag{1.39}$$

For a cubic crystal the directions [100], [110] and [111] (and the related ones [010], [101], etc.) are called symmetry directions, since the lattice has rotational symmetry about these lines of four-, two- and three-fold symmetry, respectively (i.e. a point symmetry O, which has, as axes of symmetry, the group $3C_4, 6C_2, 4C_3$). For these three directions the eigenvectors are independent of the magnitude of the wave vector. This follows because the waves are truly longitudinal or transverse. For the general direction this is no longer true, the polarization of the waves are not strictly longitudinal or transverse, and the polarization vectors become dependent on $|\mathbf{k}|$ as well as $\mathbf{k}$. Nevertheless, the diagonalization of the dynamical matrix still provides a method for finding $\omega^2(\mathbf{k}, j)$, since it is not necessary to find $\mathbf{e}(\mathbf{k}, j)$ explicitly. If we use the secular equation

$$|D_{\alpha\beta} - \omega^2 \delta_{\alpha\beta}| = 0 \qquad (1.40)$$

and solve for ω^2, we can then find $\mathbf{e}(\mathbf{k}, j)$ if information is required about the polarization of the wave. It is conventional to refer to the highest-frequency acoustic mode as longitudinal, even though the polarization is not exactly parallel to the direction of propagation. Some examples of these are included in Chapter 2.

1.10   Wave-vector, momentum and reciprocal space

If it is valid to treat a normal mode of vibration of a crystal as a quantum energy, and hence as a particle, we may also associate with it a momentum $\hbar\mathbf{k}$. The literature contains many discussions on the significance of the momentum associated with a phonon. The terms 'pseudomomentum', 'quasimomentum' and 'crystal momentum' are used. The last of these is ambiguous, but the use of a special term such as pseudo- or quasi- may be justified, since the phonon momentum is unlike a 'particle momentum' in that it cannot increase indefinitely. Every time it increases by $\hbar\mathbf{K}$, this amount is 'transferred' to the lattice as a whole, because the phonon can exist only in a lattice. Provided this transfer is taken into account, the term 'momentum' is safe. Of course, the sum over all momenta transferred to the lattice is zero, and the crystal does not gain momentum from its own lattice waves. As with material particles, the momentum is of no interest unless an interaction is involved—the momentum of a bus is academic unless it runs into something. This subject is discussed in detail in Chapter 5.

We have seen earlier in this chapter that the energy of a phonon is localized in a space defined by $\mathbf{k}$; thus it will be of interest to look at the properties of $\mathbf{k}$ space in some detail. Since $\mathbf{k}$ was initially introduced as a wave vector, it is clear that it has dimensions of reciprocal length. We can define a new space to be related to the real crystal lattice space by the relations between basis vectors:

$$\mathbf{a}^* = 2\pi \frac{\mathbf{b} \wedge \mathbf{c}}{\mathbf{a} \cdot (\mathbf{b} \wedge \mathbf{c})} \tag{1.41a}$$

$$\mathbf{b}^* = 2\pi \frac{\mathbf{c} \wedge \mathbf{a}}{\mathbf{a} \cdot (\mathbf{b} \wedge \mathbf{c})} \tag{1.41b}$$

$$\mathbf{c}^* = 2\pi \frac{\mathbf{a} \wedge \mathbf{b}}{\mathbf{a} \cdot (\mathbf{b} \wedge \mathbf{c})}. \tag{1.41c}$$

These new basis vectors define a new lattice, called the reciprocal lattice. The reciprocal lattice vectors, defined in this way, have the property

$$\mathbf{a}_i^* \cdot \mathbf{a}_j = 2\pi \delta_{ij}. \tag{1.42}$$

The reciprocal space is spanned by the three vectors $\mathbf{a}_1^*$, $\mathbf{a}_2^*$ and $\mathbf{a}_3^*$, and the reciprocal lattice is generated by

$$\mathbf{K} = n_1 \mathbf{a}_1^* + n_2 \mathbf{a}_2^* + n_3 \mathbf{a}_3^*. \tag{1.43}$$

$\mathbf{K}$ is a reciprocal lattice vector, and it joins two reciprocal lattice points. The scalar product of any reciprocal lattice vector with any direct lattice vector yields an integer multiple of 2π:

$$\mathbf{K} \cdot \mathbf{l} = (n_1 \mathbf{a}_1^* + n_2 \mathbf{a}_2^* + n_3 \mathbf{a}_3^*) \cdot (l_1 \mathbf{a}_1 + l_2 \mathbf{a}_2 + l_3 \mathbf{a}_3)$$

$$= 2\pi(n_1 l_1 + n_2 l_2 + n_3 l_3) = 2\pi n \tag{1.44}$$

since n_i and l_i are all integers.

Consider now the wave vector $\mathbf{k}$ in the dynamical matrix of equation (1.12). It appears only through the term

$$\mathrm{e}^{-i\mathbf{k} \cdot \mathbf{r}^l}.$$

Now $\mathbf{r}^l = l_1 \mathbf{a}_1 + l_2 \mathbf{a}_2 + l_3 \mathbf{a}_3$, and thus every time $\mathbf{k}$ increases by a reciprocal lattice vector $\mathbf{K}$, it produces no new values, i.e.

$$(\mathbf{k} + \mathbf{K}) \cdot \mathbf{r}^l = \mathbf{k} \cdot \mathbf{r}^l + 2\pi n \tag{1.45}$$

so that

$$\mathrm{e}^{-i(\mathbf{k} \cdot \mathbf{r}^l + 2\pi n)} = \mathrm{e}^{-i\mathbf{k} \cdot \mathbf{r}^l}$$

Therefore $\mathbf{k}$ and $\mathbf{k} + \mathbf{K}$ are equivalent. Hence in consideration of all values of $\mathbf{k}$ it is only necessary to include values in the range

$$\mathbf{k} = \mathbf{a}_1^*$$

$$\mathbf{k} = 0 \quad \text{to} \quad \mathbf{k} = \mathbf{a}_2^*$$

$$\mathbf{k} = \mathbf{a}_3^*$$

For reasons that will become apparent, it is convenient to take the range

$$-\mathbf{a}_1^*/2 < \mathbf{k} \leq \mathbf{a}_1^*/2 \tag{1.46a}$$

$$-\mathbf{a}_2^*/2 < \mathbf{k} \le \mathbf{a}_2^*/2 \qquad (1.46b)$$

$$-\mathbf{a}_3^*/2 < \mathbf{k} \le \mathbf{a}_3^*/2 \qquad (1.46c)$$

Thus, treating $\mathbf{k}$ as a vector in our reciprocal space, we can see that distinct values of $\mathbf{k}$ are all included in a volume surrounding one lattice point, for convenience chosen to be the origin: $n_1 = n_2 = n_3 = 0$. This volume may be constructed geometrically by joining the origin to all neighbouring reciprocal lattice points and bisecting the lines with perpendicular planes. The construction is easily drawn in two dimensions, and, as an example, consider the following steps to find the area which contains all distinct $\mathbf{k}$ values for a simple square lattice.

Stage 1: Square lattice—join nearest lattice points [Figure 1.9(a)].

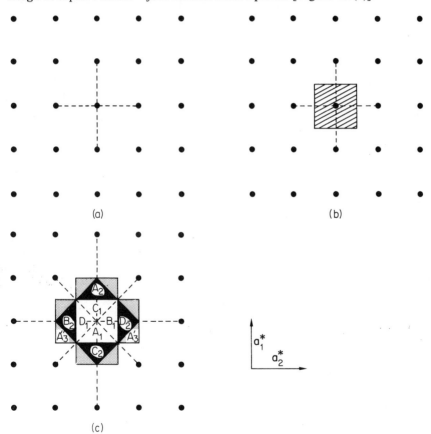

Figure 1.9 The three-dimensional construction is similar, but the bisections are planes instead of lines. The volume enclosed by the construction in (b) is called the first Brillouin zone (see, for example, Ziman[6]). If we continue the construction as in (c) we define a second and a third Brillouin zone

Stage 2: Bisect the lines [Figure 1.9(b)]. The shaded area contains all distinct **k** values (in this case in two dimensions).

Stage 3: Bisect next nearest reciprocal lattice vectors and third nearest vectors.

It is easy to see that the four separated parts of the second zone fit exactly into the first zone if they are translated by a suitable reciprocal lattice vector, e.g. area A_2 becomes superimposed on A_1 if it is translated by $\mathbf{K} = \mathbf{a}_1^*$. Similarly

$$B_2 \rightarrow B_1 \quad \text{for translation } \mathbf{K} = \mathbf{a}_2^*$$

$$C_2 \rightarrow C_1 \quad \text{for translation } \mathbf{K} = \mathbf{a}_1^*$$

$$D_2 \rightarrow D_1 \quad \text{for translation } \mathbf{K} = -\mathbf{a}_2^*$$

The same will hold for the eight parts of the third zone, but with different translation vectors; for example, A_3' and A_3'' fit into A_1.

Since the dynamical matrix is unchanged by the addition of any reciprocal lattice vector, these higher zones are exact repetitions of the first Brillouin zone, and the energy of a mode corresponding to $\mathbf{k} + \mathbf{K}$ is identical with that for $\mathbf{k}$, i.e.

$$\omega(\mathbf{k} + \mathbf{K}, j) \equiv \omega(\mathbf{k}, j) \quad \text{for all } j.$$

An instructive method of interpreting the equivalence of $\mathbf{k}$ and $\mathbf{k} + \mathbf{K}$ is the following. Consider a linear chain as in Figure 1.7(a). The first reciprocal lattice vector is $K = 2\pi/a$ and this corresponds to a mode with wavelength $\lambda = 2\pi/K = a$; i.e. all atoms move in phase the same as for $k = 0$ ($\lambda = \infty$) [Figure 1.10(a)].

Figure 1.10(b) shows the mode corresponding to $2K$, i.e. $\lambda = a/2$, and the atoms still move in phase. Since there are no atoms in the space between,

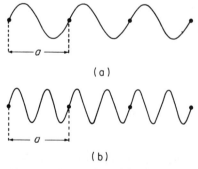

(a)

(b)

Figure 1.10   Mode with (a) wavelength $\lambda = a$ and (b) wavelength $\lambda = a/2$

the wave form is a convenient concept used only to represent the atomic motions as a wave. Hence the atoms (the only relevant points) cannot distinguish between $k = 0$ and $k = nK$, where n is an integer. The general argument follows easily by adding **k** to each of the reciprocal lattice vectors and showing that there can be no distinction between **k** and **k** + n**K**.

The reciprocal space we have defined is sometimes called **k** space and it is sometimes called momentum space. The alternative names which are used follow from the properties of **k** in the reciprocal lattice and from the relation between **k** and momentum. It is clear analytically why **k** and **k** + **K** are equivalent, but what is the physical significance of this if we are thinking in terms of a phonon with momentum $\hbar$**k**? If the momentum of the phonon is increased beyond the range we have discussed (say by 'collision' with another momentum-bearing particle), it apparently transfers the momentum in units of $\hbar$**K**. This must be transferred to the lattice and is effectively a series of Bragg reflections from the atomic planes of the crystal. A phonon $\hbar$**K** is destroyed and the momentum is taken up by the mode of the crystal for which **k** = 0 and **k** = **K** is equivalent to **k** = 0. This is the infinite-wavelength acoustic mode in which all the atoms move in phase—i.e. a crystal translation. Thus we retain conservation of momentum. Events involving phonons with values of **k** that fall within the first zone are called 'normal processes'; those involving a **k** which falls outside the zone and hence are brought back inside by subtracting a reciprocal lattice vector, are called 'umklapp processes'. The same effect is experienced by electrons, and the same terminology is used. We shall discuss this further in Chapter 2 when more general properties of periodic structures arise.

1.11 Summary

We have seen that the concept of a **phonon** arises from the properties of an **ordered** system of atoms characterizing that state of matter called **'solid'**. The long-range order has been described in terms of a lattice of points, and our model associates an atom or a group of atoms with each lattice point. The geometrical configuration can be established by, for example, X-ray diffraction. This atom or group of atoms, called a **unit cell**, executes three-dimensional **harmonic oscillations** about the lattice point. In addition, the unit cell has a number of **internal degrees of freedom** that may also be excited into vibrational states.

The atomic motions are coupled by cross terms in the **harmonic** Hamiltonian, but these may be resolved by a transformation to a set of **normal coordinates**. This procedure reduces the complex coupled equations to a set of **independent normal modes**. The energy of these modes may be found from the secular equation of the **dynamical matrix** which is expressed in terms of second-order interatomic **force constants** and a phase factor which involves the **wave vector** of the plane wave. Although the energy of these modes may be expressed as a sum of particle-like energies localized in a **reciprocal space**, they are modes belonging to the whole crystal.

The quantum mechanics of the atomic vibrations, assumed to be small vibrations so that the harmonic approximation is valid, shows a quantization of the energy of each particle oscillator—**first quantization**. The quantization of the energy of a normal mode is **field quantization** or **second quantization**. In this respect a phonon is analogous to a **photon**. However there are some very significant limitations on the analogy; for example, since a phonon can only be present in matter, we cannot expect it to have the same relativistically invariant properties of the photon. Clearly we must be cautious in pursuing the analogy too far.

If we treat the lattice purely as a medium in which a plane wave may propagate, we effectively consider a continuous medium and describe the excitation in terms of field variables. This is the formalism of classical field theory, and summations over particle energies become integrations over Lagrangian or Hamiltonian density functions. The terms involving differences in displacements of neighbouring atoms due to phase differences become infinitesimals. Thus, having set up a field theory, we find the equations of motion from Hamilton's Principle (see, for example, Leech[7]). By analogy with particle quantization, we replace the field variables by operators and introduce commutation relations. The latter will be expressed in terms of Dirac delta functions rather than Kronecker delta functions (see, for example, Merzbacher[2]). The introduction of the operators quantizes the amplitudes (one of the field variables) and hence the energies of the waves that may propagate in the crystal. Thus the second quantization procedure is a way of dealing with the many particles that may be present in the volume of space in which the field extends.

Finally we have seen that the properties of reciprocal space, which is conceived for convenience and defined relative to the real crystal space, are periodic, and thus that the wave vector and the de Broglie related momentum take distinct values only in a finite range. All values outside this range have an equivalent value in the range. The equivalent points are joined by a **reciprocal lattice vector**.

Chapter notes

[a] Three-body interactions take account of the change in the interaction energy of two atoms owing to the presence of a third. This occurs, for example, by the distortion of the wave functions by the third atom. In a uniform crystal one hopes for a large cancellation of such terms, but obviously to include them would involve very complex summations when all possible triplets of atoms are considered. For a fuller discussion see the work of Jansen.[8–10]

^b This implicitly assumes an infinite crystal and, since we wish summations to be finite, strictly we are considering part of an infinite crystal. We shall see that we cannot often associate one atom with one lattice point, but more generally we talk of a *unit cell* which may contain more than one atom. However, for the present discussion we need not consider the structure of this cell and we need only think of a single mass located at the lattice point.

^c We shall follow the convention of using square brackets to denote lines (directions), i.e. [110]; round brackets to denote points, i.e. (0 0 0); curly brackets to denote planes, i.e. {111}.

References

1. Woolfsen, M. M., *X-Ray Crystallography*, Cambridge University Press, 1970.
2. Merzbacher, E., *Quantum Mechanics*, 2nd ed., Wiley, New York, 1970.
3. Dekker, A. J., *Solid State Physics*, Macmillan, London, 1960.
4. *International Tables of X-Ray Crystallography*, Vols. 1, 2 and 3, Kynock Press, Birmingham, 1952.
5. Wyckoff, R. W. G., *Crystal Structures*, Vols. 1–4, 2nd ed., Wiley-Interscience, New York, 1963.
6. Ziman, J. M., *Electrons and Phonons*, Oxford University Press, 1960.
7. Leech, J. W., *Classical Mechanics*, Methuen, London, 1958.
8. Jansen, L., *Phys. Rev.*, **125**, 1798–1804 (1962).
9. Jansen, L., *Phys. Letters*, **4**, 91–94 (1963).
10. Jansen, L., *Phil. Mag.*, **8**, 1305–1311 (1963).

2

Dispersion

2.1 Introduction

In Chapter 1 we have discussed the analysis of atomic vibrations and the idea of a normal mode of vibration of a crystal. We restricted the discussion to single modes and only in passing acknowledged that there would be a large number of such modes present simultaneously. A close inspection of the motion of an individual atom would reveal a complex dependence of displacement on time. The complex, but periodic, motion may be Fourier analysed to resolve it into the component harmonic oscillations. Thus the resolution into normal modes is the same procedure as the Fourier analysis of a periodic function, the Fourier transform taking the system into a Fourier space which we have called reciprocal, momentum or $\mathbf{k}$ space.

The energy associated with the normal mode will be dependent on its wave vector, since it is travelling in a dispersive medium. The function relating $E(\mathbf{k})$ [or $\hbar\omega(\mathbf{k})$] and $\mathbf{k}$ is called a **dispersion relation**. It is not always possible to express this relation in closed form, but more usually it must be found numerically at a set of points for different values of $\mathbf{k}$. We look first at two theories that make assumptions about the form of the dispersion relations and then at the lattice dynamical method that we have formulated in Chapter 1.

2.2 Einstein and Debye models of a solid

The classical theory of specific heat does not provide an acceptable result when applied to a solid. It has been observed that the specific heat of a solid is reduced below the classically predicted constant if the temperature of the solid is lowered. The specific heat approached zero close to absolute zero. In 1906 Einstein[1,2] published a paper which reported the first successful treatment of the specific heat of a solid. He applied the idea that Planck had proposed seven years earlier in connection with the radiation of a black body. Einstein proposed that not only did the body emit or absorb energy in quantized units, but that it existed in the oscillators in quantized units. In order to process his theory to evaluate the specific heat, he needed to know the values of the angular frequencies of the atomic oscillators. He postulated a simple model in which the thermal energy of the solid was associated with $3N$ linear oscillators all having the same frequency which we shall call ω_E. With this simplest of all frequency distributions, Einstein was able to show that quantum theory was compatible with the observed temperature dependence of the specific heat of a solid. We shall look at the results of this frequency distribution in Chapter 4, where it may be compared with other theories.

A few years later, in 1912, Debye[3] published another calculation of specific heat. He assumed that the solid was a continuum capable of carrying a number of travelling waves. Since it was a continuum, the number of modes would be infinite, but the model must represent a set of atoms. Therefore Debye normalized the number of allowed modes to $3N$ for a solid of N atoms. By looking at the solution of the wave equation for standing waves, we can find the number of modes of vibration within a given frequency range (see, for example, Dekker[4]). For a three-dimensional continuum we get:

$$Z(\omega)\,d\omega = \frac{V}{2\pi^2}\left(\frac{2}{v_t^3} + \frac{1}{v_l^3}\right)\omega^2\,d\omega \tag{2.1}$$

where V is the volume, and v_t and v_l are the velocities of the transverse and longitudinal modes, respectively. The normalizing condition gives

$$\int_0^{\omega_D} Z(\omega)\,d\omega = 3N \tag{2.2}$$

and thus we have that the maximum frequency, the Debye frequency, is

$$\omega_D^3 = 18\pi^2\frac{N}{V}\left(\frac{2}{v_t^3} + \frac{1}{v_l^3}\right)^{-1}. \tag{2.3}$$

With these relations Debye treated each mode as a quantized harmonic oscillator and integrated over all angular frequencies up to ω_D. This resulted in a calculated specific heat that was exceedingly close to the experimental curve at very low temperatures. Since we are primarily concerned with dispersion relations at present, we shall leave further discussion of this also until Chapter 4.

In the same year as Debye published his theory of specific heat, Born and von Karman[5,6] laid out the method of lattice dynamics more or less as we know it today. Since it appeared to be rather complex manipulatively, compared to the theory of Debye, and since it also required a knowledge of the way in which atoms interact, the Debye method was more appealing and became widely applied, while the Born–von Karman method was shelved. Blackman[7-12] made the first serious attempts to apply the method in 1933, again to the theory of specific heat.

2.3   Further properties arising from lattice periodicity

So that we would not be troubled by surface effects and so that all lattice points could be regarded as equivalent, we regarded our solid as a part of an infinite crystal. The mathematical method for dealing with this is to introduce 'cyclic boundary conditions'. The physical significance of these is clear in one and two dimensions. The $(N + 1)$th atom of a linear chain is identified with the first atom, so that in moving N lattice spacings along the chain we arrive back at where we started. This is effectively joining the ends of the chain to form a circle as in Figure 2.1 drawn for $N = 8$.

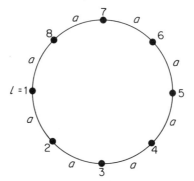

Figure 2.1   Cyclic boundary conditions for a linear chain of eight atoms

In two dimensions, a square lattice is joined first along one side forming a cylinder. The two open ends are then joined to form a torus. Thus $l_x = 1$ and $l_x = 6$ (in general $N + 1$) are equivalent, as are $l_y = 1$ and $l_y = 6$.

In three dimensions the construction cannot be conceived by extension of these diagrams, but the analytical meaning is clear. We consider cyclic boundary conditions in the direction of all three basis vectors. These boundary conditions provide numerous practical simplifications without affecting the properties of the crystal. Consider the effect of these on the number of distinct values of **k** that are allowed. Cyclic boundary conditions impose the requirement

$$e^{iN_j \mathbf{k}.\mathbf{a}_j} = 1 \quad \text{for} \quad j = 1, 2 \text{ or } 3 \tag{2.4}$$

where $N = N_1 N_2 N_3$ = number of atoms.

Now we have seen in Chapter 1 that it is convenient to think of **k** as a vector in reciprocal space, and that in this space all the distinct values of **k** are included in the first Brillouin zone. Equation (2.4) is satisfied by

$$\mathbf{k} = \frac{1}{L}\mathbf{K} = \frac{1}{L}(n_1 \mathbf{a}_1^* + n_2 \mathbf{a}_2^* + n_3 \mathbf{a}_3^*). \tag{2.5}$$

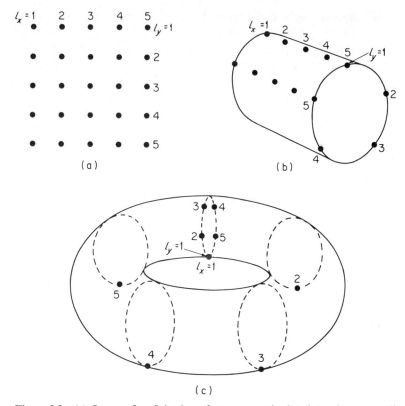

Figure 2.2 (a) Square 5×5 lattice of atoms manipulated to show a cyclic boundary condition (b) for l_y and (c) for l_x and l_y

For example, for a simple cubic lattice

$$k_x = \frac{n_1}{N_1} a_x^*$$

$$= 0, \quad \pm\frac{1}{N_1}\frac{2\pi}{a}, \quad \pm\frac{2}{N_1}\frac{2\pi}{a}, \quad \pm\frac{3}{N_1}\frac{2\pi}{a}, \quad \text{etc.} \qquad (2.6)$$

So we see that, in general, the **k** may take N values in the first Brillouin zone and the integers n_j run from $-N_j/2$ to $+N_j/2$. The number of allowed **k** values in the first Brillouin zone is equal to the number of unit cells in the crystal. The three eigenvalues of the dynamical matrix solved for N points in **k** space correspond to the $3N$ modes of vibration of the system of interacting unit cells. When the cells have more than one atom, the dynamical matrix becomes larger and the new eigenvalues correspond to the internal degrees of freedom of the unit cells which also produce crystal modes.

We commented early in Chapter 1 that the most important property characterizing a crystalline solid is the space periodicity of the sites that are the equilibrium positions of the atoms. We have considered the effect of this periodic structure on the vibrational properties of a solid and hence on the passage of a travelling wave. The effect of periodicity is extensive, and, to emphasize this, let us look at another entity travelling in the lattice—an electron. An electron in a crystalline solid will experience an electrostatic force that is dependent on the electronic structure of the atoms making up the solid, but, however complex this force becomes, it will have the same symmetry as the lattice. The electron sees a potential with the same periodicity as the lattice. The lattice points are given by the position vectors,

$$\mathbf{r}^l = l_1\mathbf{a}_1 + l_2\mathbf{a}_2 + l_3\mathbf{a}_3 \tag{2.7}$$

and if $\mathbf{r}$ is the position vector of the electron, we can write the potential seen by it as

$$V(\mathbf{r}) \equiv V(\mathbf{r} + \mathbf{r}^l). \tag{2.8}$$

Equation (2.8) expresses the symmetry requirements for the potential field in which the electron moves. Since $V(\mathbf{r})$ is a periodic function, we may write it as a Fourier series

$$V(\mathbf{r}) = \sum_{\mathbf{k}} V_{\mathbf{k}}\, e^{i\mathbf{k}\cdot\mathbf{r}} \tag{2.9}$$

which has the required periodicity if

$$\mathbf{k} = n_1\mathbf{a}_1^* + n_2\mathbf{a}_2^* + n_3\mathbf{a}_3^* \tag{2.10}$$

where

$$\mathbf{a}_i^* \cdot \mathbf{a}_j = 2\pi\delta_{ij}.$$

Equation (2.10) is identical with the reciprocal lattice vectors of Chapter 1. Now consider the effect of this potential on the motion of the electron.

The one-electron model considers a single electron in a periodic potential due to the ions at the lattice sites and a uniform background due to the other mobile electrons; the effects of electron–electron interactions are not included. If we employ this model and, for convenience, apply to a one-dimensional chain, we can obtain a solution that will highlight the points of interest.

Figure 2.3   A one-dimensional lattice showing an arbitrary periodic potential due to ions at the lattice points

The Schrödinger equation for one of these electrons is

$$\frac{\partial^2 \psi(x)}{\partial x^2} + \frac{2m}{\hbar^2}[E - V(x)]\psi(x) = 0 \tag{2.11}$$

which has a most general solution of the form

$$\psi(x) = A\alpha(x) + B\beta(x). \tag{2.12}$$

From the physics of the problem, we can invoke the periodicity and see that any linear combination of $\alpha(x + a)$ and $\beta(x + a)$ must also be a solution to equation (2.11). The basic postulates of quantum mechanics require that these are not distinct states and that they may be expressed as linear combinations of basic states. So we may write

$$\alpha(x + a) = a_1\alpha(x) + b_1\beta(x) \tag{2.13a}$$

$$\beta(x + a) = a_2\alpha(x) + b_2\beta(x) \tag{2.13b}$$

where a_i and b_i are constants.

We may also write

$$\psi(x + a) = A\alpha(x + a) + B\beta(x + a)$$
$$= (a_1 A + a_2 B)\alpha(x) + (b_1 A + b_2 B)\beta(x) \tag{2.14}$$

using equation (2.13). However, if $\psi(x + a)$ and $\psi(x)$ are to be non-distinct, they must be related by a constant independent of x, i.e.

$$\psi(x + a) = \lambda\psi(x). \tag{2.15}$$

Substituting equation (2.12) into the right-hand side of equation (2.15) and the result into equation (2.14), we may equate coefficients of $\alpha(x)$ and of $\beta(x)$ to ensure non-trivial solution for $\alpha(x)$ and $\beta(x)$. This gives us (assuming that A and B are non-zero)

$$\begin{vmatrix} a_1 - \lambda & b_1 \\ a_2 & b_2 - \lambda \end{vmatrix} = 0 \tag{2.16}$$

Thus the λ in the relation (2.15) has two solutions and, since both $\psi(x + a)$ and $\psi(x)$ will be normalized, we have

$$|\lambda^2| = 1 \tag{2.17a}$$

and hence, most generally

$$\lambda_1 = e^{ik_1 a} \tag{2.17b}$$

$$\lambda_2 = e^{ik_2 a}. \tag{2.17c}$$

Defining two functions

$$U_{k_1}(x) = e^{-ik_1 x}\psi(x) \tag{2.18a}$$

$$U_{k_2}(x) = e^{-ik_2 x}\psi(x) \tag{2.18b}$$

which clearly have the periodicity of the lattice, we see that the wave function for an electron in a periodic potential may be written

$$\psi_k(x) = e^{ikx}U_k(x). \tag{2.19}$$

Equation (2.19) is a plane wave modulated by a function with lattice periodicity—and is due to Bloch,[13] who first applied a mathematical theorem due to Floquet. (For a proof of this theorem, see, for example, Whittaker and Watson.[14]) This equation may also be interpreted as the most general solution of the Schrödinger equation [equation (2.11)] such that the probability density $\psi^*(x)\psi(x)$ for the electron is the same at equivalent points in the crystal, *viz*

$$\psi^*(x + l_1 a)\psi(x + l_1 a) = \psi^*(x)\psi(x). \tag{2.20}$$

The corresponding treatment for a three-dimensional crystal introduces no special difficulties.

We can find solutions (2.19) for all values of the energy E within defined ranges, and for each E there are two values of **k**. If we have an infinite crystal all values of E are allowed, but if we impose cyclic boundary conditions such that

$$\psi(x + Na) = \psi(x) \tag{2.21}$$

we have, from equation (2.15), that $e^{ikNa} = 1$.

Thus, using the standard solutions to the Nth root of unity

$$e^{ika} = 1^{1/N}$$

$$= e^{2\pi i(l_1/N)} \tag{2.22}$$

where l_1 is an integer, and hence

$$ika = 2\pi i(l_1/N)$$

or

$$k = \frac{2\pi}{a}\frac{l_1}{N}. \tag{2.23}$$

This is the same set of discrete values for k as we found for the phonon. The similarity arises solely from the common feature—the lattice structure.

2.4 Dispersion

In the preceding section, we made reference to the energy corresponding to a particular **k** value. In Chapter 1 we discussed the number of eigenvalues corresponding to a particular point in **k** space. Suppose now we look at a particular degree of freedom (labelled by a j value) and consider the relation between the energy and the **k** value for this branch. If we look first at the one-dimensional linear chain, we have that the dispersion relationship is given by equation (1.33a), which, for nearest-neighbour interactions only, becomes

$$\omega = 2\left(\frac{\alpha}{m}\right)^{1/2} \sin\left(\frac{ka}{2}\right) \qquad (2.24)$$

if we write $\phi_{zz}^{l=1} = \alpha$.

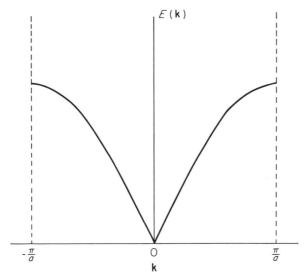

Figure 2.4 $E(\mathbf{k})$ against **k** for a linear chain of atoms with only nearest-neighbour interactions included. This is for the chain of Figure 1.7(a) vibrating as in Figure 1.7(c), i.e. for the longitudinal acoustic mode

If we now consider a linear diatomic lattice we have two modes, and the expressions for these may be found as follows. Let m_1 and m_2 be the mass of the two atoms, and let the spacing between cells be a and the spacing between atoms in the same cell be b, as in Figure 2.5.

Figure 2.5 Linear diatomic chain of atoms with only nearest-neighbour interactions

There will be two 'nearest-neighbour' force constants involved, α_1 between atoms in the same cell and α_2 between the nearest atoms in adjacent cells. The equation of motion for this system become

$$m_1\ddot{u}_1 = \text{force on A} = -\alpha_1 u_1 - \alpha_2 u_1 + \alpha_1 u_2 \cos kb + \alpha_2 u_2 \cos k(b-a) \quad (2.25a)$$

$$m_2\ddot{u}_2 = \text{force on B} = -\alpha_1 u_2 - \alpha_2 u_2 + \alpha_1 u_1 \cos kb + \alpha_2 u_1 \cos k(a-b). \quad (2.25b)$$

We have assumed displacements that differ by a phase factor corresponding to a travelling plane wave, and if we substitute this as a solution and require that the amplitudes are non-trivial, we have

$$\begin{vmatrix} \alpha_1 + \alpha_2 - m_1\omega^2 & -\alpha_1 \cos kb - \alpha_2 \cos k(b-a) \\ -\alpha_1 \cos kb - \alpha_2 \cos k(a-b) & \alpha_1 + \alpha_2 - m_2\omega^2 \end{vmatrix} = 0 \quad (2.26)$$

This has two roots, giving the energies of the two modes for a given k. Consider the special case $b = a/2$ and hence $\alpha_1 = \alpha_2 \equiv \alpha$, the solution is then

$$\omega^2(k, j = 1) = \frac{\alpha}{\mu}\left\{1 - \left[1 - \frac{4m_1 m_2}{(m_1 + m_2)^2}\sin^2\left(k\frac{a}{2}\right)\right]^{1/2}\right\} \quad (2.27a)$$

$$\omega^2(k, j = 2) = \frac{\alpha}{\mu}\left\{1 + \left[1 - \frac{4m_1 m_2}{(m_1 + m_2)^2}\sin^2\left(k\frac{a}{2}\right)\right]^{1/2}\right\} \quad (2.27b)$$

where

$$\frac{1}{\mu} \equiv \frac{1}{m_1} + \frac{1}{m_2}. \quad (2.28)$$

The solution (2.27a) is the acoustic mode, since it approaches zero if k approaches zero. The second solution is the optical mode, and this remains finite with a value of $(2\alpha/\mu)^{1/2}$ for the frequency at $k = 0$. At the zone boundaries, i.e. when $k = \pm\pi/a$, it is easy to see that

$$\omega^2\left(k = \frac{\pi}{a}, j = 2\right) \geq \omega^2\left(k = \frac{\pi}{a}, j = 1\right) \quad (2.29)$$

and that the equality holds only when $m_1 = m_2$. These two cases are shown in Figure 2.6.

The energy gap representing a region of forbidden frequencies disappears in the case of equal masses. This is still true when $b \neq a/2$. The analysis of these linear chains is closely analogous to that for an electromagnetic wave in a periodically loaded waveguide or an elastic wave in a periodically loaded sonometer wire. Simple experiments can be devised to illustrate the dispersion shown above. The model represented by Figure 2.6(b) is an equally spaced chain of identical atoms distance $a/2$ apart. If we treated it as such we would expect a dispersion curve as in Figure 2.4, but which extended

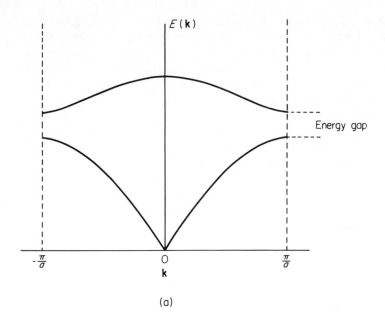

(a)

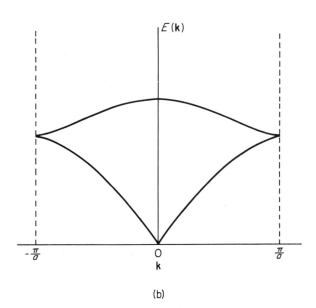

(b)

Figure 2.6 $E(\mathbf{k})$ against $\mathbf{k}$ for a diatomic linear chain in one dimension with $b = a/2$: (a) $m_1 \neq m_2$ and (b) $m_1 = m_2$. Situation (b) is the same physical system as a monatomic linear chain with spacing $a/2$

to $k = \pm 2\pi/a$. The artificial device of treating it as a diatomic chain has taken the parts of the curve which now fall outside the zone and subtracted $K_1 = 2\pi/a$ from $k > \pi/a$ and added $K_1 = 2\pi/a$ to $k < -\pi/a$. When the dispersion is drawn across several zones instead of restricting it to the first zone it is called an extended zone scheme. Dispersion curves are usually drawn in the reduced zone scheme. The apparent increase in the number of branches only occurs if a unit cell that is larger than necessary is used.

If we now look at a real crystal in three dimensions we can follow the same procedure, provided that we have some knowledge of the interatomic interactions. The cubic crystal that we discussed in Section 1.9 has three acoustic branches.

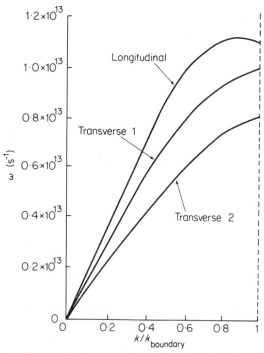

Figure 2.7   Typical dispersion relation in a face-centred cubic crystal in the [210] direction (data are for solid argon)

A cubic crystal with two atoms per unit cell has six branches. An example of this is germanium, which has a face-centred cubic lattice of unit cells, each containing two germanium atoms. The two atoms in each of the cells are separated by a vector $\left(\dfrac{a}{4} \; \dfrac{a}{4} \; \dfrac{a}{4} \right)$ as shown in Figure 2.8(a). The dispersion relations for germanium as given by Cochran[16] are shown in Figure 2.8(c) for a sample direction.

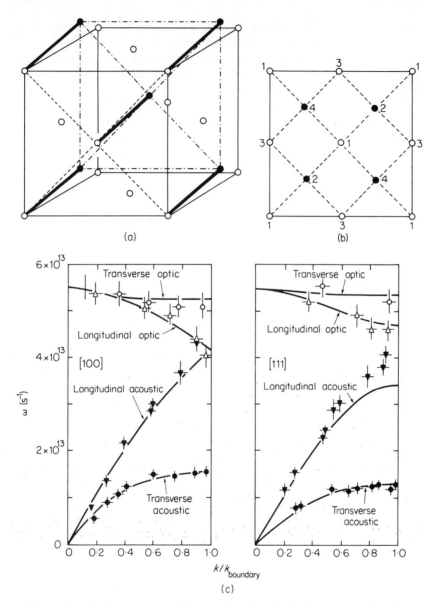

Figure 2.8   Lattice structure of germanium showing (a) interpenetrating face-centred cubic lattices displayed by a vector ($a/4$ $a/4$ $a/4$) and (b) the lattice of (a) projected on to the front face. Atoms labelled 1 are in the plane of paper; atoms 2, 3 and 4 are $a/4$, $a/2$ and $3a/4$, respectively, into the paper. Curves (c) show the dispersion relations for the [100] and [111] directions in germanium and are reproduced from Cochran, W., *Proc. Roy. Soc.*, **A253**, 260–276 (1959), by permission of the Council of The Royal Society, London

Calculations of $E(\mathbf{k})$ require assumptions about the form of the interatomic force law in order to evaluate the dynamical matrix.

This is the core problem of most lattice dynamical calculations. It is not possible to describe a single model and to vary the details to suit the crystal. In principle we could solve the quantum-mechanical problem of the interaction between any two atoms and use this result as our interatomic force law. In practice the interaction of many-electron atoms is too complex, and approximations must be made. Different approximations must be made for different classes of crystals, and this leads to apparently different forms of lattice dynamics. We shall separate discussion on the interatomic force laws for various classes of crystals from the lattice dynamical methods used to process them. The rest of this chapter is devoted to four classes of crystals into which most crystalline solids may be placed; neutral (or molecular) crystals, ionic crystals, covalent crystals and metallic crystals.

2.5 Classification of crystal types

The forces between atoms are governed by the electronic structure of the atoms involved. This is not only of importance for the vibrational properties of the crystal, but controls the electrical conductivity, the optical and magnetic properties and the mechanical strength of the crystal.

The feature common to all crystals is a periodic arrangement of unit cells and atoms within the unit cells. We have seen in Section 2.3 that the periodicity imposes conditions such that solutions (2.19) may be found within specified energy ranges. If the crystal is infinite, there are an infinite number of allowed states within each band. If the crystal has N atoms, the boundary conditions impose a quantization and there are $2N$ states. The Schrödinger equation [equation (2.11)] may be solved for some simple choice of periodic potential and the band structure calculated. The first exact solution of this type was the famous Kronig–Penny model. The potential used by them was a square well centred on each atom and solved in one dimension. The solution show that there are regions of energy that would correspond to imaginary values of k; these are therefore forbidden. The result is not dependent on the choice of potential, only on its periodicity. Figure 2.9 (dotted lines) shows a typical extended zone representation of $E(\mathbf{k})$ against $\mathbf{k}$ for an electron in a periodic structure.

It would be interesting to discuss the implications of the result shown in Figure 2.9 on the behaviour of an electron and such ideas as the effective mass, Zener oscillations, group and phase velocities, the variation of the width of the forbidden band as energy increases, etc. However we are interested in this band model as a means of a broad classification of crystals. Consider bands as in Figure 2.10.

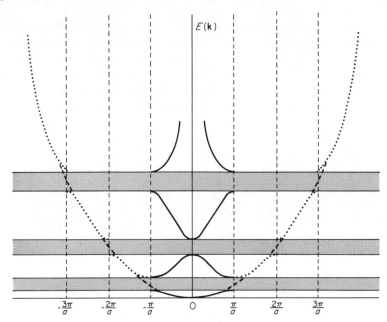

Figure 2.9 Dotted lines .... show an extended zone plot of $E(\mathbf{k})$ against $\mathbf{k}$ for an electron in a periodic structure. Full lines ――――― show the corresponding reduced zone scheme. The broken line ――――――― shows the free-electron solution. a is the distance between equivalent points on the periodic potential. The shaded regions are forbidden energy bands

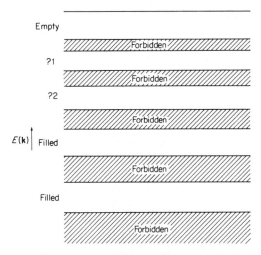

Figure 2.10 Schematic form of allowed and forbidden energy bands of an electron in a crystal

From the statistical properties of fermions, we know (see Chapter 4) that at absolute zero the lowest energy states will be filled up to an energy called the Fermi level. At other temperatures electrons close to the Fermi level will be excited above it, leaving some states just below the Fermi level empty. The lowest energy states are not disturbed. Thus if a low energy band is filled, we may assume that it will remain so and that we need only consider the higher occupied bands. A filled band cannot contribute to conduction since the electrons cannot gain ₤nergy and remain in the band (Pauli exclusion principle). An empty band cannot conduct and hence let us consider the bands in Figure 2.10 marked ?1 and ?2. All bands below ?2 are full; all bands above ?1 are empty.

There are two possibilities:

(i) ?1 is empty, ?2 is full. In this case the crystal will be non-conducting unless some electrons are excited from ?2 into ?1.
(ii) ?2 is full, ?1 is partially occupied. This will be a good conductor, since the electrons can take up kinetic energy easily.

Case (ii) corresponds to a metal. Case (i) corresponds to an insulator at absolute zero. If the forbidden band is wide, the electrons require large energies before they can make the transition into the higher band, so the crystal remains a good insulator. If, however, the width is comparable with thermal energies ($\sim k_B T$), the crystal will become more conducting as the temperature increases. Such a crystal is an intrinsic semiconductor. (Intrinsic is merely to distinguish it from semiconductors whose conductivity is controlled by the impurity content.) So we see that insulators and semiconductors differ because of quantitative differences in the energy scheme, whereas metals are quite distinct. This distinction will be raised again.

Although this classification is made with respect to the properties of electrons, the same broad divisions are reflected in the vibrational properties, primarily through the effect on the interatomic interactions.

2.6 Interatomic force law—neutral atoms

Hitherto we have avoided the issue of finding the force constants that appear in the dynamical matrix. We have made certain restrictions, namely that they are central and that only two-body forces will be treated, but we have not needed to venture beyond these generalities. Some explicit examples will serve to illustrate the principles involved.

Consider first the interaction between two neutral atoms. When there are no monopole electrostatic forces the only long-range interaction between two atoms are dipole–dipole and higher-order interactions. These are the van der Waals forces and were first given a quantum-mechanical treatment by London and Eisenshitz in 1930.[17] It is not difficult in principle to deal with the case of any two neutral atoms, but, if there are a large number of electrons involved, the algebraic form conceals the physics. We can indicate the origin of these forces perfectly satisfactorily by treating two hydrogen atoms.

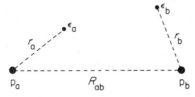

Figure 2.11 Notation for two hydrogen atoms; p_a and p_b are the nuclei, ε_a and ε_b are the two electrons

We assume that the two hydrogen atoms shown in Figure 2.11 are far enough apart for exchange effects (i.e. interactions between ε_a and p_b and between ε_b and p_a) to be negligible. Hence the Hamiltonian is

$$H = H_a(r_a) + H_b(r_b) + W(r_a, r_b, R_{ab}) \tag{2.30}$$

for $R_{ab} \gg r_a, r_b$. $H_a(r_a)$ is the hydrogenic wave function for atom a, W is the energy of interaction of two electric dipoles. From electrostatics (see, for example, Scott[18]) we have that

$$W = \frac{e^2}{4\pi\varepsilon_0 R_{ab}^3}\left[\mathbf{r}_a \cdot \mathbf{r}_b - \frac{3(\mathbf{r}_a \cdot \mathbf{R}_{ab})(\mathbf{r}_b \cdot \mathbf{R}_{ab})}{R_{ab}^2}\right]. \tag{2.31}$$

Choosing a set of axes such that z lies along $\mathbf{R}_{ab}$, equation (2.31) becomes,

$$W = \frac{e^2}{4\pi\varepsilon_0 R^3} w \tag{2.32}$$

where

$$w = x_a x_b + y_a y_b - 2z_a z_b.$$

The dipole–dipole term w may be treated as a perturbation on the state of two non-interacting hydrogen atoms. The unperturbed part is

$$[H_a(\mathbf{r}_a) + H_b(\mathbf{r}_b)]|n_a, n_b\rangle = [E_{n_a} + E_{n_b}]|n_a, n_b\rangle \tag{2.33}$$

and we are interested in perturbation of the ground state energy $n_a = 1$, $n_b = 1$. Unless an atom is exposed to a polarizing force, it will not have a permanent dipole moment, and the first-order perturbation energy will vanish since

$$\langle 1, 1|w|1, 1\rangle = 0 \tag{2.34}$$

i.e. the averages

$$\langle z_a z_b \rangle = \langle y_a y_b \rangle = \langle x_a x_b \rangle = 0.$$

However, the second-order perturbation term is non-zero (since this involves averages over $x_a^2 x_b^2$, etc.) and is

$$\Delta E = \frac{e^4}{16\pi^2 \varepsilon_0^2 R^6} \sum_{n_a, n_b} \frac{|\langle 1, 1|w|n_a, n_b \rangle|^2}{2E_1 - E_{n_a} - E_{n_b}}. \tag{2.35}$$

This is always negative since $E_{n_a} + E_{n_b} > 2E_1$. We can see from equation (2.35) that the dipole–dipole interaction of two hydrogen atoms contributes a potential energy of the form

$$W = -\frac{\alpha}{r^6} \tag{2.36}$$

where α is known as the dipole–dipole van der Waals coefficient and is given by

$$\alpha = -\frac{e^4}{16\pi^2 \varepsilon_0^2} \sum_{n_a, n_b} \frac{|\langle 1, 1|w|n_a, n_b \rangle|^2}{2E_1 - E_{n_a} - E_{n_b}}. \tag{2.37}$$

This van der Waals interaction is a weak attractive force. We may obtain an estimate of α for two hydrogen atoms as follows. The two atoms are in their ground states (1s) and the energies of the excited states are given by

$$E_n = -\frac{me^4}{2\hbar^2} \cdot \frac{1}{n^2} \cdot \frac{1}{(4\pi\varepsilon_0)^2} \tag{2.38}$$

(see, for example, Merzbacher[19]).

Thus the largest term in the denominator of equation (2.37) is

$$2E_1 - E_2 - E_2 = -\frac{me^4}{2\hbar^2}(2 - \tfrac{1}{4} - \tfrac{1}{4})\frac{1}{(4\pi\varepsilon_0)^2}$$

$$= -\frac{3}{4} \cdot \frac{me^4}{\hbar^2} \cdot \frac{1}{(4\pi\varepsilon_0)^2}$$

and the smallest term is

$$2E_1 - E_\infty - E_\infty = -\frac{me^4}{2\hbar^2}(2 - 0)\frac{1}{(4\pi\varepsilon_0)^2}$$

$$= -\frac{me^4}{\hbar^2} \cdot \frac{1}{(4\pi\varepsilon_0)^2}$$

so that we can write, to a reasonable accuracy

$$2E_1 - E_{n_a} - E_{n_b} = -\frac{me^4}{\hbar^2} \cdot \frac{1}{(4\pi\varepsilon_0)^2}$$

for all n_a and n_b.

This gives us

$$\alpha = e^4 \langle 1, 1|w^2|1, 1\rangle \frac{\hbar^2}{me^4}. \qquad (2.39)$$

Exploiting the spherical symmetry, we can simplify this further:

$$\langle x^2 \rangle = \langle y^2 \rangle = \langle z^2 \rangle = \tfrac{1}{3}\langle r^2 \rangle \qquad (2.40)$$

and we know that the hydrogen ground state is

$$|1, 1\rangle = \left(\frac{1}{\pi a^3}\right)^{1/2} e^{-r/a} \qquad (2.41)$$

where $a(\equiv 4\pi\varepsilon_0\hbar^2/me^2)$ is known as the first Bohr radius.[a] Therefore

$$\langle r^2 \rangle = \int_0^\infty \int_{-(\pi/2)}^{+(\pi/2)} \int_0^{2\pi} \frac{1}{\pi a^3} e^{-2r/a} r^4 \sin\theta \, dr \, d\theta \, d\phi \qquad (2.42)$$

which may be integrated by parts to give

$$\langle r^2 \rangle = 3a^2. \qquad (2.43)$$

Now since all the cross terms such as $\langle x_a x_b y_a y_b \rangle$ vanish

$$\langle w^2 \rangle = \langle (x_a x_b)^2 + (y_a y_b)^2 + 4(z_a z_b)^2 \rangle \qquad (2.44)$$

and using the results (2.40) and (2.43)

$$\langle w^2 \rangle = 6a^4.$$

Hence, substituting into equation (2.39):

$$\alpha = \frac{6e^2}{4\pi\varepsilon_0} a^5. \qquad (2.45a)$$

Clearly our approximation for the denominator is crude, and the average would be between

$$-\frac{me^4}{\hbar^2}\frac{1}{(4\pi\varepsilon_0)} \quad \text{and} \quad -\frac{3}{4}\frac{me^4}{\hbar^2}\frac{1}{(4\pi\varepsilon_0)^2}.$$

London and Eisenshitz made a more careful evaluation and found that

$$\alpha = \frac{6.47}{4\pi\varepsilon_0} e^2 a^5. \qquad (2.45b)$$

If we take higher orders of perturbation the interaction becomes a series:

$$V(r) = -\frac{\alpha}{r^6} - \frac{\beta}{r^8} - \frac{\gamma}{r^{10}}. \qquad (2.46)$$

β corresponds to a dipole–quadrupole interaction and γ corresponds to a quadrupole–quadrupole interaction. Born and Huang[20] have given a set of values for some of these coefficients, and there is a good review by Margenau[21] for complete details.

The analysis has been for hydrogen, but we will take the result to be the general form where the values of α, β, etc., will depend on the particular atoms. This is not a fanciful assumption; it implies merely that we may write the interaction as a multipole expansion. For the areas in which the expression (2.46) is applied, the series exhibits rapid convergence.

Equation (2.46) describes the long-range weak attractive force between a pair of neutral atoms. When these two atoms come close together, strong repulsive forces arise from exchange effects. These may be derived quantum mechanically, but the calculations are not reliable because of the large number of electrons that may be involved, and it is customary to choose an empirical law. This law must be a short-range strong force, and the most widely used expressions have been a large inverse power or an exponential, i.e.

$$V(r) \propto r^{-m} \quad \text{or} \quad e^{-\alpha r}.$$

Since the hydrogen wave function involves an exponential, it is easy to see that, at least for a hydrogen atom, the second has more quantum-mechanical justification. However, the first is easier to handle and is just as effective in computing results in agreement with experiment.

The simplest, and probably most useful, expression for the total potential function for a pair of neutral atoms is thus

$$\phi(r) = \frac{A}{r^m} - \frac{\alpha}{r^6} \qquad (2.47)$$

where the higher-order attractive terms have been dropped. This form with $m = 12$ is due to Mie[2] and Lennard Jones.[23] The form of this potential is shown in Figure 2.12.

The parameters A and α may be written in terms of the equilibrium spacing σ and the depth ε of the potential well. The most critical part of this potential is around the minimum, and it may be helpful to have a third term that is effective in this region. Let us consider a three-parameter potential of which equation (2.47) is a special case:

$$\phi(r) = \frac{A}{r^m} + \frac{B}{r^n} + \frac{C}{r^6}. \qquad (2.48)$$

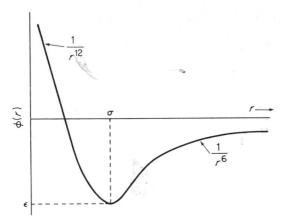

Figure 2.12 Two-body interaction potential between
neutral atoms

Now $\phi(r) = \varepsilon$, $\phi'(r) = 0$ when $r = \sigma$, so that we have

$$0 = m\frac{A}{\sigma^m} + n\frac{B}{\sigma^n} + 6\frac{C}{\sigma^6}$$

$$\varepsilon = \frac{A}{\sigma^m} + \frac{B}{\sigma^n} + \frac{C}{\sigma^6}$$

which leads to

$$\phi(r) = \frac{\varepsilon}{(m-n)}\sum_p x^{-p}(\xi_{pmn6}G + \xi_{pnm}) \qquad (2.49)$$

where $G \equiv C/\varepsilon\sigma^6$, $x \equiv r/\sigma$ and the properties of ξ are

$$\xi_{pqr} \equiv \begin{cases} q - r \\ r - s \\ s - q \\ 0 \end{cases} \text{ for } p = \begin{cases} s \\ q \\ r \\ \neq q, r \text{ or } s \end{cases} \qquad (2.50a)$$

i.e., ignore the suffix equal to p and ξ_{pqrs} is the difference, taken cyclically, of the other two.

$$\xi_{pqr} = \begin{cases} r \\ -q \\ 0 \end{cases} \text{ for } p = \begin{cases} q \\ r \\ \neq q \text{ or } r \end{cases} . \qquad (2.50b)$$

It is a useful abbreviation to write

$$\phi = \sum_p \frac{1}{x^p} \tag{2.51}$$

where

$$\sum_p \equiv \frac{\varepsilon}{m - n} \sum_p (\xi_{pmn6} G + \xi_{pnm}).$$

Equation (2.51) reduces to equation (2.47) by writing $G = 0$ and $n = 6$.

Thus we have an interatomic force law suitable for neutral atoms or molecular crystals, and the parameters may be found by fitting to experimental data. Since neither ε nor σ are directly observable quantities, this is the best we can expect. Appendix A contains some examples of this procedure for the solidified inert gases.

2.7 Interatomic force law—ionic crystals

In 1910, Born (see Reference 20) and Madelung[24] independently made calculations on the energy of an ionic crystal. They treated the lattice as a system of positive and negative ions. The Coulombic potential energy of an ion in the crystal is a series of the form

$$E = -\frac{e^2}{4\pi\varepsilon_0}\left(\pm\frac{z_1}{r_1} \pm \frac{z_2}{r_2} \pm \frac{z_3}{r_3} \pm \cdots\right) \tag{2.52}$$

where z_1 is the number of ions at distance r_1 from the reference ion, and the positive sign is for ions with opposite charge to that of the reference ion. For sodium chloride the structure is as in Figure 2.13 and thus

$$E = -\frac{2e^2}{4\pi\varepsilon_0 a}\left(6 - \frac{12}{\sqrt{2}} + \frac{8}{\sqrt{3}} - \cdots\right). \tag{2.53}$$

However equation (2.53) does not converge rapidly because the Coulomb force extends over a long range. A method due to Evjen[25] deals successfully with the problem. He wrote the energy (with $b \equiv a/2$)

$$E = -\frac{Ae^2}{4\pi\varepsilon_0 b} \tag{2.54}$$

and showed that A could be found by the use of weighting factors. The method is to sum the potentials due to ions within a cube $(na)^3$ surrounding the central ion, where n is an integer. The contributions of ions inside the cube are given a weighting factor $W = 1$; those ions on the surface, edges and corners are assigned $W = \frac{1}{2}, \frac{1}{4}$ and $\frac{1}{8}$, respectively. (Ions on the surface are shared by two crystal cubes; ions on an edge are shared by four cubes and those on corners by eight cubes.)

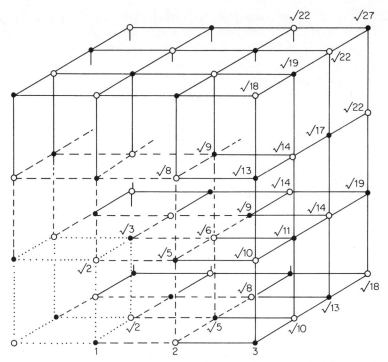

Figure 2.13   Sodium chloride structure. Sodium-ion sites are marked by a circle ●
and chlorine-ion sites are marked by a circle ○. The dotted line . . . . is an octant
of the cube $n = 1$, the broken line $-----$ is an octant for $n = 2$ and the solid line
$\underline{\qquad}$ is an octant for $n = 3$. The numbers at the sites show the distance from the
origin in units of $a/2$

This procedure is equivalent to summing by cells rather than ions. Increasing the integer n by unit steps produces a rapidly convergent series with
alternating signs.

If $n = 1$ (i.e. the dotted-line cube of Figure 2.13)

$$A = 6 \cdot \frac{1}{2} \cdot 1 - 12 \cdot \frac{1}{4} \cdot \frac{1}{\sqrt{2}} + 8 \cdot \frac{1}{8} \cdot \frac{1}{\sqrt{3}}$$

$$= 1 \cdot 456.$$

If $n = 2$ (i.e. the broken-line cube of Figure 2.13)

$$A = \left(6 - \frac{12}{\sqrt{2}} + \frac{8}{\sqrt{3}}\right) \cdot 1 - \left(\frac{6}{\sqrt{4}} - \frac{24}{\sqrt{5}} + \frac{24}{\sqrt{6}}\right) \cdot \frac{1}{2} + \left(-\frac{12}{\sqrt{8}} + \frac{24}{\sqrt{9}}\right) \cdot \frac{1}{4}$$

$$- \frac{8}{\sqrt{12}} \cdot \frac{1}{8} = 1 \cdot 751.$$

If $n = 3$ (i.e. the full-line cube of Figure 2.13)

$$A = 1 \cdot 746.$$

Thus the slowly convergent Columb form has become a rapidly convergent series. A is known as the Madelung constant, and the attractive long-range part is expressed in terms of the nearest ionic distance. The Madelung constant depends only on the structure of the crystal.

The repulsive part is very short range and may be neglected beyond the nearest ions; so we have an ionic potential energy of the form

$$\phi(r) = -\frac{Ae^2}{4\pi\varepsilon_0 r} + 6v(r) \tag{2.55}$$

where $v(r)$ is a function representing all the other contributions to the inter-action energies (the dominant contribution being repulsive) and A is a constant for the structure, e.g. $A_{NaCl} = 1.746$, $A_{ZnS} = 1.638$, $A_{CaF_2} = 1.681$. Fuller details of the calculations of lattice energies may be found in References 26–30.

If a potential of the form of equation (2.55) is used in the equations of motion, the lattice sums in the corresponding dynamical matrix converge too slowly for the method to be of value. Ewald[27] solved this by introducing a theta transformation into the Coulomb part. The l summation is divided into two rapidly convergent series, one requiring a direct lattice summation and the other a reciprocal lattice summation. A summary of this technique is given as Appendix B. The method was applied first by Kellerman to a rigid ion model, and this is mentioned in Section 2.10. The main advantage of the potential of equation (2.55) is that it is defined in terms of only two parameters and these may be established as follows. At equilibrium

$$\left.\frac{d\phi}{dr}\right|_{r=b} = 0$$

$$= \frac{Ae^2}{4\pi\varepsilon_0 b^2} + 6\left.\frac{dv}{dr}\right|_{r=b} \tag{2.56}$$

Therefore we have

$$\left.\frac{dv}{dr}\right|_{r=b} \equiv v'(r) = -\frac{A}{6}\cdot\frac{e^2}{b^2}\cdot\frac{1}{4\pi\varepsilon_0}\left(= -1.165\frac{e^2}{4b^2}\frac{1}{4\pi\varepsilon_0} \text{ for NaCl}\right). \tag{2.57}$$

We may use the compressibility $1/B$ to find the second derivative:

$$B \equiv -V\left(\frac{\partial P}{\partial V}\right)_T$$

$$= V\left(\frac{\partial^2 F}{\partial V^2}\right)_T \tag{2.58}$$

since $P = -\partial F/\partial V$, where F is the free energy. Now if the constant temperature is $T = 0$, the free energy per unit cell is

$$F = \phi \tag{2.59}$$

and therefore

$$B = V\left(\frac{\partial^2 \phi}{\partial V^2}\right)_T. \tag{2.60}$$

For NaCl, $v = 2b^3$; so it is readily seen that

$$\frac{\partial^2 \phi}{\partial V^2} = -\frac{1}{18b^5}\frac{\partial \phi}{\partial b} + \frac{1}{36b^4}\frac{\partial^2 \phi}{\partial b^2}$$

$$= \frac{1}{36b^4}\frac{\partial^2 \phi}{\partial b^2} \tag{2.61}$$

since

$$\left.\frac{\partial \phi}{\partial r}\right|_{r=b} = 0.$$

Thus we have

$$B = \frac{1}{18b}\frac{\partial^2 \phi}{\partial b^2} = \frac{1}{18b}\left[-\frac{2Ae^2}{4\pi\varepsilon_0 b^3} + 6\left.\frac{\partial^2 v(r)}{\partial r^2}\right|_{r=b}\right] \tag{2.62}$$

or

$$\left.\frac{\partial^2 v(r)}{\partial r^2}\right|_{r=b} = 3bB + \frac{Ae^2}{3b^3}\cdot\frac{1}{4\pi\varepsilon_0}\left(= 10\cdot18\frac{e^2}{4b^3}\frac{1}{4\pi\varepsilon_0}\text{ for NaCl}\right). \tag{2.63}$$

These results were used in the rigid ion model, so called because it used
Born's model of an ionic crystal. The crystal is treated as a lattice of point
ionic charges. However, although there are some areas where this may be
regarded as successful (see Section 2.10) it predicts poor values for the
dielectric constants. Also it has been shown by Herman[31] that it requires at
least fifth-neighbour interaction to be explicitly included before agreement
with experiment is attained. This introduces fifteen parameters and the
procedure loses all physical significance. Dick and Overhauser[23] proposed
a **shell model** where each ion could be polarized. Their model of a unit cell
was a pair of ions each made up of a core (nucleus and inner electrons) and a
shell of valence electrons as in Figure 2.14. The forces indicated in Figure
2.14 are included in the equations of motion, and a number of experimental
quantities are needed to establish values for the parameters. The actual
number of parameters varies according to the approximations made. These
approximations and variations on the basic shell model are raised again in
Section 2.10.

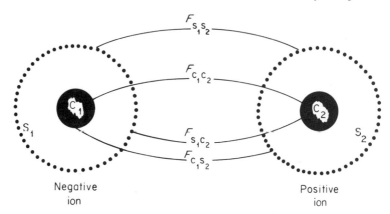

Figure 2.14   Shell model of Dick and Overhauser, showing the forces $F_{C_1C_2}$ (force of interaction between core 1 and core 2), $F_{S_1S_2}$, $F_{C_1S_2}$ and $F_{S_1C_2}$

2.8   Interatomic force law—covalent crystals

There are considerable similarities in the properties of solids bound by covalency and those that are ionic. However, they warrant a separate class if only because of their conduction properties. Whereas ionic crystals are mainly insulators, the conductivity of covalent crystals varies from good insulators (diamond) through semiconductors (silicon and germanium) to reasonable conductors (some forms of tin).

Covalent crystals form two structures—the diamond [as shown in Figure 2.8(a)] and the zinc blende [as is formed by ZnS, Figure 2.8(a) with one faced-centred cubic lattice formed by Zn and the other by S]. Cochran[16] applied the model of Dick and Overhauser (see Section 2.10) to covalent crystals, originally to germanium. This was very successful and underlines the similarity, at least in some areas, between ionic and covalent solids. For our discussion of lattice dynamical treatments we shall not distinguish these two classes.

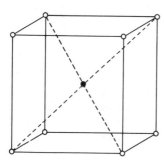

Figure 2.15   Caesium chloride structure. Cs atoms are shown as ● and Cl atoms as ○ (or vice versa)

2.9 Interatomic force law—metals

In addition to the periodic potential of the lattice ions, a potential for the atoms of a metal must take account of the larger number of electrons present with properties very similar to those of free electrons. The lattice does not play a significant role in determining the energy bands. However, the lattice contribution is important when dealing with vibrations. Metals must be treated by methods that are completely different from those of the other three classes. Perhaps the most important feature which makes this clear is that each atom is no longer subjected to a potential function from which its motion may be calculated. The existence of non-localized electrons which are continually involved in energy transfers with the ions tends to blur the concept of a normal mode.

The theory of phonons in metals is based on the idea of a 'pseudopotential'. This is introduced into the Schrödinger equation and then certain approximations are made to localize the pseudopotential to the ion sites. Since the theory for metals requires special and involved techniques and we shall not normally choose a metal as a sample crystal in our discussions, the methods are not described here. However, Appendix C outlines the procedure and summarizes the way in which a pseudopotential is defined. A full treatment of the method and its application to metals appears in an article by Harrison.[33,34]

2.10 Dispersion curves

We have made some general points about the relation between the energy and momenta of phonons in Section 2.4. Evaluation of these relations requires explicit knowledge of the interatomic force law for the material of interest. If this information is available, the elements of the dynamical matrix may be calculated for a particular value of $\mathbf{k}$ and hence, by diagonalization, the energy of any normal mode may be obtained. We have divided crystals into three groups: molecular crystals (including neutral atoms), ionic crystals (for our purposes including covalent crystals) and metals.

The solidified inert gases are a convenient and simple example of the first group. We shall consider only the face-centred cubic structure, although under some conditions these atoms form the hexagonal close-packed structure.[35] The unit cells of these lattices contain only one atom. A potential-energy function [for example, equation (2.51)] is substituted into the dynamical matrix, in this case of order three. The elements involve sums over the lattice of the form

$$\sum_{l} \frac{l_1^{n_1} l_2^{n_2} l_3^{n_3}}{l^m} (1 - \cos \mathbf{k} \cdot \mathbf{r}^l) \qquad (2.64)$$

where $\mathbf{r}^l = (a/2)(l_1\, l_2\, l_3)$ for a face-centred cubic lattice with $l_1 + l_2 + l_3 =$ an even integer; n_1, n_2 and n_3 are integers. Some of these sums are tabulated in Appendix D.

A thorough investigation of this application to neon, argon, krypton and xenon has been made by Horton and Leech,[15] and many other authors[35] have made use of the same kind of potentials. The dispersion in a sample direction [210] has been shown in Figure 2.7. Horton and Leech have computed these for six directions: the three symmetry directions [100], [110] and [111], and directions [210], [211] and [221]. The dynamical matrix factorizes into a linear and a quadratic equation for all points on these lines, which considerably decreases the computational labour. The general point requires the solution of a cubic equation.

This group of crystals provides the most direct application of the lattice dynamical methods as they have been described. A suitable potential is chosen and substituted into the basic equations. The lattice sums are performed over the required number of surrounding atoms. By this method it is easy to carry out sets of calculations to investigate the sensitivity of the results to changes in the potential parameters, the number of neighbours included, different species of the same group of crystals and the temperature dependence. It is not possible to present all these variations in the text, but some attempt is made in Appendix E to give sets of results, and a sample calculation is included to clarify the procedure. It is hoped that this, together with the references indicated, is sufficient to provide a working knowledge of the essential steps in calculating the lattice dispersion.

Unlike the inert gases, the forces of interionic interaction in ionic solids are large, and thus a given thermal energy in the lattice produces relatively small amplitude vibrations. Thus the harmonic approximation is entirely adequate at most temperatures, whereas for molecular crystals, particularly the lighter inert-gas solids such as neon and argon, anharmonic effects may be expected to play an important role in the thermal properties. This is discussed in some detail in Chapter 5. The energy levels of the ions of the alkali halides are such that the electrons follow the motion of their nuclei instantaneously. This requirement, known as the adiabatic approximation, is basic to Born–von Karman lattice dynamics; so, in satisfying it, an ionic crystal provides a suitable system for investigation. The adiabatic approximation is justified by Born and Oppenheimer[36] and confirms that it is valid to express the forces in terms of an interaction potential involving only nuclear coordinates.

Kellerman[37] applied the Born model of point ions of positive and negative charges to a detailed study of the vibrational spectra of sodium chloride. It is customary to refer to this as the 'rigid ion model', since no account is taken of the effect of any deformation (or polarization) on the interaction between ions. The ions are assumed to be spherical and not deformable in any way. The Coulomb field due to the ion at points distant from the ion is that of a point charge. A method due to Ewald[27] (see Appendix B) makes it possible to carry out the summations even though their convergence is very slow.

The model provides a relatively simple method of obtaining the dispersion curves, and Kellerman evaluated the energies of modes at 48 points in the first Brillouin zone. The basic expressions are derived in Appendix F. Karo[38,39] has applied the method to the structurally similar halides of lithium, sodium, potassium, rubidium and caesium.

The rigid ion model predicts a frequency spectrum in which acoustic branches are in fairly good agreement with neutron-scattering measurements (see Section 8.6) but whose optic branches are too large—sometimes by more than 50 per cent. It has been found that models that allow ions to become polarized can overcome these discrepancies and also provide a realistic mechanism for the interpretation of dielectric properties.

It is not possible to mention all the attempts to extend the Born model description of ionic crystals, neither is it particularly desirable, otherwise this book would become a catalogue. The most prominent advances on the rigid ion model can be summarized as the deformation–dipole model[40–47] and shell models.[16,32,48–56] The latter exist in many forms and are taken to include the exchange–charge model. The interest in these models has set up Kellerman's work in a position of central importance.

In recent years Hardy[43,44,46] and Karo[45] have developed the deformation–dipole method introduced by Szigeti,[40,41] and it is their treatment that is outlined here. The Born model gives a good account of the cohesive energy of ionic crystals, but falls down when lattice excitations are directly involved. The plane waves cause distortions within the crystal which produce ionic distortions. From this, dipole–dipole and higher-multipole terms appear in the interaction energy. The deformation–dipole model neglects the higher terms, and Hardy argues a justification of this for all modes except very long wave acoustic (see Appendix A of Reference 46).

At a given ion lattice site (l, K) (see Section 1.8), the dipole moment has two contributions. Kellerman (using the Born model) included the part due to the displacement of the ion, but there is also the dipole moment produced when there is a relative displacement of outer electrons from the centre of the 'sphere'. Both of these contributions should be included. Lyddane and Herzfeld[57] introduced this in a direct way using the classical expression and writing the dipole moment as being proportional to an effective field. They used the free-ion polarizability data.[58] The results were not encouraging—some of the modes were predicted with imaginary frequencies under conditions where the lattice is known to be stable. Later,[43] when the polarizabilities more applicable to the ions in the crystal^b are used,[59] the imaginary frequencies are eliminated, but the corresponding results (for the specific heat) are worse than those of the rigid ion model. Szigeti[33] pointed out that the predicted static dielectric constants are compatible with the experimental values only if the charge is treated as a parameter, and he found, for example, $e_{eff}(NaCl) = 0.74e$. Szigeti suggested that polarization could also be produced by a short-range effect, perhaps associated with the repulsive forces due to overlap. The shell model was originally introduced by Dick and Overhauser[32] to account for Szigeti's results, but before continuing our discussion of shell models, let us look at distortion-produced dipoles. Figure 2.16 is a diagrammatic representation of the charge distributions surrounding a negative ion.

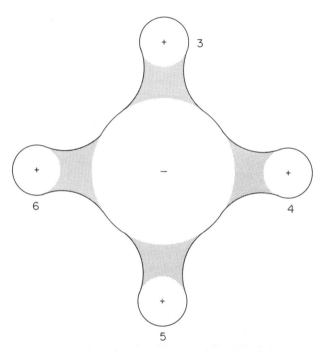

Figure 2.16   Four of the six nearest neighbours in two dimensions. The shaded regions are those in which the surrounding ions cause distortions to the electronic distribution and hence the region in which the dipole moment originates. Ions 1 and 2 are not shown—they are out of the plane of the page and into the page, respectively

Consider the dipole moment arising from relative displacements of the nearest-neighbour ions. The component into the plane of the paper (say cartesian α direction) due to ions 3, 4, 5 and 6 is

$$\sum_{i=3}^{6} \gamma_{-}[U_{\alpha}(i) - U_{\alpha}(0)] \tag{2.65a}$$

(0 being the negative ion), while while ions 1 and 2 contribute

$$\sum_{i=1}^{2} \gamma'_- [U_\alpha(i) - U_\alpha(0)] \qquad (2.65b)$$

where

$$\gamma_- = \frac{m_-(r_0)}{r_0}$$

$$\gamma'_- = \frac{d}{dr}[m_-(r)]|_{r=r_0}$$

and $m_-(r_0)$ is the dipole moment on the negative ion due to its bond with a nearest neighbour. The term (2.65a) represents the component of perpendicular m_- which becomes directed along α; term (2.65b) arises from the change in m_- as the ions change their separation. Similar expressions, with m_+ replacing m_-, hold for the dipole moment induced on the positive ion.

To compute the energies of the modes of the system on this model, the forces may be separated into Coulomb and non-Coulomb parts. The short-range repulsive part is the same as for the rigid ion model and hence is as deduced by Kellerman. However, the force acting on an ion, due to the field of the other ions, now includes the dipoles induced on all the other ions by the displacement of the reference ion. (The force on the dipole associated with the reference ion is usually neglected, since it is a second-order effect.)

Hardy deduces by studying the effect of various approximations that the deformation primarily affects the negative ion and that there is no improvement to be gained by allowing for a polarization on the positive ion (Figure 2.18 shows dispersion relations calculated by this method and compares with the alternative models.)

The basic idea of the shell model, introduced by Dick and Overhauser[32] as a model to explain relative permittivity, is shown in Figure 2.14. The simple classical model for the theory of dielectric behaviour of ionic crystals supposes polarizable ions with charges $\pm Ze$ and polarizabilities $\alpha\pm$. The model yields relations between the limiting high- and low-frequency relative permittivities [$\varepsilon(\infty)$ and $\varepsilon(0)$, respectively] and the reststrahlen frequency ω_0. The latter is the transverse optic mode for long wavelengths which interacts with infrared radiation, so called from the German for residual rays. (If an ionic crystal is irradiated by a wide band of frequencies in the infrared region, after several successive reflections the beam becomes almost monochromatic. The wavelength which remains corresponds to the only frequency with significant reflectivity, i.e. the resonant frequency of the lattice. This does not occur in a covalent crystal, since the atoms are not charged and the mode can be excited.) The corresponding longitudinal mode is given by the

Lyddane–Sachs–Teller[60] relation

$$\omega_{\text{long}}^2 = \omega_0^2 \frac{\varepsilon_{(0)}}{\varepsilon_{(\infty)}}.$$

Szigeti[40,41] eliminated the unknown $\alpha\pm$ and obtained two relations

$$B = \frac{m\omega_0^2}{3a} \cdot \frac{\varepsilon_{(0)} + 2}{\varepsilon_{(\infty)} + 2} \tag{2.66a}$$

where B is the bulk modulus (inverse compressibility) and (taking care not to confuse $\varepsilon_{(0)}$ with ε_0, which is the permittivity of free space in farad metre^{-1})

$$\varepsilon_{(0)} - \varepsilon_{(\infty)} = \left(\frac{\varepsilon_{(\infty)} + 2}{3}\right)^2 \cdot \frac{N}{\varepsilon_0} \cdot \frac{(Ze)^2}{m\omega_0^2}. \tag{2.66b}$$

Table 2.1(a) The ratio $s = e^*/e$ from the work of Szigeti.[40,41] 'a' is NaCl structure (see Figure 2.13), 'b' is CsCl structure [see Figure 2.15] and 'c' is zinc blende (ZnS) structure [see Figure 2.8(a)]

Crystal	Structure	s	r	$\varepsilon_{(0)}$	$\varepsilon_{(\infty)}$
LiF	a	0·87	2·07	9·27	1·92
NaF	a	0·93	2·31	6·0	1·74
NaCl	a	0·74	2·81	5·62	2·25
NaBr	a	0·69	2·97	5·99	2·62
NaI	a	0·71	3·23	6·60	2·91
KCl	a	0·80	3·14	4·68	2·13
KBr	a	0·76	3·29	4·78	2·33
KI	a	0·69	3·53	4·94	2·69
RbCl	a	0·84	3·27	5	2·19
RbBr	a	0·82	3·42	5	2·33
RbI	a	0·89	3·66	5	2·63
CsCl	b	0·84	3·56	7·20	2·60
CsBr	b	0·79	3·71	6·51	2·78
TlCl	b	1·08	3·33	31·90	5·10
CuCl	c	1·10	2·34	10	3·57
CuBr	c	0·995	2·46	8	4·08
MgO	a	0·88	2·10	9·80	2·95
CaO	a	0·76	2·40	11·80	3·28
SrO	a	0·58	2·57	13·30	3·31
ZnS	c	0·48	2·33	8·30	5·07

Neither of these relations satisfy the experimental values as they stand. Szigeti introduces the effective charge e^* in place of e, and an effective compressibility $(B^*)^{-1}$ in place of B^{-1}. These are defined so that equations

(2.66) are satisfied by experimental observations; for example

$$s \equiv \frac{e^*}{e} = \left[\frac{\varepsilon_{(0)} - \varepsilon_{(\infty)}}{(\varepsilon_{(\infty)} + 2)^2} \cdot \frac{\varepsilon_0}{N} \cdot \frac{9m\omega_0^2}{(Ze)^2} \right] \tag{2.67}$$

in order that equation (2.66b) is satisfied by the observed values of $\varepsilon_{(0)}$, $\varepsilon_{(\infty)}$ and ω_0. Table 2.1(a) shows some values of e^* (from Szigeti[40,41]) and indicates the discrepancies inherent in the classical model. Table 2.1(b) is included to show experimental values of some of the quantities involved in the theory we have been discussing. They are, in general, more recent values than those used by Szigeti.

Table 2.1(b) Experimental values of $\varepsilon_{(0)}$ (the static relative permittivity, $\varepsilon_{(\infty)}$ (the optical-frequency relative permittivity), ω_0 (the reststrahlen frequency), ω_L (deduced using the Lyddane–Sachs–Teller relation) and the lattice constant. The data is mainly from a compilation by Burstein[42]

Crystal	$\varepsilon_{(0)}$	$\varepsilon_{(\infty)}$	ω_0 $(10^{13}\,\text{s}^{-1})$	ω_L $(10^{13}\,\text{s}^{-1})$
LiF	8·9	1·9	5·783	12·52
NaF	5·1	1·7	4·502	7·80
NaCl	5·9	2·25	3·089	5·00
NaBr	6·4	2·6	2·524	3·96
NaI		3·1		
KCl	4·85	2·1	2·675	4·07
KBr	4·9	2·3	2·129	3·11
KI	5·1	2·7	1·902	2·61
RbCl	4·9	2·2	2·185	3·26
RbBr	4·9	2·3	1·658	2·42
RbI	5·5	2·6	1·413	2·06
CsCl	7·2	2·6	1·865	3·10
CsBr	6·5	2·8	1·375	2·10
TlCl	31·9	5·1	1·187	2·97
CuCl		3·7		
CuBr		4·5		
MgO	9·8	2·95	7·535	13·73
CaO		3·4		
SrO		3·3		
ZnS	8·3	5·0	5·161	6·65

The simple classical theory does not include a polarization mechanism arising from the short-range repulsive overlap forces. It is these forces that are responsible for the apparent loss of ionic character of the crystal suggested by Tables 2.1. The existence of these interactions can be justified on a quantum-mechanical basis by looking at the exchange interaction between two atoms with saturated electronic configuration. The important factor in the model is that the repulsive interaction is taken to act through the **shells**, not the nuclei, i.e. $F_{s_1 s_2}$ in Figure 2.14. This shell–shell repulsion reduces the polarization of the negative ion and increases that of the positive ion (for a polarizing field along the line joining the positive ion to the negative ion). This is shown in Figure 2.17.

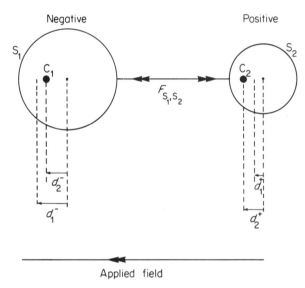

Applied field

Figure 2.17 Showing the two polarization effects in terms of the displacements between the centre of the shell and the core. $d_1^\pm$ are the displacements if there is no shell–shell repulsion, $d_2^\pm$ is the additional effect when this is included

As we saw with the deformation–dipole method, there are two polarization mechanisms—(i) the polarization caused because the ions move together (or apart) under the action of a field (shown in Figure 2.17 as $d_1^\pm$) and (ii) the polarization due to the change of overlap charge (exchange charge) (shown in Figure 2.17 as $d_2^\pm$).

The details of the shell model involve varying degrees of approximation. The 'simple' shell model[50,51] allows for a polarization only of the negative ion. Developments of this include a model in which both ions are polarizable[50,51] and a complex model in which there is a new degree of freedom—the isotropic 'breathing' mode, in which the shell pulsates.[52] Within these there are wide ranges of approximations in the fitting of parameters. The adiabatic approximation may be retained by putting the masses of the shells to zero.

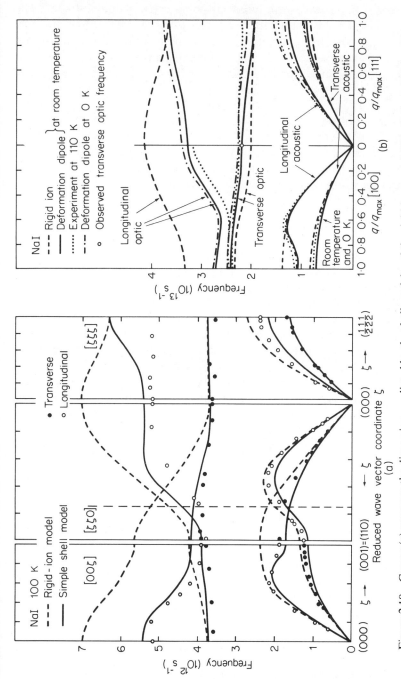

Figure 2.18   Curves (a) compare the dispersion predicted by the shell model and the rigid ion model. The single points have been measured by neutron scattering.[50,51] [Reproduced, with permission, from Woods, A. D. B., Cochran, W., Brockhouse, B. N., and Cowley, R. A., *Phys. Rev.*, **131**, 1025–1029 (1963).] Curves (b) compare the dispersion predicted by the deformation-dipole method and the rigid ion model. [Reproduced, with permission, from Karo, A. M., and Hardy, J. R., *Phys. Rev.*, **129**, 2024–2036 (1963).]

The shell model was introduced for ionic crystals and justified by a quantum-mechanical treatment of saturated shells. Cochran[16] applied the theory to the covalent semiconductor germanium with far greater success than one might expect. In this work he emphasizes the importance of the shell–shell repulsion for the lattice dynamics of germanium. By allowing κ, labelling the atoms within the unit cell, to take four values (two for core coordinates and two for shell coordinates) Cochran's analysis retains the basic form of Born–von Karman. Cowley, Woods, Cochran and Brockhouse have produced a series of papers[16,48–51,55] reporting experimental results of neutron scattering and have discussed them on a shell-model basis. A simple example of a shell model calculation is performed in Appendix G. Figure 2.18 compares the dispersion predicted using various models.

2.11   Long waves and elasticity

In the five preceding sections we discussed theories that are applicable to particular types of crystals. We now return to a more general discussion and consider the relation between the travelling waves in the lattice and the elastic properties of the solid.

If the travelling wave has a wavelength which is long compared with the spacing between the atoms, the crystal will look like an elastic continuum to the wave. Thus we expect that, as **k** tends to zero, the acoustic mode will be describable in terms of the macroscopic elastic properties of the crystal. Since there are no details of crystal structure to take into account, the equation of motion of the travelling wave may be found by simple application of Hooke's law and Newton's second law. (We stress that this is for $\lambda \gg a$.) Let us first relate the macroscopic elastic constants to those of the lattice.

For a general (anisotropic) material, Hooke's law is a tensor relation of the form

$$T = \lambda E \qquad (2.68)$$

where $\lambda \equiv \{C_{ijkl}\}$, T is the stress tensor and E is the strain tensor.

Consider first the stress tensor T. The stresses in a material may cause dilations or torques, and we distinguish between these by labelling the former P (for pressure) and the latter S (for shear). Figure 2.19 shows these stresses in an infinitely small volume (such that the stress is uniform).

If the element of volume in Figure 2.19 is to be in equilibrium and not to rotate under the action of the couples, then we must have

$$t^S_{\alpha\beta} = t^S_{\beta\alpha} \qquad (2.69)$$

so that the stress tensor in its most general form is defined in terms of six

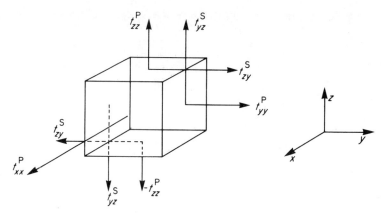

Figure 2.19   Stresses in an infinitely small volume; $t^S_{\alpha\beta}$ are shear stresses, $t^P_{\alpha\alpha}$ are compressional stresses

independent components, namely

$$T \equiv \begin{pmatrix} t^P_{xx} & t^S_{xy} & t^S_{xz} \\ t^S_{xy} & t^P_{yy} & t^S_{yz} \\ t^S_{xz} & t^S_{yz} & t^P_{zz} \end{pmatrix}. \tag{2.70}$$

The stresses produce strains and these are described by the strain tensor E. Since there are a maximum of six independent stress components, there are also a maximum of six independent strain components, and these may be written explicitly from equation (2.68):

$$t^P_{xx} = C_{11}e_{xx} + C_{12}e_{yy} + C_{13}e_{zz} + C_{14}e_{yz} + C_{15}e_{zx} + C_{16}e_{xy} \tag{2.71a}$$

$$t^P_{yy} = C_{21}e_{xx} + C_{22}e_{yy} + C_{23}e_{zz} + C_{24}e_{yz} + C_{25}e_{zx} + C_{26}e_{xy} \tag{2.71b}$$

$$t^P_{zz} = C_{31}e_{xx} + C_{32}e_{yy} + C_{33}e_{zz} + C_{34}e_{yz} + C_{35}e_{zx} + C_{36}e_{xy} \tag{2.71c}$$

$$t^S_{yz} = C_{41}e_{xx} + C_{42}e_{yy} + C_{43}e_{zz} + C_{44}e_{yz} + C_{45}e_{zx} + C_{46}e_{xy} \tag{2.71d}$$

$$t^S_{zx} = C_{51}e_{xx} + C_{52}e_{yy} + C_{53}e_{zz} + C_{54}e_{yz} + C_{55}e_{zx} + C_{56}e_{xy} \tag{2.71e}$$

$$t^S_{xy} = C_{61}e_{xx} + C_{62}e_{yy} + C_{63}e_{zz} + C_{64}e_{yz} + C_{65}e_{zx} + C_{66}e_{xy}. \tag{2.71f}$$

In equations (2.71) the conventional abbreviations for the subscripts on the coefficients has been employed: $xx \to 1$, $yy \to 2$, $zz \to 3$, $yz \to 4$, $zx \to 5$ and $xy \to 6$. The C_{ij} are called elastic constants and may be related to the moduli of elasticity theory. The requirement that the body be in equilibrium has reduced the number of equations from nine to six and hence has reduced the number of elastic constants from 81 to 36. Even for the general case we can reduce this further. Consider the energy of an elastically strained crystal W.

$$-dW = t_{xx}\,de_{xx} + t_{yy}\,de_{yy} + t_{zz}\,de_{zz} + t_{yz}\,de_{yz} + t_{zx}\,de_{zx} + t_{xy}\,de_{xy}. \tag{2.72a}$$

We may also write formally

$$dW = \frac{\partial W}{\partial e_{xx}}\,de_{xx} + \frac{\partial W}{\partial e_{yy}}\,de_{yy} + \frac{\partial W}{\partial e_{zz}}\,de_{zz} + \frac{\partial W}{\partial e_{yz}}\,de_{yz} + \frac{\partial W}{\partial e_{zx}}\,de_{zx} + \frac{\partial W}{\partial e_{xy}}\,de_{xy} \tag{2.72b}$$

and comparing coefficients

$$t_{\alpha\beta} = -\frac{\partial W}{\partial e_{\alpha\beta}}. \tag{2.73}$$

Now, from equations (2.71)

$$C_{\alpha\beta,\gamma\delta} = \frac{\partial t_{\alpha\beta}}{\partial e_{\gamma\delta}}$$

or

$$C_{ij} = \frac{\partial t_i}{\partial e_j} \tag{2.74}$$

(using the same abbreviated notation as before for i, j from 1 to 6). Thus, from equations (2.73) and (2.74) we have

$$C_{ij} = -\frac{\partial}{\partial e_j}\frac{\partial W}{\partial e_i}.$$

Similarly

$$C_{ji} = -\frac{\partial}{\partial e_i}\frac{\partial W}{\partial e_j}$$

and we see the general result

$$C_{ij} = C_{ji} \tag{2.75}$$

making the matrix of the elastic constants symmetric and the number of independent elements 21.

Further reductions may be made in the number of independent elastic constants by taking account of the symmetry of the crystal and the form of the interatomic interactions. The relations between the constants C_{ij} and the moduli of macroscopic elasticity theory are best derived for specific symmetries, since the algebra is tedious for the general case of 21 constants. As an example of the procedure consider the simplest case—a cubic crystal.

For a cubic crystal:

$$C_{ij} = 0 \quad \text{for } i \neq j \quad \text{and} \quad i > 2 \quad \text{or } j > 2$$

$$C_{11} = C_{22} = C_{33}$$

$$C_{44} = C_{55} = C_{66}$$

$$C_{12} = C_{23} = C_{31}.$$

Hence the elastic constant matrix is

$$
\begin{pmatrix}
C_{11} & C_{12} & C_{12} & 0 & 0 & 0 \\
C_{12} & C_{11} & C_{12} & 0 & 0 & 0 \\
C_{12} & C_{12} & C_{11} & 0 & 0 & 0 \\
0 & 0 & 0 & C_{44} & 0 & 0 \\
0 & 0 & 0 & 0 & C_{44} & 0 \\
0 & 0 & 0 & 0 & 0 & C_{44}
\end{pmatrix}
\tag{2.76}
$$

in which there are only three independent constants: C_{11}, C_{12} and C_{44}.

Young's modulus is defined as the longitudinal stress produced by a unit strain when the body is unconstrained in the transverse directions, i.e. $E = t^P_{xx}/e_{xx}$ when e_{yy} and e_{zz} are free to change and $t^P_{yy} = t^P_{zz} = 0$.

Using equations (2.71a, b and c) we get

$$t^P_{xx} = C_{11}e_{xx} + C_{12}(e_{yy} + e_{zz})$$

$$0 = C_{11}e_{yy} + C_{12}(e_{xx} + e_{zz})$$

$$0 = C_{11}e_{zz} + C_{12}(e_{xx} + e_{yy})$$

and it is a simple matter to eliminate e_{yy} and e_{zz} to find

$$E = \frac{(C_{11} - C_{12})(C_{11} + 2C_{12})}{C_{11} + C_{12}}. \tag{2.77}$$

Similarly, relations for the other elastic moduli may be derived and these may be used to compare experimental results with elastic constants calculated from lattice dynamics.

The velocities of elastic waves in crystals may be expressed in terms of the constants C_{ij}; for example, it is easily seen that

$$v_{\text{long}}[100] = \left(\frac{C_{11}}{\rho}\right)^{1/2} \tag{2.78a}$$

$$v_{\text{trans}}[100] = \left(\frac{C_{44}}{\rho}\right)^{1/2} \tag{2.78b}$$

$$v_{\text{trans}}[110] = \left(\frac{C_{11} - C_{12}}{2\rho}\right)^{1/2}. \tag{2.78c}$$

Equations (2.78b and c) provide a useful condition of isotropy. For an isotropic body the transverse velocity should be the same in all directions; so, from equations (2.78)

$$C_{11} - C_{12} = 2C_{44} \tag{2.79}$$

for isotropy. Thus Young's modulus for an isotropic material is

$$E_{\text{iso}} = \frac{C_{44}(3C_{12} + 2C_{44})}{C_{12} + C_{44}}. \tag{2.80a}$$

[The corresponding expression from classical elasticity theory is $E_{\text{iso}} = \mu(3\lambda + 2\mu)/(\lambda + \mu)$ where λ and μ are Lamé's constants.]

The other isotropic moduli are:
Bulk modulus:

$$B_{\text{iso}} = C_{12} + \tfrac{2}{3}C_{44}. \tag{2.80b}$$

Poisson ratio:

$$v_{\text{iso}} = \frac{C_{12}}{2C_{12} + C_{44}}. \tag{2.80c}$$

Modulus of rigidity (or shear modulus):

$$S = C_{44} \tag{2.80d}$$

If the forces acting between atoms (or molecules) are central, no internal strains will be created by elastic stresses and the elastic constants obey the relations

$$C_{12} = C_{66}, \quad C_{23} = C_{44}, \quad C_{31} = C_{55}$$
$$C_{14} = C_{56}, \quad C_{25} = C_{64}, \quad C_{36} = C_{45}. \tag{2.81a}$$

These are the Cauchy relations and for a cubic crystal become

$$C_{12} = C_{44}. \tag{2.81b}$$

We shall discuss later the extent to which this relation is obeyed by real crystals.

Although we shall not pursue it in our discussions, the theory of elasticity outlined in this section (due mainly to Cauchy) is not strictly general. The symmetry assumptions for the tensor quantities are not necessarily valid if the crystal is anisotropic and there are non-central contributions to the force of interaction. There are experimental measurements (for example, measurements of the transverse velocity of sound to show $C_{44} \neq C_{55}$ in some cubic crystals) to invalidate the reduction to 21 independent elastic constants and to support the theory due to Laval[61-63] in which there are 45 independent elastic constants. Nevertheless the Cauchy theory is adequate for our discussions. For some crystals (e.g. ionic crystals) the theory must include piezoelectric effects and the stress–strain relationships are not purely elastic in their coupling.

Equations (2.78) and corresponding equations for other directions give the velocity of waves in the lattice whose wave vectors tend to zero. Measurements of these velocities yield values for the elastic constants. Born and Huang have discussed at length the elastic, dielectric and piezoelectric effects in crystals, and we shall be making reference to some of their results and detailed derivations. Our lattice dynamical methods enable values of C_{ij} to be calculated. For a cubic crystal, the theory of elasticity yields the relation (known sometimes as the Green–Cristoffel equation; see, for example, Love[64]):

$$
\begin{vmatrix}
C_{11}k_1^2 + C_{44}(k_2^2 + k_3^2) & (C_{12} + C_{44})k_1k_2 & (C_{12} + C_{44})k_1k_3 \\
- \rho v^2 k^2 & & \\
(C_{12} + C_{44})k_1k_2 & C_{11}k_2^2 + C_{44}(k_3^2 + k_1^2) & (C_{12} + C_{44})k_2k_3 \\
& - \rho v^2 k^2 & \\
(C_{12} + C_{44})k_1k_3 & (C_{12} + C_{44})k_2k_3 & C_{11}k_3^2 + C_{44}(k_1^2 + k_2^2) \\
& & - \rho v^2 k^2
\end{vmatrix} = 0.
$$

$$(2.82)$$

For small values of **k** (long waves) the dynamical matrix may also be expressed in this form and, by comparing coefficients, expressions for the elastic constants in terms of the interatomic force law may be obtained. Tables 2.2 show some selected experimental and theoretical values of the quantities discussed in this section.

Our treatment has concerned perfect crystals; however, many solids cannot be obtained in single-crystal form, and experimental work must be carried out on polycrystalline material. Thus, to compare theory and experiment, averages over the theoretical results must be made. Hill[65] has deduced one such average for the shear modulus of a polycrystal in terms of the basic elastic constants for a cubic crystal:

$$
S_{(\text{Hill})} = \frac{(C_{11} - C_{12}) + 3C_{44}}{10} + \frac{5}{2}\left[\frac{4}{C_{11} - C_{12}} + \frac{3}{C_{44}}\right]^{-1}. \qquad (2.83)
$$

The bulk elastic properties of a polycrystalline material are istropic and may be described in terms of the bulk modulus B and the shear modulus S. We may suppose, reasonably, that B is the same for a polycrystal as for an

Table 2.2(a) Elastic constants for the inert-gas solids Ne, Ar, Kr and Xe. The lattice dynamical model employed is shown in the first column: n.n.o. = nearest neighbours only, a.n. = all neighbours (meaning the lattice sums include as many neighbours as are necessary to achieve convergence). For the three-parameter potential, C is the value of the van der Waal's coefficient. The parameters of all these potentials are included in the tables in Appendix A. All results refer to $T = 0$ unless otherwise stated. $A = 2C_{44}/(C_{11} - C_{12})$ measures the departure from isotropy. In addition to these results Gsänger et al.[69] have measured $v_l[110] = 1446 \pm 7$ m/s at $T = 4.2$ K and 1291 ± 6 m/s at $T = 76.8$ K. It can be seen from earlier in this section that $v_l[110] = [(C_{11} + C_{12} + 2C_{44})/2\rho]^{1/2}$ which gives, for example, 1584 m/s (n.n.o. 12-6).

It is important to note that the meaning of the results depends on the correct interpretation of the experiment. Different measurements (e.g. low-frequency inelastic neutron scattering) yield the adiabatic elastic constants (Cowley[70]).

Model	Single crystal $v_l[100]$ $(10^2$ m/s)	$v_t[100]$ $(10^2$ m/s)	$v_t[110]$ $(10^2$ m/s)	C_{11} $(10^9$ N/m²)	C_{12} $(10^9$ N/m²)	C_{44} $(10^9$ N/m²)	A	B^{theor} $(10^9$ N/m²) 71,72,76	Polycrystal S_{Hill} $(10^9$ N/m²)	S_{HL} $(10^9$ N/m²)	$a_{l,HL}$ $(10^2$ m/s)	$a_{t,HL}$ $(10^2$ m/s)
Neon												
12-6 (a.n.)	7.47	6.36	4.05	0.84	0.34	0.61	2.47		0.453*†	0.435*†	8.29*†	5.17*†
12-6 (n.n.o.)								1.02	0.462*†	0.457*†	8.24*†	5.30*†
12-9-6 (a.n., $C = -0.47 \times 10^{-78}$)									0.505†			
									0.42			
Argon												
12-6 (a.n.)	13.70	10.62	6.56	3.32	1.80	1.99	2.22		1.36	1.31*	15.12*	8.58*
12-6 (n.n.o.)	14.20	10.19	7.40	3.57	1.63	1.84	1.89	2.62	1.42	1.40*	15.29*	8.88*
12-9-6 (a.n., $C = -5.57 \times 10^{-78}$)	15.21	11.63	7.41	4.10	2.15	2.40	2.46		1.67			
Krypton												
12-6 (a.n.)	11.77	9.00	5.54	4.28	2.38	2.50	2.64		1.70	1.63	12.96*	7.27*
12-6 (n.n.o.)	12.18	8.68	6.22	4.58	2.19	2.32	1.94	3.21	1.78	1.75*	13.12*	7.52*
12-9-6 (a.n., $C = -10.72 \times 10^{-78}$)	13.19	9.96	6.32	5.37	2.91	3.06	2.48		2.13			
Xenon												
12-6 (a.n.)	11.44	8.71	5.35	4.96	2.79	2.88	2.65		1.95	1.90	12.60	7.03
12-6 (n.n.o.)	11.84	8.41	5.99	5.31	2.59	2.68	1.97	3.64	2.04	2.03	12.75	7.27
12-9-6 (a.n., $C = -27.62 \times 10^{-78}$)	12.69	9.54	6.03	6.10	3.35	3.45	2.51		2.39			

* Results taken from Horton and Leech.[15]

† Calculated using an incorrect value of the lattice spacing ($a = 4.350$ Å instead of 4.460 Å)

Table 2.2(b) Experimental quantities for comparison

	B[73] (10^9 N/m^2)	v_l (polycrystal) (10^2 m/s)	v_t (polycrystal) (10^2 m/s)
Neon	1·12 ± 0·03	11·31 ± 0·14[74]	6·33 ± 0·09[74]
Argon	2·67 ± 0·04	16·40[75]	9·44[75]
			9·7 ± 0·3[77]
Krypton	3·44 ± 0·04		
Xenon	3·6 ± 0·1		

Table 2.2(c) Crystalline elastic constants of some ionic crystals

Ionic crystals	C_{11} (10^9 N/m^2)	C_{12} (10^9 N/m^2)	C_{44} (10^9 N/m^2)
NaCl	49·4	13·7	12·8
NaBr	33·0	13·1	13·3
KCl	37·0	8·1	7·9
KBr	33·0	5·8	5·2
KI	26·7	4·3	4·2
AgCl*	60·5	36·4	6·24
CaF$_2$*	164	44·8	33·8

Table 2.2(d) Crystalline elastic constants of some metals (for good review and tables of elastic constants see Huntingdon[79])

Metals (cubic)	C_{11} (10^9 N/m^2)	C_{12} (10^9 N/m^2)	C_{44} (10^9 N/m^2)
Al	108	62	28
Cu	170	123	75
Pb	48	41	14
K	4·6	3·7	2·6
Fe	237	1·41	1·16
Ag	120	89·7	43·6
Au	194	166	40
W	513	206	153

isotropic single crystal, namely as given by equation (2.80b). S is more difficult. Horton and Leech[15] found it necessary to convert their calculations of the elastic properties of the inert gas solids into those appropriate to polycrystalline samples, since at that time there were no single crystals available for experiment. The found a value for $S_{\text{(polycrystal)}}$ by assuming that the polycrystal was a Debye solid, and hence obtained a value for the Debye temperature [$\theta_D \equiv (\hbar/k_B)\omega_D$, where ω_D is given by equation (2.3)]. The transverse and longitudinal velocities involved are related to B and S. Horton and Leech substituted into this expression a value of θ_D evaluated by a method due to de Launay[66-68] and thus obtained values of v_l, v_t and S to compare with measurements on polycrystals. Although the method is open to some criticism of the interpretation in equating these two expressions for the Debye temperature, it does provide a simple and convenient comparison between theory and experiment. The experimental errors in results available to these authors at the time certainly exceeded the inaccuracy in the identity invoked. Some of their results are included in Table 2.2(a).

The examples quoted in the Tables 2.2 show clear groupings. Apart from those marked with an asterisk, the ionic crystals in Table 2.2(c) show a close approximation to the Cauchy relation (2.81b). Silver chloride has a sodium chloride structure, but the silver ion is clearly non-symmetrical and calcium fluoride has no centre of symmetry [all others included in Table 2.2(c) do]. They are included to show the effect of symmetry on the elastic behaviour. The metals in Table 2.2(d) have considerably greater elastic strength and they exhibit strong violation of the Cauchy relation, thus indicating that it would be wrong to assume a spherical symmetry in the bonding between atoms. AgCl has elastic constants more appropriate to the group of metals than to ionic crystals, and this property is exploited in stress–strain models which need to be transparent and to represent metallic behaviour.

Table 2.2(a) is of a different character in that it compares the results calculated using various models. Some corresponding experimental values are shown in Table 2.2(b). It is not intended that it should be complete, and further comparisons are readily available in the quoted sources. The value of $A[\equiv 2C_{44}/(C_{11} - C_{12})]$ is a crude measure of the degree of isotropy; for isotropy $A = 1$. It is apparent that the inclusion of more atoms in the model introduces greater anisotropy. This is physically unsatisfactory and probably results from the same inadequacy of the form of the potential that leads to the findings of Horton and Leech. They conclude that a nearest-neighbour-only model gives results in better agreement with experiment. We see also that the heavier atoms are more anisotropic but that they obey Cauchy's relation more closely. Elastic constants are discussed again in Section 4.7, where further and more recent references are included.

2.12   The frequency distribution

The Debye model expresses the summation over the allowed modes in terms of a frequency distribution or density of states rather than in terms of a dispersion relation. The dispersion contains much more detailed information than averages such as are produced by summations. Thermodynamic quantities are averages over the details of the fundamental excitations of the lattice. This suggests that it may be possible to express them directly in terms of averages over the frequency spectrum. Such averages are the 'moments' of the frequency spectrum. The average over the frequency itself is the 'first moment' μ_1, the average of the squares of the frequencies is the 'second moment' μ_2, the average over the cubes of the frequencies is the 'third moment' μ_3, and so on.

$$\mu_n \equiv \frac{1}{3N} \int_0^{\omega_{max}} \omega^n Z(\omega)\, d\omega. \qquad (2.84)$$

The first attempt to make use of such averages was by Thirring.[80,81] He expressed the high-temperature specific heat as a series of even moments:

$$\frac{C_V}{3Nk_B} = 1 - \frac{B_2}{2!}\left(\frac{\hbar}{k_B T}\right)^2 \mu_2 + \frac{3B_4}{4!}\left(\frac{\hbar}{k_B T}\right)^4 \mu_4 - \frac{5B_6}{6!}\left(\frac{\hbar}{k_B T}\right)^6 \mu_6 \qquad (2.85)$$

where the general term is (for n even integers only)

$$(-1)^{n/2} \frac{(n-1)}{n!} B_n$$

and B_n is a Bernoulli number, some of which are given in Table 2.3. The method was taken up by Montroll[82-84] in a series of papers and he devised expressions for the even moments up to the fourteenth. Barron[85] and Horton and Schiff[86] have used the method for other thermodynamic quantities. Salter[87,88] in a thesis and in a publication with Domb[89] has dealt with the problem of calculating the moments without having first to calculate details of the spectrum. In particular they show how the first moment (related to the zero point energy of the lattice) may be expressed in terms of these known even moments. For a face-centred cubic crystal they deduced (for nearest neighbours only) that:

$$\text{zero point energy} = 1{\cdot}0225\hbar\left(\frac{8\alpha}{m}\right)^{1/2}. \qquad (2.86)$$

where α is the nearest-neighbour force constant and m the atomic mass, i.e. $(8\alpha/m)^{1/2}$ is the maximum lattice frequency. Later, more accurate, work[90] found a value of $1{\cdot}02266215 \pm 5$ in the last figure; this work also gives calculations up to the 34th even moment to the same accuracy.

Table 2.3 Bernoulli numbers up to B_{14}. (Care must be taken with these in the literature. Some authors use slightly different definitions than the one employed here)

n	0	2	4	6	8	10	12	14
B_n	1	$\frac{1}{6}$	$\frac{1}{30}$	$\frac{1}{42}$	$\frac{1}{30}$	$\frac{5}{66}$	$\frac{691}{2730}$	$\frac{7}{6}$

Although initially based on a high-temperature series expansion, the method has been extended into the low-temperature region by Domb and Isenberg[91] who analytically continued the series of equations (2.85) by the use of Padé approximants.[92-94]

At the present time the determination of density of states or frequency distribution presents no particular problems beyond the determination of the normal modes. Modern large and fast computers deal with the equivalent of 10^6 modes in times of the order of 10^3 s. Hence accurate densities of states may be obtained quite painlessly. This, however, was not the case in 1940, when much interest was being revived in the problem. Sampling methods were tedious, and analytical methods were proposed to avoid the vast numerical task. Although no analytical method succeeded in producing a satisfactory frequency distribution, two of the methods proved useful in other contexts. One of these we have already discussed—the moments method; the other was an attempt by Houston[95] to find the distribution by evaluating the normal modes at points at which it was easy to do so (along symmetry lines) and to interpolate between these points, invoking the symmetry of the lattice. The method has been developed[96] to provide a very useful technique for the evaluation of thermodynamic quantities.

Houston's method exploits the symmetry of the Brillouin zone. A sum over the reciprocal lattice of any function is carried out by replacing it by an integral (this is a very good approximation, since there are N values of $\mathbf{k}$ in each Brillouin zone, where N is the number of unit cells) and then evaluating that integral along certain directions distributed in the irreducible part of the zone. The values of the function between these lines are found by interpolation by expanding the function in terms of polynomials with the same symmetry as the function. For example, all cubic crystals (simple, body-centred and face-centred cubic) are invariant under transformations of the full cubic symmetry group (the irreducible portion of the Brillouin zone being $\frac{1}{48}$th part of the whole), and so the lowest-order polynomials with this symmetry are used; for tetragonal structures[97] we would use polynomials with tetragonal symmetry, and so on. Appendix H contains some tables of functions that are suitable for this procedure for various structures.

Suppose we are interested in a cubic crystal and choose the three symmetry directions—we have seen in Section 2.10 that the dispersion is easier to calculate along six particular directions (including the symmetry directions) in which the dynamical matrix factorizes. We must select three lowest-order polynomials which possess full cubic symmetry, i.e. they have the same value if the sign of any component (cartesian) is changed or for any permutation of the components. Moreover, they must be mutually orthogonal with all other members of the set, otherwise they are not independent and the expansion contains redundancies.

Von der Lage and Bethe[98] have given a classification of 'Kubic' harmonics which Houston used in his original paper. These are also contained, along with other polynomials for various crystals, in Reference 99 (see Appendix H). If $f(\mathbf{k})$ is the function to be integrated over the Brillouin zone, we expand

$$f(\mathbf{k}) = \sum_{i=1}^{n} C_i \chi_i(\mathbf{k}) \qquad (2.87)$$

where n is the number of directions, in this case three. Therefore the required integral

$$F = \int_0^{\pi} \int_0^{2\pi} f(\mathbf{k}) \sin \theta \, d\theta \, d\phi$$

$$= 4\pi C_1 \qquad (2.88)$$

since the lowest-order polynomial is $\chi_1 = 1$ and all other χ_i must be orthogonal to χ_1. Hence from the value of $f(\mathbf{k})$ along $\mathbf{k}$, we can find F from the coefficient of χ_1 in the expansion. Generalizing this we may write

$$F = \sum_{[\mathbf{k}]} C(\mathbf{k}) f(\mathbf{k}) \qquad (2.89)$$

and hence we have n simultaneous equations:

$$\sum_{[\mathbf{k}]} C(\mathbf{k}) = 1 \qquad (2.90a)$$

$$\sum_{[\mathbf{k}]} C(\mathbf{k}) \chi_i(\mathbf{k}) = 0, \qquad i = 2, 3, \cdots, n. \qquad (2.90b)$$

Using the chosen set of $\chi_i(\mathbf{k})$, we may solve equations (2.90) and find the n values of $C(\mathbf{k})$.

Using three directions and

$$\chi_1 = 1 \qquad (2.91a)$$

$$\chi_2 = x^4 + y^4 + z^4 - 3/5 \qquad (2.91b)$$

$$\chi_3 = x^2 y^2 z^2 + \chi_2/22 - 1/105 \qquad (2.91c)$$

Houston found

$$C[100] = \frac{4\pi}{35} \cdot 10 \qquad C[110] = \frac{4\pi}{35} \cdot 16 \qquad C[111] = \frac{4\pi}{35} \cdot 9. \qquad (2.92)$$

Thus we can find the integral of $f(\mathbf{k})$ by integrating along each of the three lines (say by Simpson's rule) and the angular integration is performed using equation (2.89) together with the constants (2.92). Betts *et al.*[96] have calculated up to six direction formulae and discussed the relative merits of eight expressions with different choices of directions. The expression involving the six directions along which the dynamical matrix factorizes is the most satisfactory. This is

$$I = \frac{4\pi}{1081080}\{117603\,I[100] + 76544\,I[110] + 17496\,I[111]$$

$$+ 381250\,I[210] + 311040\,I[211] + 177147\,I[221]\}. \qquad (2.93)$$

Another method used in the 1940s was remarkable for its originality. Leighton[100] made models of constant-frequency curves in plaster of paris. By weighing different sections of the model he was able to produce the most satisfactory frequency distribution available at the time, and hindsight shows just how meticulous he must have been with the structure and measurements.

One of the problems generating much of the difficulty was the existence of singularities.[101] van Hove[102] has shown that these arise from points of zero gradient in the dispersion $[\partial\omega(\mathbf{k}, j)/\partial\mathbf{k} = 0]$ and they yield discontinuities in $\partial g(\omega)/\partial\omega$. By a topological method he proved a theorem that requires that there must be at least one of these discontinuities (critical points) and also that the gradient of $g(\omega)$ against ω at ω_{max} must tend to $-\infty$.

The analysis of van Hove and the subsequent calculations enable the frequency spectrum to be investigated with accuracy, even close to these singularities.

Figures 2.20 are examples of frequency distributions.

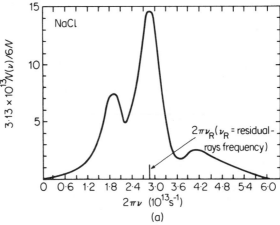

Figure 2.20   Sample frequency-distribution curves: (a) Kellerman's rigid ion model,[37] (b) shell model,[49] (c) deformation dipole,[45] (d) deformation dipole[45] and (e) measured by neutron scattering. [(a) is reproduced from Kellerman, E. W., *Proc. Roy. Soc.*, **A178**, 20, (1941), by permission of The Council of The Royal Society, London; (b) and (e) are reproduced, with permission, from Cowley, R. A., Cochran, W., Brockhouse, B. N., and Woods, D. B., *Phys. Rev.*, **131**, 1030–1039 (1963); (c) and (d) are reproduced, with permission, from Karo, A. M., and Hardy, J. R., *Phys. Rev.*, **129**, 2024–2036 (1963).]

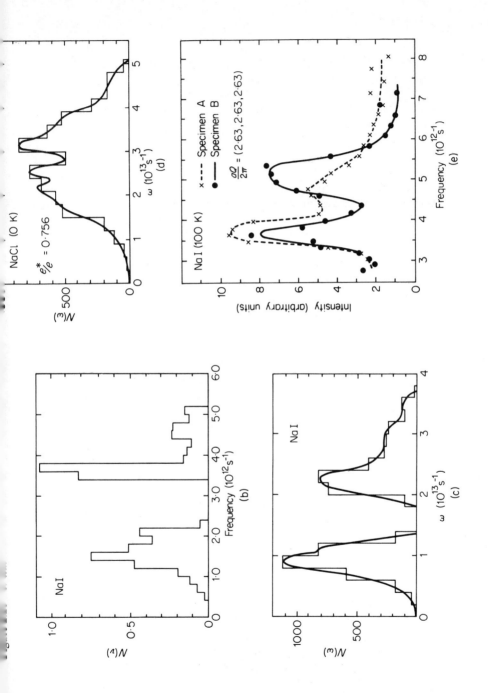

(b)

NaI

(c)

NaI

NaCl (0 K)

$e^*/e = 0.756$

(d)

NaI (100 K)

× × × × × Specimen A

●————● Specimen B

$\frac{aQ}{2\pi} = (2.63, 2.63, 2.63)$

(e)

2.13 Summary

We began this chapter with the approximations used by **Einstein** and by **Debye** in their treatments of the theory of **specific heat** of a solid. These were highly successful and were recognized immediately to be so; moreover, the approximations are useful in some circumstances even today. The more fundamental approach of **Born and von Karman** dealt directly with the equations of motion of atoms of a solid. However, the complexity of the **interatomic interactions** resulted in the passing of nearly twenty-five years before it was seriously taken up as a method of calculating the thermodynamic properties of a solid.

The theory of solids is considerably simplified by exploiting the **space periodicity** that characterizes **crystalline** solids. There has been much interest recently in amorphous solids,[103,104] but we shall not consider these. The properties of any **excitation** in the lattice (including electrons and the like) are governed by the periodicity, the effects being summarized by a **Bloch wave function**. In order that the problem is not complicated by **surface effects**, we would like to regard the atoms we consider as forming part of an **infinite crystal**. However, this introduces other problems such as the **extensive thermodynamic functions** becoming infinite. A mathematical device provides a solution to this; the surfaces are eliminated by the use of **cyclic boundary conditions**.

The lattice is a **dispersive medium** to any of the excitations it can support; the **group velocity** of the excitations is dependent on the **wave vector** (or the momentum). Thus the relation between the **energy** and the wave vector (or momentum) is not simple. The **normal modes** belong to distinct **branches** of the frequency spectrum corresponding to the different **degrees of freedom** of the lattice. If there is only **one** atom per **unit cell**, there are three branches, one being **longitudinal** type and the other two being **transverse** types. They are truly longitudinal and transverse only along **symmetry** directions. These three are **acoustic** modes. When there is more than one atom in each unit cell there are more degrees of freedom, and these account for the **optic** modes. Acoustic modes are characterized by having energies which tend to zero for infinite wavelength (zero wave vector); optic modes have high energies for infinite wavelength. The details of the **dispersion** are computed by **lattice dynamical** procedures such as the Born–von Karman method, which assumes that the interactions between atoms may be expressed in terms of a **potential function** involving only the **nuclear coordinates**. Thus a knowledge of the forces between atoms is required—a problem that is not easily soluble. It is usually necessary to invoke an **empirical** law of interaction and fit the parameters to experimental data (although there is often a broad theoretical justification for the form used). We have discussed the necessity of **classifying** crystals into certain groups, since no theory is valid over the whole range of solids.

It becomes impossible to treat calculations of the dispersion at a general level, and we resorted to examples representative of each of the classes.

For very **long waves** of the acoustic branches, the solid behaves like an **elastic continuum**. The crystalline **elastic constants** (evaluated in terms of **force constants** summed over the lattice) may be related to the elastic constants of macroscopic theory. This provides us with one method of fitting the parameters of the interatomic potential function. From the elastic constants we may also calculate a value of the **equivalent Debye temperature** (see Chapter 4). Elastic constants also provide information about the **symmetry** of the forces (**Cauchy's relation**) and the degree of **anisotropy** (**isotropy** being defined by equating velocities of waves in different directions).

As a prelude to the discussion of thermodynamics in Chapter 4, we have seen that it is possible to avoid the vast calculation of all the modes by averaging techniques. These are not very satisfactory for deducing the **frequency distribution** itself, but can be made very accurate for quantities that are, essentially, average—the **thermodynamic quantities**. The computation of the **dispersion relations** and the frequency distribution (or the **density of states**) is the prime object of lattice dynamics; it is a short step from there to the equilibrium properties of the solid.

Chapter notes

[a] This is a relic of old quantum theory. It should be remembered that $r = a$ represents the locus of the maximum probability density for the electron in its lowest level. The mean is given by $\langle r \rangle = \frac{3}{2}a$ and $\langle r^2 \rangle$ is given by equation (2.43).

[b] These were computed from the refractive indices in the optical region by Tessman, Kahn and Shockley,[59] and are somewhat larger than Pauling's values[58] for the positive ions and somewhat smaller for the negative ions.

References

1. Einstein, A., *Ann. Physik*, **22**, 180–190, 800 (1906).
2. Einstein, A., *Ann. Physik*, **35**, 679–694 (1911).
3. Debye, P., *Ann. Physik*, **39**, 789–839 (1912).
4. Dekker, A. J., *Solid State Physics*, Macmillan, London, 1960.
5. Born, M., and von Karman, Th., *Z. Phys.*, **13**, 297–309 (1912).
6. Born, M., and von Karman, Th., *Z. Phys.*, **14**, 15–19 (1913).
7. Blackman, M., *Z. Phys.*, **86**, 421 (1933).
8. Blackman, M., *Proc. Roy. Soc. (London)*, **A148**, 365–406 (1935).
9. Blackman, M., *Proc. Roy. Soc. (London)*, **A159**, 416–431 (1937).
10. Blackman, M., *Proc. Camb. Phil. Soc.*, **33**, 94–103 (1937).
11. Blackman, M., *Rep. Prog. Phys.*, **8**, 11–30 (1941).
12. Blackman, M., in *Handb. der Physik* (Ed. S. Flugge), Vol. 7, Part 1, Springer Verlag, Berlin, 1955.
13. Bloch, F., *Z. Physik*, **52**, 555–600 (1928).
14. Whittaker, E. T., and Watson, G. N., *Modern Analysis*, Cambridge University Press, New York, 1943, p. 412.

15. Horton, G. K., and Leech, J. W., *Proc. Phys. Soc.*, **82**, 816–854 (1963).
16. Cochran, W., *Proc. Roy. Soc.*, **A253**, 260–276 (1959).
17. London, F., and Eisenshitz, R., *Z. Physik*, **60**, 491–527 (1930).
18. Scott, W. T., *The Physics of Electricity and Magnetism*, 2nd ed., Wiley, 1966, p. 107.
19. Merzbacher, E., *Quantum Mechanics*, 2nd ed., Wiley, New York, 1970, p. 204.
20. Born, M., and Huang, K., *Dynamical Theory of Crystal Lattices*, Oxford University Press, 1954.
21. Margenau, H., *Rev. Mod. Phys.*, **11**, 1–40 (1939).
22. Mie, G., *Ann. Phys. Lpz.*, **11**, 657–697 (1903).
23. Lennard Jones, J. E., *Proc. Roy. Soc.*, **A106**, 463–477 (1924).
24. Madelung, E., *Z. Physik*, **11**, 898–905 (1910).
25. Evjen, H. M., *Phys. Rev.*, **39**, 675–687 (1932).
26. Madelung, E., *Z. Physik*, **19**, 524–532 (1918).
27. Ewald, P. P., *Ann. Physik*, **64**, 253 (1921).
28. Mott, N. F., *Rep. Prog. Phys.*, **25**, 218–242 (1962).
29. Mott, N. F., and Gurney, R. W., *Electronic Processes in Ionic Crystals*, 2nd ed., Oxford University Press, 1948.
30. Slater J. C., *Quantum Theory of Molecules and Solids*, Vols. 1, 2 and 3, McGraw-Hill, New York, 1965. (Volume 2 is particularly useful; this book contains a comprehensive list of references.)
31. Herman, F., *J. Phys. Chem Solids*, **8**, 405–418 (1959).
32. Dick, B. G., and Overhauser, A. W., *Phys. Rev.*, **112**, 90–103 (1958).
33. Harrison, W. A., in *Phonons, Scottish University Summer School, 1965* (Ed. Stevenson), Oliver and Boyd, London, 1966, pp. 73–109.
34. Harrison, W. A., *Pseudopotentials in the Theory of Metals*, Benjamin, New York, 1966.
35. Pollack, G. L., *Rev. Mod. Phys.*, **36**, 748–791 (1964).
36. Born, M., and Oppenheimer, J. R., *Ann. Physik*, **84**, 457–484 (1927).
37. Kellerman, E. W., *Phil. Trans. Roy. Soc.*, **A238**, 513–548 (1940).
38. Karo, A. M., *J. Chem. Phys.*, **31**, 1489–1499 (1959).
39. Karo, A. M., *J. Chem. Phys.*, **33**, 7–20 (1960).
40. Szigeti, B., *Trans. Far. Soc.*, **45**, 155–166 (1949).
41. Szigeti, B., *Proc. Roy. Soc. (London)*, **A204**, 51–62 (1950).
42. Burstein, E., *Phonons and Phonon Interactions* (Ed. T. A. Bak), Benjamin, 1964.
43. Hardy, J. R., *Phil. Mag.*, **4**, 1278–1281 (1959).
44. Hardy, J. R., *Phil. Mag.*, **6**, 27–35 (1961).
45. Karo, A. M., and Hardy, J. R., *Phys. Rev.*, **129**, 2024–2036 (1963).
46. Hardy, J. R., *Phil. Mag.*, **7**, 315–336 (1962).
47. Jaswal, S. S., and Montgomery, D. J., *Phys. Rev.*, **135**, A1257–A1261 (1964).
48. Cowley, R. A., *Proc. Roy. Soc.*, **A268**, 109–119 (1962).
49. Cowley, R. A., Cochran, W., Brockhouse, B. N., and Woods, D. B., *Phys. Rev.*, **131**, 1030–1039 (1963).
50. Woods, A. D. B., Cochran, W., and Brockhouse, B. N., *Phys. Rev.*, **119**, 980–998 (1960).
51. Woods, A. D. B., Cochran, W., Brockhouse, B. N., and Cowley, R. A., *Phys. Rev.*, **131**, 1025–1029 (1963).
52. Nusslein, V., and Schroder, U., *Phys. Stat. Sol.*, **21**, 309–314 (1967).
53. Haywood, B. C. G., and Collins, M. F., *J. Phys. (C)*, **2**, 46–51 (1969).
54. Peckham, G., *Proc. Phys. Soc.*, **90**, 657–670 (1967).
55. Cochran, W., *Rep. Prog. in Phys.*, **26**, 1–45 (1963).

56. Hanlon, J. E., and Lawson, A. W., *Phys. Rev.*, **113**, 472–478 (1959).
57. Lyddane, R. H., and Herzfeld, K. F., *Phys. Rev.*, **54**, 846–861 (1938).
58. Pauling, L., *Proc. Roy. Soc.*, **A114**, 181–211 (1927).
59. Tessman, J. R., Kahn, A. H., and Schockley, W., *Phys. Rev.*, **92**, 890–895 (1953).
60. Lyddane, R. H., Sachs, R. G., and Teller, E., *Phys. Rev.*, **59**, 673–676 (1941).
61. Laval, J., *C.R. Acad. Sci. (Paris)*, **232**, 1947–1948 (1951).
62. Laval, J., *C.R. Acad. Sci. (Paris)*, **238**, 1773–1775 (1954).
63. Laval, J., *Bull. Soc. Franc. Mineral. Crist.*, **77**, 219–227 (1954).
64. Love, A. E. H., *Treatise on the Mathematical Theory of Elasticity*, Dover, New York, 1944.
65. Hill, R., *Proc. Phys. Soc.*, *A*, **65**, 349–354 (1952).
66. de Launay, J., *J. Chem. Phys.*, **22**, 1676–1677 (1954).
67. de Launay, J., *J. Chem. Phys.*, **24**, 1071 (1956).
68. de Launay, J., *J. Chem. Phys.*, **30**, 91–92 (1959).
69. Gsanger, M., Egger, H., and Luscher, E., *Phys. Letters*, **24A**, 135–136 (1967).
70. Cowley, R. A., *Proc. Phys. Soc.*, **90**, 1127–1147 (1967).
71. Barron, T. H. K., and Klein, M. L., *Proc. Phys. Soc.*, **82**, 161–173 (1963).
72. Barron, T. H. K., and Klein, M. L., *Proc. Phys. Soc.*, **85**, 523–558 (1965).
73. Urvas, A. O., Losee, D. L., and Simmons, R. O., *J. Phys. Chem. Solids*, **28**, 2269–2281 (1967).
74. Batchelder, D. N., Losee, D. L., and Simmons, R. O., *Phys. Rev.*, **162**, 767–775 (1967).
75. Peterson, O. G., Batchelder, D. N., and Simmons, R. O., *Phys. Rev.*, **150**, 703–711 (1966).
76. Brown, J. S., and Horton, G. K., *Canad. J. Phys.*, **45**, 2995–2997 (1967).
77. Jones, G. O., and Sparkes, A. R., *Phil. Mag.*, **10**, 1053–1057 (1964).
78. Bolz, L. H., and Mauer, F. A., *Advances in X-Ray Analysis*, **6**, 242–249 (1963).
79. Huntington, H. B., *S.S.P.*, **7**, 213–351 (1958).
80. Thirring, H., *Z. Phys.*, **14**, 867–873 (1913).
81. Thirring, H., *Z. Phys.*, **15**, 127–133 and 180–185 (1914).
82. Montroll, E. W., *J. Chem. Phys.*, **11**, 481–495 (1943).
83. Montroll, E. W., *J. Chem. Phys.*, **12**, 98–106 (1944).
84. Montroll, E. W., and Peaslee, D. C., *J. Chem. Phys.*, **10**, 218–229 (1942).
85. Barron, T. H. K., *Phil. Mag.*, **46**, 720–734 (1955).
86. Horton, G. K., and Schiff, H., *Proc. Roy. Soc.*, **A250**, 248–265 (1959).
87. Salter, L., *Proc. Roy. Soc.*, **A233**, 418–427 (1955).
88. Salter, L., *Phil. Mag.*, **45**, 360–368 (1954).
89. Domb, C., and Salter, L., *Phil. Mag.*, **43**, 1083–1089 (1952).
90. Isenberg, C., *Phys. Rev.*, **132**, 2427–2433 (1963).
91. Domb, C., and Isenberg, C., *Proc. Phys. Soc.*, **77**, 659–662 (1962).
92. Baker, G. A., Jr., and Gammel, J. L., *J. Mathematical Analysis and Applications*, **2**, 21–30 (1961).
93. Baker, G. A., Jr., Gammel, J. L., and Wills, J. G., *J. Mathematical Analysis and Applications*, **2**, 405–418 (1961).
94. Baker, G. A., Jr., *Phys. Rev.*, **124**, 768–774 (1961).
95. Houston, W. V., *Rev. Mod. Phys.*, **20**, 161–165 (1948).
96. Betts, D. D., Bhatia, A. B., and Wyman, M., *Phys. Rev.*, **104**, 37–42 (1956).
97. Begum, N. A., Cracknell, A. P., Joshua, S. J., and Reissland, J. A., *J. Phys. C (Solid St. Phys.)*, **2**, 2329–2334 (1969).
98. Von der Lage, F. C., and Bethe, H. A., *Phys. Rev.*, **71**, 612–622 (1947).
99. Bell, D. G., *Rev. Mod. Phys.*, **26**, 311–320 (1954).

100. Leighton, R. B., *Rev. Mod. Phys.*, **20**, 165–174 (1948).
101. Phillips, J. C., *Phys. Rev.*, **104**, 1263–1277 (1956).
102. van Hove, L., *Phys. Rev.*, **89**, 1189–1193 (1953).
103. Frechette, V. D. (Ed.), *Non-Crystalline Solids*, Wiley, New York, 1960.
104. Mott, N. F., and Davies, E. A., *Electronic Processes in Non-Crystalline Materials*, Clarendon Press, Oxford, 1971.

3

Vibrational States of a Crystal

3.1 Introduction

In Chapter 1 we considered the Hamiltonian and its energy eigenvalues for the vibrational motions of the atoms of a crystal. We limited discussion of the state itself to a few brief and qualitative comments. We have deduced the vibrational states for a single oscillator and, since we identify a crystal mode with an oscillator, we may suppose the vibrational state of the whole crystal to be a product of these non-interacting single-oscillator states. Clearly this would be a cumbersome formalism, but, since each of the $3N$ states are independent, we need only consider that part of it relevant to the phonons of interest. In fact for all practical purposes we require only a limited description:

(i) the quantum number for the state
(ii) the state of polarization
(iii) the corresponding wave vector.

(i) tells us how many units of energy are associated with a particular mode, (ii) describes the type of atomic motions carrying the energy (this is particularly important when it comes to interactions and to the excitation of states) and (iii) gives us more information about the atomic vibrations, namely (a) the phase difference between neighbouring atoms, i.e. the wavelength, (b) the momentum of the associated phonon and (c), together with the dispersion relation, the energy of the mode.

This simplified description forms the basis of a formalism which we shall use extensively.

3.2 Occupation numbers

The state (state function, eigenfunction or equivalent term) of a system is a detailed description of the condition of that system. Thus we may expect that there will be more than one method of describing states. For example, if we wished to write down the state for a gas, we might specify the positions and momenta of all the atoms making up the gas; alternatively, we could specify the allowed energies for the atoms and list how many atoms there are with each of these energies. The statistics of this is discussed in Chapter 4. The quantum mechanics of oscillators was discussed in some detail in Section 1.7, and in Section 1.8 we equated a normal mode of the whole crystal to an oscillator. Figure 1.6 is reproduced here as Figure 3.1 because we wish to relabel it according to a different interpretation.

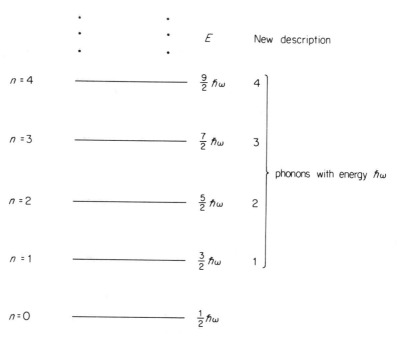

Figure 3.1   The relation between Figure 1.6 and the description of the corresponding state in terms of numbers of phonons

In describing the state of our solid, we make use of 'occupation numbers'. Figure 3.1 shows the correspondence between these and the energy levels of the oscillator. We have seen in Chapter 2 that there are $3N$ allowed modes of vibration of the crystal (not necessarily all with different frequencies) and that the angular frequency of these modes may (at least in principle) be calculated. The excitation of these modes is represented by the equivalent oscillator moving up a ladder of energy eigenvalues. Thus the state is expressed as the quantum levels of $3N$ oscillators. In our phonon description we have $3N$ distinguishable phonons (not necessarily all with different energies) which can exist in the solid. There can be any number of each such that their total energy is fixed and that they are distributed among the allowed energies according to the statistical laws governing such particles. When energy is put into the crystal more phonons are created; if energy is removed, phonons are destroyed.

The occupation number is the number of phonons of a particular kind. Thus the state is described by $3N$ integers which signify how many phonons exist with each of the allowed energies. These integers are the same set of integers as those that are the set of quantum levels on the oscillator model. The creation or annihilation of one phonon $\hbar\omega(\mathbf{k}j)$ corresponds to an oscillator moving up or down one step on the energy-level diagram. We now think in terms of a gas of particles whose number is not conserved.

It is always necessary to interpret and to compare models of physical systems with some caution. At this stage we can make some useful comparisons without undue worry. If energy is fed into an oscillator its amplitude increases. While it remains harmonic there is no change in the frequency. Energy will be absorbed or rejected by a quantum oscillator only in integer multiples of $\hbar\omega$. If energy is fed into the oscillator so that it works its way stepwise up the energy ladder, the amplitude increases and the harmonic approximation becomes invalid. Remembering that the oscillator here represents a normal mode of the crystal, the breakdown of harmonic theory occurs because the atoms (executing larger-amplitude motions) become closer together and the potential energy of interaction requires third- and higher-order terms in equation (1.1) to describe it adequately. Thus our collection of oscillators remain independent only so long as the amplitudes are small. Clearly when the harmonic approximation is not valid the ladder of eigenvalues is also modified, as we shall see in Chapter 5.

Now consider the same situation described in terms of phonons. Energy put into the solid causes phonons to be created. Provided that these are present in limited numbers they will remain independent. However if their 'density' becomes great their interaction will become non-negligible. Thus the anharmonic terms are now accounted for as interactions between phonons. Having seen how this model takes us from low energies to those outside the range of validity of the harmonic approximations (i.e. outside that region in which the concept of a phonon was introduced), we shall be able to exploit the idea with some confidence.

A state of thermal equilibrium (i.e. no temperature gradients and no heat flow to or from the system) is specified by a set of occupation numbers $n(\mathbf{k}j)$ representing the number of each kind of allowed phonon. Since $n(\mathbf{k}j)$ are integers and may be greater than unity, the phonons are a set of particles obeying Bose–Einstein statistics. Chapter 4 discusses the statistics. Figure 3.2 is a schematic summary of the foregoing discussion.

In the next section these qualitative ideas are formalized into the language of quantum field theory. Although at this stage it is the proverbial sledge-hammer to a nut (*par excellence*), it is better to introduce new ideas to simple systems and in this case the procedure is a particularly simple application.

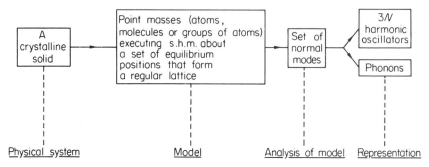

Figure 3.2   Stages in the theory of lattice vibrations

3.3   Annihilation and creation operators—introduction

The central importance of a quantum oscillator has been well stressed. The properties of a single oscillator are reflected strongly in the thermal properties of a solid. We shall first develop the formalization of the occupation-number concept for a single oscillator and in Section 3.5 we shall extend it to cover all the oscillators representing the crystal.

Consider the Hamiltonian of an oscillator as in equation (1.15):

$$H = \frac{p^2}{2m} + \tfrac{1}{2}m\omega^2 x^2. \tag{3.1}$$

The eigenvalues of this Hamiltonian may be found by making a transformation so that H is written in terms of operators with known properties. Suppose we look at the simplest (non-trivial) transformations conceivable for x and p—linear transformations of the form:

$$x = \chi_x(a^+ + a) \tag{3.2a}$$

$$p = \chi_p(a^+ - a) \tag{3.2b}$$

where χ_x and χ_p are dimensional constants, and a^+ and a are real dimensionless operators.

Now we know from basic quantum mechanics (see, for example, Reference 2 of Chapter 1) that x and p are conjugate variables and that they obey the commutation relation

$$[x, p] = i\hbar. \tag{3.3}$$

If we write this in terms of a^+ and a by using the transformations (3.2), we see that

$$xp - px = \chi_x\chi_p(a^+a^+ - aa - a^+a + aa^+ - a^+a^+ + aa - a^+a + aa^+)$$

$$= 2\chi_x\chi_p(aa^+ - a^+a)$$

$$= 2\chi_x\chi_p[a, a^+] = i\hbar. \tag{3.4}$$

Thus, since we have assumed a^+ and a to be real and dimensionless, we may write

$$[a, a^+] = 1. \tag{3.5}$$

Now expressing H in terms of these operators,

$$H = \frac{\chi_p^2}{2m}(a^+a^+ + aa - a^+a - aa^+) + \frac{m\omega^2}{2}\chi_x^2(a^+a^+ + aa + a^+a + aa^+). \tag{3.6}$$

Since we know something about a^+a and aa^+ through equation (3.4), let us choose the relative magnitudes of χ_x and χ_p to eliminate a^+a^+ and aa from the expression for H. This is achieved if we write

$$\frac{\chi_p^2}{2m} = -\tfrac{1}{2}m\omega^2\chi_x^2 \equiv -\chi^2 \tag{3.7}$$

where χ is to be determined.

Now we have, from equations (3.4) and (3.5),

$$\chi_x\chi_p = \frac{i\hbar}{2}$$

and writing this in terms of χ from equation (3.7), we have

$$i\chi^2\frac{2}{\omega} = \frac{i\hbar}{2}$$

and therefore

$$\chi^2 = \frac{\hbar\omega}{4}. \tag{3.8}$$

Hence we get from the definition (3.7) that

$$\chi_x = \left(\frac{\hbar}{2m\omega}\right)^{1/2} \tag{3.9a}$$

$$\chi_p = i\left(\frac{m\omega\hbar}{2}\right)^{1/2} \tag{3.9b}$$

and that the transformations (3.2) take the explicit form

$$x = \left(\frac{\hbar}{2m\omega}\right)^{1/2}(a^+ + a) \tag{3.10a}$$

$$p = i\left(\frac{m\omega\hbar}{2}\right)^{1/2}(a^+ - a). \tag{3.10b}$$

Using these, the Hamilton (3.1) becomes

$$H = \frac{\hbar\omega}{2}(a^+a + aa^+) = \frac{\hbar\omega}{2}(2a^+a + 1)$$

$$= \hbar\omega(a^+a + \tfrac{1}{2}).$$

(3.11)

3.4   Annihilation and creation operators—basic properties

The expression (3.11) for the Hamiltonian is a concise form defining the quantum properties of the system. These have been introduced by the use of the commutation relations. The next stage is to investigate the properties of a^+ and a. Since the product a^+a occurs frequently and, as we shall see, plays a dominant role, we shall define an operator v,

$$v \equiv a^+a.$$

(3.12)

Consider first the commutation of v with a^+ and a

$$[v, a] = va - av$$

$$= a^+aa - aa^+a$$

$$= (a^+a - aa^+)a$$

and, using equation (3.5), we see that

$$[v, a] = -a.$$

(3.13a)

Similarly

$$[v, a^+] = a^+.$$

(3.13b)

The eigenvalues of the Hamiltonian are determined by the eigenvalues of v, as is easily seen from equations (3.12) and (3.11). So let us write an eigenvalue of v as $\bar{v}$ and an eigenvector (or eigenstate) as $|\rangle$.

This is the Dirac notation. A wave function ψ is written $|\rangle$ and called a 'ket vector'. The complex conjugate of a ket vector, i.e. ψ^*, is written $\langle|$ and called a 'bra vector'. The quantity $\langle|O|\rangle$ corresponds to $\int \psi^*O\psi \, d\tau$ and is called a 'bra–ket'. This is a convenient notation for use with occupation numbers, since we can write inside the vector any labels to characterize a particular state under discussion. For further reading see Dirac[1] and p. 309 of Reference 2 in Chapter 1.

Thus we write

$$v|\rangle = \bar{v}|\rangle.$$

(3.14)

It follows immediately from result (3.13a) that, if we operate on an eigenstate of v with the operator va,

$$va|\rangle = a(v - 1)|\rangle$$
$$= a(\bar{v} - 1)|\rangle$$
$$= (\bar{v} - 1)a|\rangle \qquad (3.15a)$$

the last step being valid since $\bar{v}$ is just a number and not an operator. Similarly

$$va^+|\rangle = (\bar{v} + 1)a^+|\rangle. \qquad (3.15b)$$

Equations (3.15) show that $a|\rangle$ and $a^+|\rangle$ are also eigenstates of the operator v and that they have eigenvalues $\bar{v} - 1$ and $\bar{v} + 1$, respectively.

Let us write the lowest eigenvalue of v as $\bar{v}_0$ and the corresponding state $|0\rangle$. Since $\bar{v}_0$ is the lowest, $\bar{v}_0 - 1$ is not an eigenvalue and therefore

$$a|0\rangle = 0. \qquad (3.16)$$

If this were not true, we see from the relation (3.15a) that $\bar{v}_0 - 1$ **would** be an eigenvalue. Also it then follows that

$$v|0\rangle \equiv a^+a|0\rangle = 0|0\rangle \qquad (3.17)$$

i.e.

$$\bar{v}_0 = 0. \qquad (3.18)$$

Now the eigenstate $a^+|0\rangle$ according to the eigenvalue equation (3.15b) corresponds to an eigenvalue $\bar{v} = 1$. Thus we can write this state

$$a^+|0\rangle = |1\rangle \, . \, \text{const.}$$

By repetition of the process, we get

$$a^+|n\rangle = |n + 1\rangle \, . \, \text{const} \qquad (3.19a)$$

and we see that these eigenstates of v produce eigenvalues which are

$$\bar{v} = 0, 1, 2, 3, \ldots$$

i.e. the set of natural positive integers. Thus v is called the 'number operator'. Similarly, by working downwards

$$a|n\rangle = |n - 1\rangle \, . \, \text{const.} \qquad (3.19b)$$

Summarizing the above, we may write

$$v|n\rangle = n|n\rangle \qquad (3.20)$$

and now it is clear why we embarked on this discussion. From equations (3.20) and (3.11), the eigenvalues of H (that is the energy levels of our oscillator) are

$$E_n = (n + \tfrac{1}{2})\hbar\omega \tag{3.21}$$

which is identical with the result obtained in equation (1.25a).

That the set of positive integers are the only eigenvalues of v, is easily confirmed. a^+, a or combinations of them are the only operators that will not commute with v. Thus no **distinct** eigenstate of v can be formed other than by operating on $|\rangle$ with a^+ or a. The set of eigenstates generated by repeated application of a^+ and a is the set $|n\rangle$ we have developed above.

The operation of a^+ on an eigenstate raises the system to the next eigenstate, hence the term 'creation operator'. The operation of a on an eigenstate lowers the state of the system to the one below, hence the term 'annihilation operator'.

Consider now the values of the constants in equations (3.19a) and (3.19b). Forming the 'bra–ket'

$$\langle n + 1|a^+|n\rangle = \langle n + 1||n + 1\rangle \cdot \text{const} = \text{const} \tag{3.22}$$

since we assume the eigenstates to be normalized to unity. We have also that

$$\langle n|a^+a|n\rangle = n$$

and we can expand the left-hand side of this in the form

$$\langle n|a^+|n - 1\rangle\langle n - 1|a|n\rangle = n.$$

The two bra–kets in this equation are equal because a^+ and a are Hermitian, and since n is real we get

$$\langle n|a^+|n - 1\rangle = \langle n - 1|a|n\rangle = n^{1/2}. \tag{3.23}$$

This result may be applied to equations (3.19) and these become [with the help of equation (3.22)]

$$a^+|n\rangle = (n + 1)^{1/2}|n + 1\rangle \tag{3.24a}$$

$$a|n\rangle = n^{1/2}|n - 1\rangle. \tag{3.24b}$$

In taking the square root to get equation (3.23), it should be observed that the general result should include a phase factor, say $e^{\pm i\theta}$. This has unit modulus and should appear on the right-hand side of equation (3.24a) as $e^{i\theta}$ and in equation (3.24b) as $e^{-i\theta}$. However, for all Bose systems we may put $\theta = 0$.

These relations have been developed in some detail so that when they are used in later chapters their origins are not clouded in mystique.

While we are discussing these single-oscillator operators, it is a worthwhile digression to indicate the distinction between these and the corresponding operators for Fermi particles. Without going into details, we note that Fermions obey anticommutation relations, namely

$$c^+c + cc^+ = 1 \tag{3.25a}$$

$$cc + cc = c^+c^+ + c^+c^+ = 0$$

or

$$cc = c^+c^+ = 0. \tag{3.25b}$$

The number operator is

$$v = c^+c.$$

Considering the square of the number operator

$$v^2 = c^+cc^+c$$

$$= c^+(1 - c^+c)c$$

$$= c^+c + c^+c^+cc$$

$$= c^+c = v. \tag{3.25c}$$

The equation $v^2 = v$ has the solutions 0 or 1; thus the eigenvalues of the Fermi-number operator are zero or one. This corresponds to the exclusion principle, and means that having created a particle in a given state, no other particle can be put into that state. The occupation number can be zero or unity. We have seen that for Bosons there is no such restriction on the number operator. We shall return to this briefly in Chapter 4.

If we now consider the Fermi-particle results corresponding to equations (3.24), we cannot ignore the phase factor. However a one-particle Fermi system is trivial, and it is only necessary to consider the phase when there are many particles and the question of symmetry arises. Thus we have

$$c^+|0\rangle = |1\rangle$$

$$c|1\rangle = |0\rangle$$

$$c^+|1\rangle = 0$$

$$c|0\rangle = 0.$$

3.5 Annihilation and creation operators—set of oscillators

The previous section has dealt with the properties of the operators that represent transitions between adjacent eigenstates of a harmonic oscillator. The oscillators of interest in the theory of solids are those which are equivalent to the normal modes of vibration of the crystal. Thus the x in equation (3.1) is to be generalized to the normal coordinates $q(\mathbf{k}j)$ and the p to the normal momenta, $p(\mathbf{k}j)$. However, before we can deduce the correct form for the real operators to replace the complex $q(kj)$ and $p(kj)$ we must consider the latter in more detail than was necessary in Chapter 1. The transformation of u_α^l and $\dot{u}_\alpha^l$ [from equations (1.4), (1.6) and (1.14)] are

$$u_\alpha^l = \left(\frac{1}{mN}\right)^{1/2} \sum_{kj} e_\alpha(kj)q(kj)\, e^{-ik.r^l} \tag{3.26a}$$

and

$$\dot{u}_\alpha^l = \left(\frac{1}{mN}\right)^{1/2} \sum_{kj} e_\alpha(kj)p(kj)\, e^{-ik.r^l}. \tag{3.26b}$$

Now u_α^l and $\dot{u}_\alpha^l$ are real, and hence if $e_\alpha(kj)$ is real,[a] the following relations must hold:

$$q^*(kj) = q(-kj) \tag{3.27a}$$

$$p^*(kj) = p(-kj) \tag{3.27b}$$

$$e_\alpha(kj) = e_\alpha(-kj). \tag{3.27c}$$

Our analysis in Section 1.5 was carried out with a little of the hand-waving technique that is useful when details threaten to obscure the point of the discussion. In particular, the use of equation (1.5) to remove the cross terms in the Hamiltonian (1.3) relied more on hindsight than may have been apparent. However, the use of equations (1.14) and (1.11) would have made the arbitrary definition of $\omega^2(kj)$ unnecessary; as we saw it was not an arbitrary quantity. Considering only the potential-energy part of the harmonic Hamiltonian

$$\Phi = \frac{1}{2mN}\Phi_{\alpha\alpha'}^{ll'}e_\alpha(kj)e_{\alpha'}(k'j')\, e^{-i(k.r^l+k'.r^{l'})}q(kj)q(k'j') \tag{3.28a}$$

[the Einstein summation convention (Section 1.4) is used in equations (3.28) and (3.33), inclusive] and, from equation (1.12), this becomes

$$\Phi = \frac{1}{2N}D_{\alpha\alpha'}(kj)e_\alpha(kj)e_{\alpha'}(k'j')q(kj)q(k'j')\sum_{l'} e^{-i(k'+k).r^{l'}}. \tag{3.28b}$$

Using the general result

$$\frac{1}{N}\sum_l e^{ik.r^l} = \Delta(k) \equiv \begin{array}{ll} 1 & \text{if } k = 0 \text{ or } K \text{ (a reciprocal lattice vector)} \\ & \text{or} \\ 0 & \text{otherwise} \end{array} \tag{3.29}$$

we find

$$\Phi = \tfrac{1}{2}D_{\alpha\alpha'}(kj)e_\alpha(kj)e_{\alpha'}(-kj)q(kj)q(-kj). \tag{3.30}$$

Now equation (1.11) may be written in terms of $e_\alpha(kj)$:

$$\omega^2(kj)e_\alpha(kj) = D_{\alpha\alpha'}(kj)e_{\alpha'}(k'j). \tag{3.31a}$$

Thus multiplying both sides by $e_\alpha(kj)$ and summing over α,

$$\omega^2(kj) = D_{\alpha\alpha'}(kj)e_{\alpha'}(kj)e_\alpha(kj). \tag{3.31b}$$

Hence using this, together with the properties (3.27), the potential energy [equation (3.30)] reduces to

$$\Phi = \tfrac{1}{2}\omega^2(kj)q^*(kj)q(kj) \tag{3.32}$$

confirming that our result in equation (1.7) was correct. The transformation of the kinetic-energy part did not cause similar problems because there were no l-dependent factors other than $(\dot{u}_\alpha^l)^2$. Hence the orthogonality conditions (1.5) were directly applicable without resort to their particular form, i.e.

$$\text{kinetic energy} = \tfrac{1}{2}m(\dot{u}_\alpha^l)^*\dot{u}_\alpha^l \tag{3.33a}$$

$$= \tfrac{1}{2}m\zeta^*(l\alpha;kj)\zeta(l\alpha;k'j')p^*(kj)p(k'j') \tag{3.33b}$$

which by the condition (1.5b) with $K^2 = m^{-1}$ gives

$$\text{kinetic energy} = \tfrac{1}{2}p^*(kj)p(kj) \tag{3.33c}$$

which, taken with Φ given by equation (3.32), yields result (1.7). **We now drop the summation convention** and write any summations explicitly. The transformations corresponding to equations (3.10) for our $3N$ normal modes are

$$q(kj) = \left(\frac{\hbar}{2\omega(kj)}\right)^{1/2}[a^+(-\mathbf{k}_j^{\,\cdot} + a(kj)] \tag{3.34a}$$

$$p(kj) = i\left(\frac{\hbar\omega(kj)}{2}\right)^{1/2}[a^+(kj) - a(-kj)]. \tag{3.34b}$$

These reflect the association of $q(kj)$ with positive and negative $\mathbf{k}$ and ensure that the conditions (3.27a) and (3.27b) hold.

A phonon is characterized by a label (kj); thus the $3N$ pairs of annihilation and creation operators correspond to the $3N$ phonons. The discussion of Section 3.2 identifies the alternative representations and we see that the effect of $a^+(kj)$ (raising the quantum level of the oscillator by one) is to create a phonon with energy $\hbar\omega(kj)$. The effect of $a(kj)$ is to destroy one of these phonons. The significance of equation (3.16) is clearly that, if there are no phonons (kj), we cannot further reduce their number.

The representation of our state is

$$|n(\mathbf{k}_1 j_1), n(\mathbf{k}_1 j_2), n(\mathbf{k}_1 j_3), n(\mathbf{k}_2 j_1), \cdots, n(\mathbf{k}_i j), \cdots, n(\mathbf{k}_N j_2)\rangle \tag{3.35}$$

where $\mathbf{k}_i$, etc., are the allowed values of $\mathbf{k}$ for each of the branches, in this case assumed to be for three branches (one atom per unit cell). This state specifies the occupation number of each of the allowed phonon states. As a more convenient notation, we shall usually write

$$|n_1, n_2, \cdots, n_i, \cdots\rangle$$

the correspondence being self evident. If we now operate on this state with a particular number operator we find, by extension of equation (3.20), that

$$v_i|n_1,n_2,\cdots,n_i,\cdots\rangle = n_i|n_1,n_2,\cdots,n_i,\cdots\rangle. \qquad (3.36)$$

The number operator does not affect any of the other occupations because they are independent. If we now apply a_i^+ and a_i to the same state, we can see from equations (3.24) and from the arguments in this section that

$$a_i^+|n_1,n_2,\cdots,n_i,\cdots,\rangle = (n_i + 1)^{1/2}|n_1,n_2,\cdots,n_i + 1,\cdots\rangle \qquad (3.37a)$$

$$a_i|n_1,n_2,\cdots,n_i,\cdots\rangle = n_i^{1/2}|n_1,n_2,\cdots,n_i - 1,\cdots\rangle. \qquad (3.37b)$$

The operators a_i^+ and a_i modify the state by changing the number of phonons $\mathbf{k},j$. Thus the set of $3N$ pairs of annihilation and creation operators can be used to build up any state. Since the number of each kind of phonon depends on the thermal properties, the temperature and the statistics which the system obeys (usually Bose–Einstein in this book), this formalism has the basic requirements for linking microscopic and macroscopic properties. The equilibrium statistical mechanics is discussed in the next chapter.

Although as yet the results (3.36) and (3.37) are only formal statements of a qualitative idea, we shall find these operators to have extensive practical value. They are used for many different excitations in periodic structures, and we shall develop their use still further when the anharmonic oscillator is introduced.

The operators corresponding to different phonons are independent and thus they commute. The full set of commutation relations[b] are

$$[a_i^+,a_j^+] = [a_i,a_j] = 0 \qquad (3.38a)$$

$$[a_i,a_j^+] = \delta_{ij}. \qquad (3.38b)$$

It is easily seen that the transformations (3.34) may be applied to the Hamiltonian to yield

$$H = \sum_{\mathbf{k}j} \hbar\omega(\mathbf{k}j)[a^+(\mathbf{k}j)a(\mathbf{k}j) + \tfrac{1}{2}] \qquad (3.39)$$

where we have used the property that the $\mathbf{k}$ summation runs symmetrically over positive and negative values so that $\sum_{\mathbf{k}} f(\mathbf{k}) \equiv \sum_{\mathbf{k}} f(-\mathbf{k})$.

3.6 Phonon gas

So long as the amount of thermal energy in a crystal is small enough for the vibrations to remain harmonic, we can represent this thermal energy by a number of non-interacting particles. In this harmonic approximation the phonons behave with many of the properties of an ideal gas. The assumptions are closely analogous. The container is the crystal and phonons are conceived as point particles in **k** space. They move independently and the 'internal energy' of the phonon gas is a function of temperature only (for a given system).

The number of phonons is not conserved. As the temperature is raised by the input of thermal energy, more phonons are created. However, the chemical potential (or Gibbs free energy per particle) for a phonon is zero; so the resulting equations from statistical mechanics remain very similar but are the limiting case of those for an ideal Boson gas.

In Chapter 1 we discussed the idea of acoustic and optic modes, and also the distinction (sometimes artificial) between transverse and longitudinal modes. If N is the number of unit cells making up the crystal (effectively assumed to be part of an infinite crystal) and S is the number of atoms in each unit cell, we have seen that the number of different phonons are as in Table 3.1.

Table 3.1 Number of different phonon states for a crystal of N unit cells each with S atoms

Phonon	Number
Longitudinal acoustic (l.a.)	N
Transverse acoustic (t.a.)	$2N$
Longitudinal optic (l.o.)	$(S - 1)N$
Transverse optic (t.o.)	$2(S - 1)N$

If S is greater than 2, the distinction between the longitudinal and transverse optic modes may become somewhat tenuous.

We have been discussing the occupation of these states and will continue to do so in the following chapter, but we have not discussed the distribution of the states as a function of **k**. Such a distribution is known as the **'density of states'**. Phonons, as we have observed, behave very similarly to photons. The density of states of photons in a cavity containing 'temperature' (or black-body) radiation may be deduced in a simple well known way. If we assume the cavity to be a cube of side L (the result should be shape independent, so this is only a convenience), the boundary conditions impose restrictions on the allowed wave vectors, namely

$$\mathbf{k} = \left(\pi \frac{n_x}{L}, \pi \frac{n_y}{L}, \pi \frac{n_z}{L} \right) \tag{3.40}$$

where n_x, n_y and n_z are integers. This result follows from the solutions of the eigenvalue equation. The allowed states may be represented by an integer plot in three dimensions. Figure 3.3 shows this in two dimensions, but the three-dimensional case follows obviously.

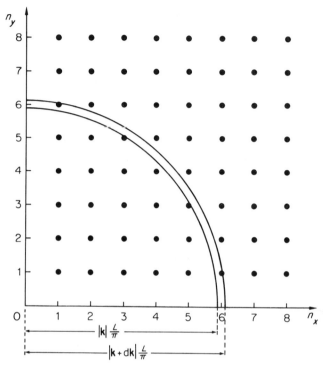

Figure 3.3   A dimensionless (integer) plot, representing the
allowed electromagnetic modes in a cubic cavity (showing only
two dimensions; the third dimension is implied)

From Figure 3.3, we can see that the number of modes lying between $\mathbf{k}$
and $\mathbf{k} + d\mathbf{k}$ is the number of points in one octant (all components positive)
of a shell with boundary radii $\mathbf{k}$ and $\mathbf{k} + d\mathbf{k}$, i.e.:

number of points lying between $\mathbf{k}$ and $\mathbf{k} + d\mathbf{k}$

$$= \frac{1}{8} \cdot \frac{\text{volume of shell}}{\text{volume occupied by each point}}$$

$$= \frac{1}{8} \cdot 4\pi \mathbf{k}^2 \, d\mathbf{k} \cdot \left(\frac{\pi}{L}\right)^{-3} \tag{3.41}$$

where $(\pi/L)^3$ is the volume occupied by each point in units of $\mathbf{k}^3$. Since there
are two states of polarization of a photon (both transverse) for all values of $\mathbf{k}$,
the expression must be multiplied by two and we see

$$\rho_k = \left(\frac{k}{\pi}\right)^2 \tag{3.42}$$

where ρ_k is the density of states such that ρ_k $\mathbf{dk}$ is the number of states between $\mathbf{k}$ and $\mathbf{k}$ + $\mathbf{dk}$ for unit volume of crystal. This expression can be shown to be volume and shape independent.

The model for phonons corresponding to black-body radiation is that of Debye (Section 1.2). The corresponding density of states is slightly different from equation (3.42) owing to the different character of waves. Equation (3.42) was deduced for photons, which all have the same velocity in vacuum according to special relativity. If we assume that all phonons have the same velocity, the density of states would be just $1\frac{1}{2}$ times result (3.42), since there are three phonon states of polarization. However, it is not a very good approximation to assume no dispersion and we have, for a Debye solid, that the density of states from equation (2.1), and written here in slightly different form, is

$$\rho(\omega) = \frac{Z(\omega)}{V} = \frac{1}{2\pi^2}\left(\frac{2}{V_t^3} + \frac{1}{V_l^3}\right)\omega^2. \tag{3.43}$$

If we are not working within the Debye model but computing the lattice dynamics by the Born–von Karman approach, the density of the states is considerably more complex. We will find the density of allowed states to be very important when considering interaction effects such as absorption of infrared radiation by a lattice. The direct method of obtaining the density of states would be to compute the frequencies of a large number of modes distributed evenly over the first Brillouin zone and then to count how many frequencies occur in a range $\delta\omega$ about a given ω. This distribution, say $g(\omega)$, may then be plotted against ω and this is equivalent to the density of states, since it may be normalized to the known total number of states. The frequency distributions of some sample crystals are shown in Section 2.12.

3.7 Summary

In this chapter we have developed the idea of the representation of the **thermal energy** of a crystal by a set of **occupied** vibrational states. These are the **phonons** introduced in Chapter 1. We can ascribe the increase in the amount of thermal energy in the crystal to the **creation** of more phonons. If energy is lost by the crystal some phonons are destroyed or **annihilated**. This process of increasing or decreasing the numbers of phonons corresponding to the allowed modes may be formalized in terms of the quantum-mechanical operators called **annihilation** and **creation operators**. The former acts on the state function and produces a new state with one less phonon of the relevant kind. The creation operator produces a state that has one more phonon. The **state** of the crystal may be expressed in terms of a set of **occupation numbers**, which are the number of phonons corresponding to each of the allowed modes.

The annihilation and creation operators are related by simple **transformations** to the normal coordinates and momenta. The product of a creation operator (on the left) and its corresponding annihilation operator is the **number** operator, which has the same eigenstates as the Hamiltonian and eigenvalues which are the set of natural positive integers. The **Hamiltonian** takes on a particularly concise form when expressed in terms of these operators [equation (3.39)]. It has been indicated that the properties of annihilation and creation operators lead them into playing a considerable role in later parts of this book.

The **phonon gas** behaves very similarly to an **ideal gas** and this will become more clear in the next chapter. By making comparisons between **electromagnetic radiation** in a **black-body cavity** and the **Debye** model of a solid, we can deduce approximate expressions for the **density of states** of a crystal. These are a density of **vibrational** states. Real crystals require much more involved computations to obtain an acceptable density of states. Reference 2 is a useful general reference.

Chapter notes

[a] $e_\alpha(\mathbf{k}j)$ is the representation of the polarization of the mode $(\mathbf{k}j)$ or equivalently it may be regarded as a component of normalized amplitude. Thus it is real in our scheme for one atom per unit cell. If there is more than one atom per unit cell, $e_\alpha(\kappa, \mathbf{k}j)$ may be complex and then $e_\alpha^*(\kappa, \mathbf{k}j) = e_\alpha(\kappa, -\mathbf{k}j)$. Throughout we have dropped the suffices referring to the atoms within the unit cell; there is no great difficulty in generalizing the expression to include them.

[b] For fermions these are

$$c_i c_j + c_j c_i = c_i^+ c_j^+ + c_j^+ c_i^+ = 0$$
$$c_i c_j^+ + c_j^+ c_i = \delta_{ij}$$

The phase factor referred to at the end of Section 3.4, is 0 or π, depending on the number of occupied states, the value alternating as each state is occupied or deoccupied. We shall not go into details here, for it is of no direct concern to us.

References

1. Dirac, P. A. M., *Quantum Mechanics*, Clarendon Press, Oxford, 1948.
2. Maradudin, A. A., Montroll, E. W., and Weiss, G. H., *Theory of Lattice Dynamics in the Harmonic Approximation* (Ed. Seitz and Turnbull), Academic Press, New York, 1963.

4

Phonon Statistics

4.1 Introduction

The concept of an individual phonon has been introduced and formalized. The vibrational energy of a solid has been reconceived as a phonon gas. Qualitatively we have seen that there are analogies between a phonon gas and an ideal gas, and between phonons and photons. When energy is absorbed by a crystal it changes the numbers of phonons present so that their distribution over the allowed states satisfies the relevant statistical-mechanical laws. Clearly, the macroscopic thermal properties are linked to those of the elementary vibrational states by these statistical-mechanical relations. In this chapter we shall introduce the statistical-mechanical ideas that we require and show how they are applied to the phonons in a solid.

In Section 3.1 we commented that the wave function for the lattice vibrational state would be a product of independent oscillator functions. This would be the whole story if the particles were 'distinguishable'. In quantum statistics we have 'indistinguishable' components. Thus any interchange of components (of the same species) must leave the modulus of the wave function unchanged; the wave function itself may change by a phase factor $e^{i\theta}$. All particles fall into one of two groups: $\theta = 0$, the wave function being symmetric with respect to interchange of any pair of components; and $\theta = \pi$, the wave function being antisymmetric with respect to an interchange. The first group are Bosons (and include phonons); the second group are Fermions. A correct description of the state of a set of identical bosons is thus a normalized linear combination of all possible permutations of the boson equilibrium states which correspond to the given conditions. However, these considerations introduce no problems. It means merely that we cannot say which bosons are associated with a particular state, only that there is a probability distribution and that there will be, say, n bosons (any n bosons) in a specified individual particle state. However, fundamentally, it does mean that the counting processes used in the statistics must take into account whether or not we can distinguish between components.

The atomic oscillators **are** distinguishable, since they are localized and remain associated with fixed reference points; the quanta of energy are not distinguishable. Thus we see the alternatives: we may treat a solid as an ensemble of distinguishable components—oscillating atoms—and use the Maxwell–Boltzmann distribution, or we may treat it as a gas of indistinguishable particles—phonons—and apply Bose–Einstein statistics. A full treatment of the background to the expressions that we require would be out of place here. We shall make use of some standard results that are well documented and shall restrict discussion to a minimum necessary to put the results we use into perspective with the general theory. The reader is referred to any standard work on statistical mechanics; in particular, Chapters III, IV, VIII and IX of Wannier[1] are recommended.

The various methods developed to compute frequency spectra (see Chapter 2) were concerned ultimately with thermodynamic quantities. However, these are not very sensitive to the details of the dispersion and do not provide critical tests of the validity of a lattice dynamical method. The effective averaging over large numbers of components blurs out all detail. Thermodynamics provides a variety of quantities which may be used to compare theory and experiment, but it must be remembered that these all compare a macroscopic measurement (the averaged effect of a microscopic property of a large number of components) with a statistical average of a theoretical model. This is like comparing a high-altitude aerial photograph of a large football crowd with the numbers of tickets sold for each part of the ground. Both lose the details and different errors may cancel, but the comparison provides a general check and may indicate serious errors. (An example of a serious discrepancy is the attempt to predict the low-temperature thermal behaviour of a solid using classical theory.) The most useful thermodynamic quantities are those that may be obtained independently from different parts of the theory. The equivalent Debye temperature (which may be obtained from elastic properties or from specific-heat calculations) is one such quantity and is discussed later in this chapter.

The significant point arising from this chapter is that many observed properties of crystals cannot be interpreted in terms of a set of uncoupled normal modes. Anharmonic terms in the potential-energy expansion are essential for a qualitative and quantitative understanding of the known physical properties of solids. These appear from Section 4.4 onwards. Apart from the statistical averaging, anharmonicity is treated at a qualitative level. The analytical details are presented in Chapter 5 and 6.

4.2   Bose–Einstein statistics

The occupation of a boson state has no limit other than the total number of particles available. In the case of a set of phonons, the limit is only that of the stability of the crystal. If the thermal energy becomes too large, the crystal structure changes or is broken up, but there is no fundamental limit due to the statistical behaviour of bosons as there is with a Fermi system. Systems made up of particles that have antisymmetric total wave functions must be described by Fermi–Dirac statistics. Those with symmetric wave functions satisfy Bose–Einstein statistics. There are two distinct classes of system to which Bose–Einstein statistics may be applied: (i) the number of component particles are conserved (e.g. a gas of helium atoms) and (ii) the number of component particles are not conserved (e.g. phonons and photons). Both of these classes are quite distinct from the properties of systems obeying Fermi–Dirac statistics.

In the introduction we said that the solid could be treated as distinguishable oscillators and hence that Maxwell–Boltzmann statistics are appropriate. In practice the only model that is conveniently treated in this way is the Einstein model. It is the source of some confusion that we get the same result using the classical idea of distinguishability as we do using Bose–Einstein indistinguishability on a different model of the same physical system. For this reason we outline the salient features of the two analyses. It is important to be clear that it is the statistical counting process that is different in the two models. Each component—an oscillator—is still a quantum system with discrete energy levels. The statistical behaviour of an assembly of identical distinguishable components is summarized in the expression

$$\bar{\eta}_n = e^{\beta(\mu - \varepsilon_n)} \tag{4.1a}$$

where $\beta \equiv (k_B T)^{-1}$, μ is the chemical potential and η_n is the number of components with energy ε_n (the corresponding expressions for all three forms of statistics are summarized for comparison purposes in Table 4.4). If this is applied to the $3N$ oscillators of the Einstein model,

$$3N = \sum_n \bar{\eta}_n = \sum_n e^{\beta(\mu - \varepsilon_n)} \tag{4.1b}$$

and thus we can eliminate μ leaving

$$\bar{\eta}_n = \frac{3N\,e^{-\beta\varepsilon_n}}{\sum_n e^{-\beta\varepsilon_n}}. \tag{4.1c}$$

Now if $\varepsilon_n = (n + \tfrac{1}{2})\hbar\omega_E$, the total vibrational energy is

$$E = \sum_n \bar{\eta}_n \varepsilon_n$$

$$= 3N\hbar\omega_E \frac{\sum_n (n + \tfrac{1}{2})\,e^{-\beta\hbar\omega_E(n + \tfrac{1}{2})}}{\sum_n e^{-\beta\hbar\omega_E(n + \tfrac{1}{2})}}.$$

We may write this (putting $\beta\hbar\omega_E = x$ for brevity),

$$E = \frac{3N}{2}\hbar\omega_E - 3N\hbar\omega_E \frac{(\partial/\partial x)(\sum_n e^{-nx})}{\sum_n e^{-nx}}$$

[Alternatively, we might have written this

$$E = -3N\hbar\omega_E \frac{\partial}{\partial x} \ln\left(\sum_n e^{-(n+\frac{1}{2})x}\right)].$$

Noting, in either of these expressions, that $\sum_n e^{-nx} = 1/(1 - e^{-x})$

$$E = \frac{3N}{2}\hbar\omega_E + 3N\hbar\omega_E(e^{\beta\hbar\omega_E} - 1)^{-1} \qquad (4.2)$$

The same result is obtained directly using the Bose–Einstein expression

$$\bar{\eta}_i = (e^{\beta(\varepsilon_i - \mu)} - 1)^{-1} \qquad (4.3)$$

for the mean occupation number for bosons with energy ε_i. For the Einstein model there is only one kind of phonon, that with energy $\hbar\omega_E$, and we shall see later that for phonons $\mu = 0$; therefore we write $\bar{\eta}_i \to \bar{n}$ and

$$E = \hbar\omega_E \cdot 3N\bar{n} \qquad (4.4)$$

which yields the temperature-dependent part of equation (4.2). The zero point energy is omitted by this approach, since it is a constant unaffected by the phonon distribution.

In the first of these two methods we asked how many ($\bar{\eta}_0$) of the $3N$ (distinguishable) oscillators are expected to be found in the ground state; how many ($\bar{\eta}_1$) are excited to the first state; and, in general, how many $\bar{\eta}_n$ oscillators are excited to the nth state? The occupation numbers $\bar{\eta}_n$ we are using to describe the state are the mean numbers of actual components in each of the allowed states ε_n, subject to the constraint $\sum_n \bar{\eta}_n = 3N$ where N is fixed.

On the other hand, in the second method we deal with different quantities. We ask what is the mean level of excitation (in terms of n) to which an oscillator of frequency ω_E will be excited.

Now

$$\bar{n} \neq \bar{\eta}_n$$

in fact

$$\bar{n} = \frac{1}{3N}\sum_n n\bar{\eta}_n \qquad (4.5)$$

and we underline that this may be traced back to the counting process and that the numbers η_n refer to distinguishable entities, while the n refer to indistinguishable entities. For any model other than an Einstein model it is impracticable to relate these two quantities.

So we have seen in equation (4.2) that the energy is a temperature-independent part (zero point energy of all the $3N$ oscillators) and a part equivalent to $3N\bar{n}$ quanta of energy $\hbar\omega_E$. This result was obtained for the oversimplified case of identical oscillators. Suppose we now consider a set of oscillators with frequencies $\omega(kj)$. In terms of phonons we may ask: 'how many phonons $\overline{n(kj)}$ are there with angular frequency $\omega(kj)$?' The answer is obviously given by equation (4.3) with $\varepsilon_i \equiv \hbar\omega(kj)$ and from this it follows that

$$E = \sum_{kj} \hbar\omega(kj)[\overline{n(kj)} + \tfrac{1}{2}]$$ (4.6)

where

$$\overline{n(kj)} = (e^{\beta\hbar\omega(kj)} - 1)^{-1}$$ (4.7)

and we have again put $\mu = 0$ for phonons.

We should consider the significance of the value of μ, the chemical potential. Equation (4.3) may be applied to a Bose–Einstein ideal gas of N particles and the quantity μ is introduced so that the summation over $\overline{n(\varepsilon_i)}$ may be made equal to the total number of particles N.

$$N = \sum_{\varepsilon_i} (e^{\beta(\varepsilon_i - \mu)} - 1)^{-1}.$$ (4.8)

From this we see that $\mu < \varepsilon_0$, the lowest energy, or otherwise N would not be limited since the sum would not converge. This highlights the difference in the behaviour of our set of phonons (or photons) and a gas of 'material' particles. The total number of phonons is **not** limited and hence the chemical potential takes the value zero (similarly for photons). This is seen as follows; the number of phonons varies so as to be in equilibrium [described by the relation (4.3)] and to take up all the thermal energy. Thus the condition of equilibrium for a given crystal is

$$\left(\frac{\partial F}{\partial N}\right)_T = 0.$$ (4.9)

From thermodynamics, the Helmholtz free energy F is

$$F = E - TS = -PV + \mu N$$ (4.10)

(see, for example, Zemansky[2]). Thus to satisfy condition (4.9), $\mu = 0$.

We saw in equation (4.1) that μ may always be eliminated from the Maxwell–Boltzmann expression. Only in special cases is this possible with equation (4.8). If $\mu \neq 0$, it is usually necessary to keep it in the expressions and carry it through the analysis to be found empirically.

Expression (4.7) first arose when Planck[3] investigated the distribution of energy in the spectrum of a black body. With hindsight, the significance of his assumptions is now clear. He departed from standard thinking at the time by assuming that energy could be emitted or absorbed only in discrete amounts—quanta of radiation. This fits into quantum-mechanical pictures of absorption and emission processes accompanying transitions between discrete energy levels. The Planck distribution law described the observations very accurately, in contrast to the Rayleigh–Jeans classical expression which was plausible only at high temperatures. Using equation (3.42) for the density of photon states and equation (4.7) for the mean number of photons in the state, the energy in the range from ω to $\omega + d\omega$ is

$$E(\omega)\,d\omega = \hbar\omega Z(\omega)n(\omega)\,d\omega \tag{4.11}$$

where

$$Z(\omega)\,d\omega = V\frac{k^2}{\pi^2}\,dk = V\frac{\omega^2}{c^3\pi^2}\,d\omega$$

giving Planck's law of energy distribution:

$$E(\omega) = \frac{V}{\pi^2 c^3}\frac{\hbar\omega^3}{e^{\beta\hbar\omega}-1}. \tag{4.12}$$

The mean energy in a particular mode is

$$\overline{\varepsilon(\omega)} = \overline{n(\omega)}\hbar\omega \tag{4.13}$$

and the fluctuation about this mean value is deducible without difficulty. The root-mean-square deviation Δn of the number of particles in a mode is given by

$$\Delta n = (\overline{n^2} - \bar{n}^2)^{1/2} \tag{4.14}$$

and

$$\overline{n^2} = \frac{\sum_n n^2\,e^{-nx}}{\sum_n e^{-nx}} \tag{4.15}$$

where $x \equiv \beta\hbar\omega$, which becomes, using the same result as before for the summation,

$$\overline{n^2} = (1 - e^{-x})\frac{\partial^2}{\partial x^2}\left(\sum_n e^{-nx}\right)$$

$$= (1 - e^{-x})\frac{\partial^2}{\partial x^2}\left(\frac{1}{1 - e^{-x}}\right)$$

and, by differentiating and noting equation (4.7)

$$\overline{n^2} = \bar{n} + 2\bar{n}^2. \tag{4.16}$$

Substituting this into equation (4.14),

$$\Delta n = (\bar{n} + \bar{n}^2)^{1/2} \tag{4.17}$$

which gives the ratio of the fluctuation to the magnitude of the mean occupation:

$$\frac{\Delta n}{\bar{n}} = \left(1 + \frac{1}{\bar{n}}\right)^{1/2} \tag{4.18}$$

$$= (1 + e^{\beta\hbar\omega} - 1)^{1/2}$$

$$= e^{\beta\hbar\omega/2}. \tag{4.19}$$

In finding this to be always greater than unity, we must remember that this is derived for a photon field, **not** for a particle system. For a steady mode (standing wave in a cavity) which is permanently excited, its intensity varies with time from zero to twice the mean value (since it is sinusoidal). n increases as $e^{\beta\hbar\omega}$ decreases and the ratio $\Delta n/\bar{n}$ approaches unity, i.e. for low frequency or high temperature. For a mode that is excited for only short periods, the fluctuations are much greater.

The same arguments apply to phonons in a solid, and the preceding results are used in treating the thermodynamic properties of a crystal. The ideas may be helped by looking at some of the magnitudes involved. Table 4.1 presents the magnitudes for an Einstein solid.

Table 4.1 Magnitudes and temperature variation of mean occupation number, total number of phonons and Einstein function for an Einstein model. $x = \beta\hbar\omega_E$, $F_E = C_V/3Nk_B = x^2 e^x(e^x - 1)^{-2}$. n_{total} is the number of phonons per mole.

	$T(K)$	x	$\exp(x)$	$\bar{n}$	$n_{total}(\times 10^{-26})$	$F_E(x)$
$\omega_E = 10^{11}$ s^{-1}	1	0·764	2·15	0·872	0·016	0·953
	2	0·382	1·47	2·15	0·039	0·988
	3	0·255	1·29	3·45	0·062	0·995
	4	0·191	1·21	4·75	0·086	0·997
	5	0·153	1·17	6·06	0·109	0·998
	10	0·076	1·08	12·6	0·228	0·999
	20	0·038	1·04	25·7	0·464	1·000
	30	0·026	1·03	38·8	0·701	1·000
	40	0·019	1·02	51·9	0·937	1·000
	50	0·015	1·02	65·0	1·17	1·000
	100	0·007	1·01	130	2·36	1·000
$\omega_E = 10^{12}$ s^{-1}	1	7·64	2080	0·000$_5$	10^{-5}	0·335
	2	3·82	45·6	0·022	0·000$_4$	0·744
	3	2·55	12·8	0·085	0·001$_5$	0·875
	4	1·91	6·75	0·174	0·003	0·927
	5	1·53	4·61	0·277	0·005	0·953
	10	0·76	2·15	0·872	0·016	0·988
	20	0·38	1·47	2·15	0·039	0·997
	30	0·26	1·29	3·45	0·062	0·999
	40	0·19	1·21	4·75	0·086	0·999
	50	0·15	1·17	6·06	0·109	1·000
	60	0·13	1·14	7·36	0·133	1·000

—continued

Table 4.1—continued

	$T(K)$	x	$\exp(x)$	$\bar{n}$	$n_{total}(\times 10^{-26})$	$F_E(x)$
$\omega_E = 10^{12}\,s^{-1}$	70	0·11	1·12	8·67	0·157	1·000
	80	0·10	1·10	9·98	0·180	1·000
	90	0·08	1·09	11·3	0·204	1·000
	100	0·076	1·08	12·6	0·228	1·000
$\omega_E = 10^{13}\,s^{-1}$	1	76·4	10^{33}	10^{-33}	10^{-34}	10^{-29}
	2	38·2	10^{16}	10^{-16}	10^{-18}	10^{-13}
	3	25·5	10^{11}	10^{-11}	10^{-13}	10^{-8}
	4	19·1	10^8	10^{-8}	10^{-10}	10^{-5}
	5	15·3	10^6	10^{-6}	10^{-8}	10^{-4}
	10	7·64	2080	$0·000_5$	10^{-5}	0·028
	20	3·82	45·6	0·022	$0·000_4$	0·335
	30	2·55	12·8	0·085	$0·001_5$	0·598
	40	1·91	6·75	0·174	$0·003$	0·744
	50	1·53	4·61	0·277	0·005	0·826
	60	1·27	3·57	0·389	0·007	0·875
	70	1·09	2·98	0·506	0·009	0·906
	80	0·95	2·60	0·626	0·011	0·927
	90	0·85	2·34	0·748	0·014	0·942
	100	0·76	2·15	0·872	0·016	0·953
	500	0·15	1·17	6·06	0·109	0·998

The value of ω_E characterizes the crystal and Table 4.1 shows that, as the binding forces become stronger (higher oscillator frequency), the number of phonons at a given temperature decreases. There are fewer phonons (for an Einstein model) in a crystal with strong interatomic forces than in one with weaker forces at the same temperature. This is, of course, intuitive. The former takes up more energy per excitation than the latter.

Table 4.2 shows the Einstein specific-heat function for values of $x(\equiv \beta\hbar\omega_E)$ from 0 to 10·9. This is useful in reverse to find the magnitude of the equivalent

Table 4.2   Values of the Einstein function $F_E = \dfrac{x^2 e^x}{(e^x - 1)^2} = \dfrac{C_{V(\text{Einstein})}}{3Nk_B}$

x	0·0	0·1	0·2	0·3	0·4	0·5	0·6	0·7	0·8	0·9
0	1·000	0·9992	0·9967	0·9925	0·9868	0·9794	0·9705	0·9602	0·9483	0·9352
1	0·9207	0·9050	0·8882	0·8703	0·8515	0·8319	0·8114	0·7904	0·7687	0·7466
2	0·7241	0·7013	0·6783	0·6552	0·6320	0·6089	0·5859	0·5631	0·5405	0·5182
3	0·4963	0·4747	0·4536	0·4330	0·4129	0·3933	0·3743	0·3558	0·3380	0·3207
4	0·3041	0·2881	0·2726	0·2578	0·2436	0·2300	0·2170	0·2046	0·1928	0·1815
5	0·1707	0·1605	0·1508	0·1416	0·1329	0·1246	0·1168	0·1094	0·1025	0·9589
6	0·8968	0·8383	0·7833	0·7315	0·6828	0·6371	0·5942	0·5539	0·5162	0·4808
7	0·4476	0·4166	0·3876	0·3605	0·3351	0·3115	0·2894	0·2687	0·2495	0·2316
8	0·2148	0·1993	0·1848	0·1713	0·1587	0·1471	0·1362	0·1261	0·1168	0·1081
9	0·1000	0·0925	0·0855	0·0791	0·0731	0·0676	0·0624	0·0577	0·0533	0·0492
10	0·0454	0·0419	0·0387	0·0357	0·0329	0·0304	0·0280	0·0258	0·0238	0·0219

Einstein temperature if C_V is known from another source. Beattie[4] has compiled a table of the Debye function F_D from $x = 0$ to 24 in steps of 0·01. Outside this range, it is proportional to x^{-2}. The range corresponding to that of Table 4.2 is shown in Table 4.3. It is seen that for larger x (lower temperatures) the Debye function is larger than the Einstein function. This arises from the omission of the low frequencies from the latter, which are significant at the lower temperatures. At high temperatures both approach the classical result.

Table 4.3   Values of the Debye specific-heat function

$$F_D = \frac{12}{x^3}\left(\int_0^x \frac{y^3\,dy}{e^y - 1} - \frac{3x}{e^x - 1} \right) = \frac{C_{v(\text{Debye})}}{3Nk_B}$$

x	0·0	0·1	0·2	0·3	0·4	0·5	0·6	0·7	0·8	0·9
0	1·000	0·9995	0·9980	0·9955	0·9920	0·9876	0·9822	0·9759	0·9687	0·9606
1	0·9517	0·9420	0·9315	0·9203	0·9085	0·8960	0·8828	0·8692	0·8550	0·8404
2	0·8254	0·8100	0·7943	0·7784	0·7622	0·7459	0·7294	0·7128	0·6961	0·6794
3	0·6628	0·6461	0·6296	0·6132	0·5968	0·5807	0·5647	0·5490	0·5334	0·5181
4	0·5031	0·4883	0·4738	0·4595	0·4456	0·4320	0·4187	0·4057	0·3930	0·3807
5	0·3686	0·3569	0·3455	0·3345	0·3237	0·3133	0·3031	0·2933	0·2838	0·2745
6	0·2656	0·2569	0·2486	0·2405	0·2326	0·2251	0·2177	0·2107	0·2038	0·1972
7	0·1909	0·1847	0·1788	0·1730	0·1675	0·1622	0·1570	0·1521	0·1473	0·1426
8	0·1382	0·1339	0·1297	0·1257	0·1219	0·1182	0·1146	0·1111	0·1078	0·1046
9	0·1015	0·0985	0·0956	0·0928	0·0901	0·0875	0·0850	0·0826	0·0803	0·0780
10	0·0758	0·0737	0·0717	0·0697	0·0678	0·0660	0·0642	0·0625	0·0609	0·0593

4.3   Comparison with other statistics

Electrons and other half-spin particles do not obey the statistical laws we have discussed in Section 4.2. Physical systems fall into two distinct and non-overlapping classes: those obeying Bose–Einstein statistics and those obeying Fermi–Dirac statistics. Since we are primarily interested in phonons, which fall into the former group, discussion of the properties of fermions is limited to a brief indication of the main points of difference.

The mean occupation number for a Fermi system is given by

$$\bar{n}(\varepsilon) = (e^{\beta(\varepsilon - \mu)} + 1)^{-1} \tag{4.20}$$

which can never exceed unity. This is a weighted average of the allowed occupations $n = 0$ or 1. For an electron system, the chemical potential μ is usually called the 'Fermi level'. This is the energy at which the mean occupation is always $\frac{1}{2}$. For energies greater than μ, $\bar{n}(\varepsilon)$ is always less than $\frac{1}{2}$; for energies less than μ, $\bar{n}(\varepsilon)$ is always greater than $\frac{1}{2}$.

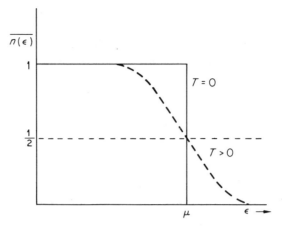

Figure 4.1 $\bar{n}(\varepsilon)$ for a Fermi system. $\mu = \varepsilon_F$, the Fermi level. At $T = 0$ all states below ε_F are occupied and those above are empty. When T is increased, particles in states close to ε_F make transitions to states above ε_F and leave states below empty

At high temperatures and low densities, equation (4.20) and the corresponding equation for bosons [equation (4.3)] both approach the same value. This is the classical limit (Maxwell–Boltzmann statistics):

$$\text{Fermi–Dirac } \bar{n} = (e^{\beta(\varepsilon-\mu)} + 1)^{-1}$$

$$e^{-\beta(\varepsilon-\mu)}.$$

$$\text{Bose–Einstein } \bar{n} = (e^{\beta(\varepsilon-\mu)} - 1)^{-1}$$

Thus, for high temperatures and low densities, the Maxwell–Boltzmann expression may be applied. An ideal gas satisfies these requirements. The electrons in a low-carrier-density semiconductor are also well described by the classical expression. The simpler expression is used when it is valid and results in considerable saving of labour. The consideration of this limiting equivalence is only applicable for $\mu \neq 0$, i.e. for a fixed number of particles. This number is distributed over many levels and all three expressions for $\bar{n}(\varepsilon)$ are less than unity at high temperature and low density. For $\mu = 0$ the expressions do not become equivalent, and $\sum_\varepsilon \bar{n}(\varepsilon)$ increases with temperature. However the classical limit is still attained, as may be seen by writing for high temperatures (small β) $e^{\beta\hbar\omega} \approx 1 + \beta\hbar\omega$, and using this in the temperature-dependent part of equation (4.2), whence

$$E_{\text{classical}} = 3N\hbar\omega \cdot \frac{1}{\beta\hbar\omega} = 3Nk_BT.$$

If a system is put into any non-equilibrium state, it will relax to the equilibrium state by a redistribution of particle energies. Thus the interactions between the components must reflect the statistical behaviour of the particles. When equilibrium is achieved, any further interactions must leave the system unchanged. Suppose we write down, on an intuitive basis, equations which might govern these transitions. Let E_k and E_l be the energies of two particles which interact; after the interaction there are two particles with energies E_m and E_n [see Figure 4.2(a)]. The density of the states will be written ρ_k, etc., so that $\rho_k \, dE_k$ is the number of states between E_k and $E_k + dE_k$. The occupation of the states is n_k, etc., such that $n_k \, dE_k$ is the number of components with energies between E_k and $E_k + dE_k$.

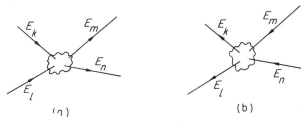

(a)
(b)

Figure 4.2(a)   An interaction of two particles. E_k and E_l are the energies before interaction and E_m and E_n are the energies after interaction. The details of the interaction are not specified. (b) is the inverse process to that of (a)

For the analysis to be applicable to discrete energy states, ρ_k, etc., should be interpreted as the degeneracy and n_k, etc., should be interpreted as the mean occupation number for a state with energy E_k, etc. We would expect the transition rate (t.r.) to increase with both

(a) the density of the states m and n
(b) the occupation of the states k and l,

but what is the effect of the occupancy of the final states? How is the transition affected if some or all of the states to which the particles are going are occupied? There are three possibilities. The occupation of the states m and n

 (i) decreases the t.r.
 (ii) does not affect the t.r.
(iii) increases the t.r.

Consider then the following expressions for the transition rate, A_i, etc., being the constants of proportionality:

(i) $$\text{t.r.} = A_i n_k n_l (\rho_m - n_m)(\rho_n - n_n) \qquad (4.21a)$$

(ii) $$\text{t.r.} = A_{ii} n_k n_l \rho_m \rho_n \qquad (4.21b)$$

(iii) $\text{t.r.} = A_{\text{iii}} n_k n_l (\rho_m + n_m)(\rho_n + n_n).$ (4.21c)

(i) When equilibrium has been achieved, the transition rate for the inverse process, Figure 4.2(b) must be equal to that of Figure 4.2(a). So we may write

$$A_i n_k n_l (\rho_m - n_m)(\rho_n - n_n) = A_i n_m n_n (\rho_k - n_k)(\rho_l - n_l).$$ (4.22)

Dividing both sides by $A_i n_m n_n n_k n_l$ and noting that

$$\frac{n_k}{\rho_k} = f_k$$

f_k being the distribution function, we see that

$$\left(\frac{1}{f_m} - 1\right)\left(\frac{1}{f_n} - 1\right) = \left(\frac{1}{f_k} - 1\right)\left(\frac{1}{f_l} - 1\right).$$ (4.23)

Since f_k is a function of E_k, f_l is a function of E_l, etc., this may be written

$$g(E_m)g(E_n) = g(E_k)g(E_l)$$ (4.24a)

where g is a function to be determined. In addition to equation (4.24a), energy is conserved, and we have

$$E_m + E_n = E_k + E_l.$$ (4.24b)

The only solution which will satisfy equations (4.24a) and (4.24b) is logarithmic:

$$E_k = B \log\left[Ag(E_k)\right]$$

where A and B are constants. Assuming the base to be natural,

$$g(E_k) = \frac{1}{A} e^{E_k/B}.$$ (4.25)

From equations (4.23), (4.24) and (4.25) we get

$$f(E_k) = \left(\frac{1}{A} e^{E_k/B} + 1\right)^{-1}.$$ (4.26)

(ii) For this case, the equation corresponding to equation (4.23) is

$$f_m f_n = f_k f_l$$ (4.27)

which, by similar arguments, yields

$$f(E_k) = A\, e^{-E_k/B}.$$ (4.28)

(iii) The equation corresponding to equations (4.23) and (4.27) is

$$\left(\frac{1}{f_m} + 1\right)\left(\frac{1}{f_n} + 1\right) = \left(\frac{1}{f_k} + 1\right)\left(\frac{1}{f_l} + 1\right)$$ (4.29)

which gives

$$f(E_n) = \left(\frac{1}{A} e^{E_\kappa/B} - 1\right)^{-1}. \tag{4.30}$$

It is immediately apparent that the three cases correspond to Fermi–Dirac statistics, Maxwell–Boltzmann statistics and Bose–Einstein statistics, respectively. The constants A and B may be identified as $e^{\beta\mu}$ and $k_B T$, respectively.

The effect of the occupation on the final states is interesting. If a Fermi state is occupied, the exclusion principle forbids other particles to enter that state; case (i) assumes this and shows that it leads to the distribution function. The behaviour of particles that satisfy Maxwell–Boltzmann statistics does not depend on whether or not the final states are occupied. Perhaps the most difficult behaviour to accept is that the transition rates for bosons are increased by the occupation. Transition probabilities to a given state are larger if that state is occupied. This effect has important consequences on the behaviour of Bose systems. The comparison between these three forms of statistics again underlines that only for distinguishable components do we have statistical independence of particles. However the occupation numbers (and probabilities of occupation) of a given state are independent of those of other states, for all three cases, except insofar as the occupation of all states depend on the temperature. Table 4.4 summarizes the important results of statistical analysis.

Table 4.4 Summary of the comparative behaviour of fermions, maxwellions and bosons

	Fermi–Dirac	Maxwell–Boltzmann	Bose–Einstein
Transition rate proportional to (ρ and n refer to final states):	$\rho - n$	ρ	$\rho + n$
Effect of n on transition:	Impeded	Unaffected	Encouraged
Probability p_i that a state ε_i has the occupation n_i:	$(e^{\beta(\varepsilon_i - \mu)} + 1)^{-1}$ $(n_i = 1)$	$\dfrac{1}{n_i!} \dfrac{e^{\beta n_i(\mu - \varepsilon_i)}}{\exp(e^{\beta(\mu - \varepsilon_i)})}$	$[1 - e^{\beta(\mu - \varepsilon_i)}] e^{\beta n_i(\mu - \varepsilon)}$
Mean occupation $\bar{n}_i$ of state ε_i (i.e. $\sum_i n_i p_i$):	$(e^{\beta(\varepsilon_i - \mu)} + 1)^{-1}$ (it is coincidence that $p_i = \bar{n}_i$ and arises since $\bar{n}_i$ is a weighted average of 0 and 1).	$e^{-\beta(\varepsilon_i - \mu)}$	$(e^{\beta(\varepsilon_i - \mu)} - 1)^{-1}$

For the case of two phonons interacting, we may write $\rho = 1$ and the subscripts may be regarded as labelling the $\mathbf{k}j$ value of each phonon involved. Phonon interactions are discussed in detail in the next chapter.

4.4   Averages

Quantum-statistical averaging is performed using the 'density matrix'.[5] This is a quantity introduced so that mixed states may be described, even though they cannot be represented as a wave function that is a linear combination of members of **one** complete set of orthonormal eigenfunctions. A mixed state arises when there are large numbers of uncorrelated particles. Consider part of a system that is a subsystem (described by coordinates x_{ss}) of the system (described by coordinates x and x_{ss}). The wave function of the whole system is $\psi(x, x_{ss})$. Now, if there is any interaction between the subsystem and the rest, x will always be involved in a wavefunction that attempts to describe the subsystem. Hence the subsystem does not have a wave function in terms of its own coordinates only. An example of this is external temperature control by isothermal contact.

To find the expectation value of some observable—represented by an operator O—we must first find the expectation value in one of the 'exact states', i.e.

$$\langle O(i) \rangle = \int \psi_i^* O \psi_i \, d\tau \tag{4.31}$$

and then average over the exact states using suitable weighting factors $W(i)$:

$$\langle O \rangle = \sum_i W(i) \langle O(i) \rangle \tag{4.32}$$

An arbitrary exact state of the subsystem $\psi(i)$ may be expanded as a linear combination of eigenstates ψ_m (for given x coordinates, i.e. for given external conditions):

$$\psi(i) = \sum_m a_m(i) \psi_m \tag{4.33}$$

and, using equation (4.33) together with equations (4.32) and (4.31),

$$\langle O \rangle = \sum_i W(i) \sum_{m,n} O_{mn} a_m^*(i) a_n(i) \tag{4.34}$$

where $O_{mn} \equiv \int \psi_m^* O \psi_n \, d\tau$. Hence we may write

$$\langle O \rangle = \sum_{m,n} O_{mn} \rho_{nm} = \sum_m (O\rho)_{mn} = \mathrm{Tr}\,\{O\rho\} \tag{4.35}$$

with $\rho_{nm} \equiv \sum_i W(i) a_m^*(i) a_n(i)$; O and ρ in the trace are the matrix representations of the operators. ρ is the **density matrix** and determines the mixed state. The elements of ρ may be complex, but they are not independent, since it must be Hermitian in order that the expectation values of O are real, i.e. in order that $\rho_{mn} = \rho_{nm}^*$. Also $\mathrm{Tr}\{\rho\} = 1$; so that the expectation value of the unit operator has the value unity. (Physically this means that the sum of the probabilities of finding the system in each of the states is unity, i.e. it is certain that the system is in one of the states.) If the number of eigenstates of the components of the system is small, it is possible to write out the elements of ρ explicitly. If there are p states, it requires $p^2 - 1$ measurements to specify the elements.

Applying this idea to an ensemble (a large number of identical non-interacting systems, each described by states ϕ_m), the state of the system is a superposition of allowed states weighted by a Boltzmann factor. We can see this as follows. From equation (4.35)

$$\langle N \rangle = \text{Tr}\,\{\rho N\}$$

$$E = \langle H \rangle = \text{Tr}\,\{\rho H\}$$

and the number of components $\langle N \rangle$ and the total energy E are fixed. Now the entropy S may be expressed in terms of the density matrix, since it depends logarithmically on the enumeration of microstates and, from its definition, ρ contains this enumeration. Thus we write

$$S = \text{Tr}\,\{\rho k_B \ln \rho\}. \tag{4.36}$$

Applying a variational method to S/k_B and introducing $\alpha\langle N \rangle$ and $\beta\langle H \rangle$ where α and β are undetermined multipliers (since the variations $\delta\langle N \rangle$ and $\delta\langle H \rangle$ are zero), we can easily show that

$$\rho = Z^{-1}\,e^{-\alpha N - \beta H} \tag{4.37a}$$

where the interpretation of α is $-\mu/k_B T$ (μ being the chemical potential) and $\beta = 1/k_B T$;

$$Z \equiv \text{Tr}\,\{e^{-\alpha N - \beta H}\}. \tag{4.37b}$$

As an example, let us apply this to find the mean number of particles occupying an energy state ε_i. In the notation of Chapter 3,

$$H = \sum_i \varepsilon_i a_i^+ a_i \tag{4.38a}$$

$$n_i = a_i^+ a_i \tag{4.38b}$$

and, using equations (4.35) and (4.37),

$$\langle n_i \rangle = \text{Tr}\,\{\rho a_i^+ a_i\} \tag{4.39a}$$

with

$$\rho = Z^{-1}\,e^{-\Sigma_i \beta(\varepsilon_i - \mu)n_i}.$$

Equation (4.39a) is of the form

$$\langle n_i \rangle = \text{Tr}\,\{e^X Y a_i\} Z^{-1} = \text{Tr}\,\{a_i\,e^X Y\} Z^{-1} \tag{4.39b}$$

where $X = -\sum_i \beta(\varepsilon_i - \mu)n_i$, $Y = a_i^+$ and the last step in equation (4.39b) invokes the cyclic theorem of traces. There is a general theorem which states that, if X and Y satisfy the relation

$$[X, Y] = \sigma Y \qquad (4.40a)$$

where σ is a constant, then

$$e^X Y e^{-X} = e^\sigma Y \qquad (4.40b)$$

or, multiplying both sides by e^X from the right,

$$e^X Y = e^\sigma Y e^X. \qquad (4.40c)$$

X and Y, as defined for equation (4.39b), satisfy the condition (4.40a). Thus we may apply equation (4.40c) to equation (4.39b), which then becomes

$$\langle n_i \rangle = Z^{-1} \operatorname{Tr} \{a_i e^\sigma Y e^X\}.$$

From commutation relation (3.13b) and condition (4.40a), we find that $\sigma = \beta(\mu - \varepsilon_i)$ (all other terms in the i summation commute with a_i^+) and the term e^σ should be taken outside the trace; hence

$$\langle n_i \rangle = Z^{-1} \operatorname{Tr} \{a_i a_i^+ e^X\} e^\sigma. \qquad (4.41)$$

Equating the right hand side of equations (4.39b) and (4.41), we see that

$$Z^{-1} \operatorname{Tr} \{e^X a_i^+ a_i\} = Z^{-1} e^\sigma \operatorname{Tr} \{a_i a_i^+ e^X\}$$

$$= Z^{-1} e^\sigma \operatorname{Tr} \{(1 + a_i^+ a_i) e^X\}$$

$$\langle n_i \rangle = e^\sigma \operatorname{Tr} \{\rho\} + e^\sigma \langle n_i \rangle$$

i.e.

$$\langle n_i \rangle = \frac{1}{e^{-\sigma} - 1} = \frac{1}{e^{\beta(\varepsilon_i - \mu)} - 1} \qquad (4.42)$$

which is the mean occupation number for bosons, as we would expect. So the density matrix given by equations (4.37) describes the same statistical behaviour as we have seen before, and this simple application is included to give some confidence in the technique before Hamiltonians which are more complicated than equation (4.38a) are involved.

Suppose now we have a Hamiltonian of the form

$$H = H_0 + H' \qquad (4.43)$$

where H_0 maybe diagonalized exactly but H' arises from higher-order terms and may not be exactly diagonalized simultaneously with H_0 (i.e. they do not commute). This is the first introduction of non-harmonic terms, and we shall see that it may be interpreted as arising from interactions between phonons. Since we are primarily interested in vibrational systems and not chemical systems, we may simplify the analysis by considering the case $\mu = 0$. Then from definition (4.37b) with $\beta = (k_B T)^{-1}$

$$Z = \operatorname{Tr} \{e^{-\beta(H_0 + H')}\}. \qquad (4.44)$$

The separation of the effects of H_0 and H' is non-trivial, since H_0 and H' do not commute, i.e.

$$e^{-\beta(H_0 + H')} \neq e^{-\beta H_0} e^{-\beta H'}$$

as may easily be confirmed by writing the series expansions for the exponentials. However, we can develop a power-series expansion for Z which is useful if H' is such that the series is convergent. We define a development operator $G(\beta, H', H_0)$ such that

$$e^{-\beta(H_0 + H')} = e^{-\beta H_0} G(\beta, H', H_0) \tag{4.45a}$$

Thus

$$G(\beta, H', H_0) = e^{\beta H_0} e^{-\beta(H_0 + H')} \tag{4.45b}$$

The derivative of $G(\beta, H', H_0)$ with respect to β is

$$\frac{\partial G(\beta, H', H_0)}{\partial \beta} = -e^{\beta H_0} H' e^{-\beta(H_0 + H')} \tag{4.46}$$

Hence, by integrating this expression, we can express $G(\beta, H', H_0)$ in the form

$$G(\beta, H', H_0) - 1 = -\int_0^\beta e^{\beta H_0} H' e^{-\beta(H_0 + H')} \, d\beta. \tag{4.47}$$

[The -1 arises from the lower limit of integration on the left-hand side of equation (4.46), since, from equation (4.45b), $G = 1$ when $\beta = 0$.] Since this is a formal process rather than a physically significant temperature integration, it is better to change to a dummy variable p and write expression (4.47)

$$G(\beta, H', H_0) = 1 - \int_0^1 e^{p\beta H_0} H' e^{-p\beta(H_0 + H')} \beta \, dp \tag{4.48}$$

where β is now a constant $[= (k_B T)^{-1}]$.

We may now build up the series by substituting equation (4.45a) into (4.48) and then replacing $G(\beta, H', H_0)$ in the integral by reusing equation (4.48). This process may be continued *ad infinitum* with the unknown $e^{-\beta(H_0 + H')}$ being pushed into higher and higher-order terms. The first few terms are

$$G(\beta, H', H_0) = 1 - \int_0^1 e^{p\beta H_0} H' e^{-p\beta H_0} \beta \, dp$$

$$+ \int_0^1 e^{p\beta H_0} H' e^{-p\beta H_0} \left\{ \int_0^1 e^{qp\beta H_0} H' e^{-qp\beta H_0} p\beta \, dq \right\} \beta \, dp$$

$$+ \cdots. \tag{4.49}$$

If we now use this series in expression (4.45a), we can write equation (4.44) as a series:

$$Z = Z_0 + Z_1 + Z_2 + Z_3 + \cdots \tag{4.50a}$$

where

$$Z_0 = \text{Tr}\{e^{-\beta H_0}\} \tag{4.50b}$$

$$Z_1 = \text{Tr}\left\{-e^{-\beta H_0}\beta \int_0^1 e^{p\beta H_0}H' e^{-p\beta H_0}\, dp\right\} \tag{4.50c}$$

$$Z_2 = \text{Tr}\left\{e^{-\beta H_0}\beta^2 \int_0^1 e^{p\beta H_0}H' e^{-p\beta H_0}\left(\int_0^1 e^{qp\beta H_0}H' e^{-qp\beta H_0}p\, dq\right)dp\right\} \tag{4.50d}$$

$$Z_3 = \text{term } O(H'^3).$$

The integrations in these expressions may be readily performed (albeit tediously for equation (4.50d)^a) to give

$$Z_0 = \langle n|e^{-\beta H_0}|n\rangle = \sum_n e^{-\beta \varepsilon_n} \tag{4.51a}$$

$$Z_1 = -\beta \sum_n e^{-\beta \varepsilon_n}\langle n|H'|n\rangle = -\beta \sum_n e^{-\beta \varepsilon_n}H'_{nn} \tag{4.51b}$$

$$Z_2 = \beta \sum_{m \neq n} \frac{\langle m|H'|n\rangle \langle n|H'|m\rangle\, e^{-\beta \varepsilon_n}}{\varepsilon_n - \varepsilon_m} = \beta \sum_{m \neq n} \frac{H'_{mn}H'_{nm}\, e^{-\beta \varepsilon_n}}{\varepsilon_n - \varepsilon_m}. \tag{4.51c}$$

[The expression for Z_2 is the symmetrized form, i.e. m and n have been interchanged in the expression obtained from (4.50d), and half the sum of the two forms has been taken to get equation (4.51c).] ε_n and ε_m are eigenvalues of H_0. Provided that the elements H'_{nn} and H'_{mn} are small compared to differences in eigenvalues of H_0, the series converges and we recognize the standard results of perturbation theory. This is a quantum-statistical formulation of perturbation theory.

From relations (4.51), the thermodynamical quantities may be obtained in the usual way, perhaps most usefully through the Helmholtz free energy:

$$F \equiv -k_B T \ln Z$$

$$= -k_B T \ln\left[Z_0\left(1 + \frac{Z_1}{Z_0} + \frac{Z_2}{Z_0} + \cdots\right)\right]$$

$$= F_0 - k_B T \ln\left(1 + \frac{Z_1}{Z_0} + \frac{Z_2}{Z_0} + \cdots\right) \tag{4.52a}$$

and hence, expanding the logarithm for $Z_1/Z_0 + Z_2/Z_0 + \cdots < 1$,

$$F = F_0 - k_B T\left(\frac{Z_1}{Z_0} + \frac{Z_2}{Z_0} + \cdots\right). \tag{4.52b}$$

Another result related to this one, and one we shall require later is

$$E = -\frac{\partial}{\partial \beta} \ln Z \qquad (4.53a)$$

$$= E_0 - \frac{\partial}{\partial \beta}\left(\frac{Z_1}{Z_0} + \frac{Z_2}{Z_0}\right). \qquad (4.53b)$$

Relations (4.52b) and (4.53b) achieve the object of separating the effects of H_0 and H' in equation (4.44) (for the conditions under which perturbation theory is valid). This result is used when explicit expressions for H' are known, for example, the cubic and quartic terms in the potential-energy expansion. In order to evaluate thermodynamic quantities from equation (4.51), the lattice dynamical problem must be solved and this is the basis of the calculation of crystalline properties.

4.5   Thermodynamics—specific heat

The first attempts to apply quantum theory to a solid were to explain the low-temperature specific heat. We have discussed the Einstein and Debye theories in Sections 2.2 and 4.2. In general terms, we may write the thermal energy of a harmonic solid as (see equation (4.6)),

$$E = \sum_{kj} \hbar\omega(kj)\bar{n}[\omega(kj)] + \text{zero point energy} \qquad (4.54)$$

where $\bar{n}[\omega(kj)] = (e^{\beta\hbar\omega(kj)} - 1)^{-1}$. Thus the specific heat is

$$C_V = \left(\frac{\partial E}{\partial T}\right)_V = k_B \sum_{kj} \left[\frac{\hbar\omega(k^j)}{k_B T}\right]^2 \frac{e^{\beta\hbar\omega(kj)}}{(e^{\beta\hbar\omega(kj)} - 1)^2}. \qquad (4.55)$$

For the Einstein model all $\omega(kj) = \omega_E$ and $\sum_{kj} \to 3N$, which gives

$$C_{V\,(\text{Einstein})} = 3Nk_B\frac{x^2 e^x}{(e^x - 1)^2} = 3Nk_B F_E(x) \qquad (4.56)$$

where $x \equiv \hbar\omega_E/k_B T$.

For the Debye model $\sum_{kj} \to \int \cdots Z(\omega)\,d\omega$ where $Z(\omega)\,d\omega$ is the number of modes in the range from ω to $\omega + d\omega$ and is given by equation (2.1) and discussed further in Section 3.5. Hence

$$E_{(\text{Debye})} = \int_0^{\omega_D} \frac{Z(\omega\hbar\omega)}{e^{\beta\hbar\omega} - 1}\,d\omega \qquad (4.57a)$$

$$C_{V\,(\text{Debye})} = \frac{9Nk_B}{x^3}\int_0^x \frac{y^4 e^y}{(e^y - 1)^2}\,dy \equiv 3Nk_B F_D(x) \qquad (4.57b)$$

where $x \equiv \hbar\omega_D/k_B T$.

The functions $F_E(x)$ and $F_D(x)$ are shown in Tables 4.2 and 4.3 for x in the range 0–10·9. It is very easy to see that $E_{(Debye)}$ yields an energy density proportional to T^4, i.e. it corresponds to the energy density of black-body radiation as given by the Stefan–Boltzmann law.

It has become common practice to express specific-heat results in terms of an 'equivalent Debye temperature'. For the Debye model, the Debye temperature is defined as $\theta_D = \hbar\omega_D/k_B$. For an experimental measurement or for a calculated value of C_V, we can define an equivalent Debye temperature. This is the value of θ_D that must be used in equations (4.57) ($x = \theta_D/T$) such that $C_{V(Debye)} = C_V$. Unless the crystal is exactly described by the Debye model (no such real crystal exists), the equivalent Debye temperature is a function of temperature, since no single value of θ_D will satisfy $C_{V(Debye)} = C_V$ at all temperatures. Thus the specific-heat data (experimental or theoretical) is usually presented as a plot of θ_D against T. In this way it shows the deviation of the crystal from a Debye solid. In the words of Professor Ziman '... the Debye temperature is a parameter in which we try to sum up the complete lattice dynamics of a given solid'. From a given value of C_V, the corresponding θ_D may be found from tables of the Debye function such as those in Beattie,[4] or N.B.S. tables.[6] An extract of these is presented as Table 4.3.

It is also possible to obtain a value for $\theta_D(T = 0 \text{ K}) (\equiv \theta_0)$ from the values of the elastic constants. de Launay (see also References 66–68 of Chapter 2) has derived an expression for θ_0 for cubic crystals which in our notation becomes

$$\theta_0 = \frac{3\hbar}{k_B}\left[\frac{6}{18 + \sqrt{3}} \cdot \frac{N}{V} \cdot f(C_{11}, C_{12}, C_{44})\right]^{1/3}\left(\frac{C_{44}}{\rho}\right)^{1/2} \tag{4.58}$$

where $f(C_{11}, C_{12}, C_{44})$ is a factor dependent on the anisotropy and is tabulated by de Launay; N/V is the atomic volume ($= a^3/2$ for body-centred cubic and $a^3/4$ for face-centred cubic) and ρ is the density ($= mN/V$).

The Debye temperature characterizes the thermal properties of a crystal. Because of the widely varying magnitudes of bonding forces in crystals, there is little meaning to the terms 'high' and 'low' as applied to absolute temperature. What is 'high' for one crystal may be 'low' for another. However, the forces between atoms are reflected in the Debye temperature, and it is useful to have this as a reference to characterize a given crystal and give a relative meaning to 'high' and 'low' temperature ranges. Table 4.6 shows representative values of θ_D and compares these with the corresponding melting points. It may be noticed that the lighter inert-gas solids melt below their Debye temperatures, while the other crystals included in the table remain solid above it. We will return later to the question of melting. Figures 4.3 show the variation of θ_D with temperature for a crystal from each of the classes defined in Chapter 2.

Table 4.5 de Launay's values of $f(s, t) \equiv f(C_{11}, C_{12}, C_{44})$ for use in equation (4.58). $s \equiv (C_{11} - C_{44})/(C_{12} + C_{44})$, $t \equiv (C_{12} - C_{44})/C_{44}$ and for positive t (i.e. $C_{12} > C_{44}$) the maximum value of t is given by $C_{12} \rightarrow C_{11}$. Thus $t_{max} = (C_{11} - C_{44})/C_{44} = 2s/1 - s$. For $C_{12} > C_{11}$ the value of f becomes complex. Reproduced, with permission, from de Launay, J., *J. Chem. Phys.*, **24**, 1071 (1956) and **22**, 1676 (1954).

s	0·1	0·2	0·3	0·4	0·5	0·6	0·7	0·8	0·9	1.0
t										
−1·0	0·6122	0·6538	0·6935	0·7315	0·7680	0·8031	0·8369	0·8695	0·9010	0·9315
−0·9	0·5854	0·6325	0·6773	0·7200	0·7608	0·7998	0·8373	0·8733	0·9080	0·9415
−0·8	0·5560	0·6091	0·6593	0·7069	0·7522	0·7953	0·8366	0·8761	0·9140	0·9506
−0·7	0·5241	0·5836	0·6396	0·6924	0·7423	0·7897	0·8348	0·8779	0·9192	0·9588
−0·6	0·4895	0·5560	0·6182	0·6764	0·7313	0·7831	0·8322	0·8790	0·9236	0·9663
−0·5	0·4522	0·5263	0·5950	0·6591	0·7191	0·7756	0·8288	0·8793	0·9273	0·9731
−0·4	0·4120	0·4944	0·5703	0·6405	0·7060	0·7672	0·8247	0·8790	0·9305	0·9794
−0·3	0·3687	0·4603	0·5438	0·6207	0·6918	0·7580	0·8199	0·8781	0·9331	0·9852
−0·2	0·3220	0·4238	0·5157	0·5996	0·6767	0·7480	0·8145	0·8767	0·9352	0·9905
−0·1	0·2710	0·3847	0·4858	0·5772	0·6606	0·7374	0·8085	0·8747	0·9369	0·9954
0·0	0·2147	0·3429	0·4542	0·5536	0·6437	0·7260	0·8019	0·8724	0·9382	1·0000
t/t_{max}										
0·1	0·2012	0·3208	0·4256	0·5202	0·6072	0·6883	0·7654	0·8413	0·9225	
0·2	0·1873	0·2979	0·3955	0·4846	0·5674	0·6455	0·7207	0·7955	0·8738	
0·3	0·1727	0·2739	0·3637	0·4465	0·5241	0·5978	0·6692	0·7399	0·8117	
0·4	0·1575	0·2488	0·3303	0·4058	0·4772	0·5455	0·6116	0·6767	0·7413	
0·5	0·1415	0·2224	0·2947	0·3623	0·4265	0·4882	0·5479	0·6064	0·6637	
0·6	0·1243	0·1942	0·2567	0·3154	0·3714	0·4254	0·4778	0·5288	0·5785	
0·7	0·1056	0·1636	0·2154	0·2642	0·3110	0·3561	0·4000	0·4428	0·4841	
0·8	0·0844	0·1293	0·1693	0·2070	0·2431	0·2781	0·3122	0·3453	0·3775	
0·9	0·0589	0·0881	0·1141	0·1386	0·1621	0·1849	0·2071	0·2288	0·2499	

Table 4.6 Some thermal properties of representative crystals. The density measurements are by X-ray analysis and the temperature (in K) at which the measurement was made is shown in brackets. The θ_D are shown as approximate values, since the values are temperature dependent. $\alpha_l \equiv (1/l)/(\partial l/\partial T)$ is the mean linear coefficient of thermal expansion up to the temperatures shown in brackets in K. For the first group, α_l varies rapidly over the whole range of solid-state temperatures.

	Structure	Density $(10^3 \, kg/m^3)$	Melting point (K)	θ_D (K)	α_l $(10^{-6} \, K^{-1})$
Ne	F.C.C.	1·503 (10)	25·4	63	340 (10)
Ar	F.C.C.	1·656 (40)	83·9	85	350 (40)
Kr	F.C.C.	3·00 (85)	116·0	63	300 (60)
Xe	F.C.C.	3·56 (88)	161·1	55	250 (80)
C (diamond)	diamond	3·516 (293)	Sublimes	~2000	1·17 (295–340)
C (graphite)	Hex. and rhom.	2·266 (293)	~4000		
Si	diamond	2·329 (293)	1685	~570	4·15 (280–330)
Ge	diamond	5·324 (298)	1231	~300	5·92 (280–330)
Na	B.C.C.	0·966 (293)	370·9	~160	71 (273–373)
K	B.C.C.	0·862 (293)	336·3	~130	80 (273–323)
Rb	B.C.C.	1·533 (293)	311·9	~70	90 (273–300)
Cu	F.C.C.	8·933 (293)	1356	~310	20 (300–1000)
Au	F.C.C.	19·281 (298)	1336	~170	15 (300–1000)
Al	F.C.C.	2·699 (293)	933	~400	29 (300–1000)
NaCl	NaCl	2·167 (293)	1074	~300	40·5 (300)
NaI	NaCl	3·667 (293)	924	~170	
KBr	NaCl	2·75 (293)	1003	~150	
KI	NaCl	3·13 (293)	959	~140	
RbF	NaCl	3·557 (293)	1048	~240	
RbI	NaCl	3·55 (293)	915	~110	

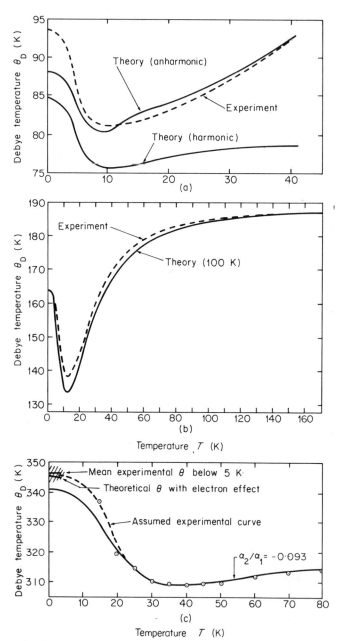

Figure 4.3 Examples of θ_D against T. For details of the theoretical model, see the reference indicated: (a) inert-gas solids,[8] (b) sodium iodide (Reference 49, Chapter 2) and (c) copper.[7] (a) is reproduced from Leech, J. W., and Reissland, J. A., *Phys. Letters*, **14**, 304–305 (1965), copyright 1965 North-Holland Publishing Co., Amsterdam; (b) is reproduced, with permission, from Cowley, R. A., Cochran, W., Brockhouse, B. N., and Woods, D. B., *Phys. Rev.*, **131**, 1036 (1963); and (c) is reproduced from de Launay, J., *Solid State Physics*, **2**, 219–303 (1956) by permission of Academic Press, Inc., New York

The expression (4.55) may be evaluated [if the $\omega(\mathbf{k}j)$ are known] using a sampling method or an interpolation method (e.g. Houston's method as in Section 2.12). However, it includes only the harmonic contributions to the specific heat. If the terms Z_1 and Z_2 in equation (4.53) are non-negligible, they also contribute to C_V through the general relation

$$C_V = -T\left(\frac{\partial^2 F}{\partial T^2}\right)_V. \qquad (4.59)$$

From the form of equation (4.52b), the contributions are additive and we may compute the anharmonic part independently of expression (4.55). If Z_1 and Z_2 are important they are also present at absolute zero and hence affect the potential parameters. These effects will be most important for the lighter atoms and those that have relatively weak forces of attraction. There has been much work on the computation of the importance of anharmonic effects in the inert-gas solids[8,10–29] (see also Reference 35 of Chapter 2). The analytical form of F_3 and F_4 (Z_2/Z_0 and Z_1/Z_0, respectively, since there is no first-order perturbation term from H_{cubic} and the second-order perturbation term involving H_{quartic} is of the order eight in the displacements) is given explicitly in the literature[b] and need not be reproduced here. However at high temperatures, the anharmonic contribution to the specific heat becomes linearly dependent on temperature. This dependence arises classically and is shown for a single anharmonic oscillator in Chapter 5. This is an important result, since at high temperatures anharmonicity may be expected to be important, i.e. when the amplitudes of the atomic vibrations are large. At lower temperatures more complex expressions must be used. Table 4.7, reproduced from Leech and Reissland,[10] shows the approach to this linear law for the inert-gas solids (these are used again as examples, since their weak interatomic forces lead to comparatively strong anharmonic effects). It can be seen that krypton and xenon exhibit the classical behaviour well below their melting points and have fairly small anharmonicity. Argon is becoming classical, but neon is a long way from being a classical solid. This behaviour follows logically from the relative masses of these crystals. The law of corresponding states and good general reviews of the thermodynamics of the inert-gas solids may be found in Horton,[11] Losee and Simmons,[12] and in Reference 35 of Chapter 2.

F_0 in expression (4.53) may be written explicitly using equations (4.51a), (4.52a) and (4.54), i.e.

$$F_0 = -k_B T \ln \text{Tr}\left(\exp\left\{-\sum_{\mathbf{k}j} \beta\hbar\omega(\mathbf{k}j)[n(\mathbf{k}j) + \tfrac{1}{2}]\right\}\right).$$

The trace is a sum over energy levels, namely $n(\mathbf{k}j)$ taking values from zero to infinity. Hence

$$F_0 = \sum_{\mathbf{k}j}[\tfrac{1}{2}\hbar\omega(\mathbf{k}j) + k_B T \ln(1 - e^{-\beta\hbar\omega(\mathbf{k}j)})]. \qquad (4.60)$$

Table 4.7 Anharmonic contributions to the specific heat, showing the approach to the linear law at high temperatures. C_V^0 is the harmonic part of the specific heat; $\Delta C_{V(\text{anh})} = -T(\partial^2 F_{(\text{anh})}/\partial T^2)_V$. The calculations all refer to constant volume corresponding to that at $T = 0$ K. Reproduced, with permission, from Leech, J. W., and Reissland, J. A., *J. Phys. C (Solid State Phys.)*, **3**, 997 (1970) copyright The Institute of Physics.

T	$F_{(\text{anh})}$ $(10^{-22}\,\text{J atom}^{-1})$	C_V^0 $(3k_B)$	$\Delta C_{V(\text{anh})}$ $(3k_B)$	$-T^{-1}\Delta C_{V(\text{anh})}$ $(10^{-4} \times 3k_B)(\text{K}^{-1})$
(a) Neon				
4	1·532	0·020	−0·015	37·5
8	1·522	0·165	−0·058	72·5
12	1·554	0·368	−0·123	102·5
16	1·653	0·536	−0·156	97·5
20	1·816	0·655	−0·175	87·5
24	2·037	0·738	−0·193	80·4
(b) Argon				
10	0·508	0·158	−0·014	14·0
20	0·564	0·523	−0·040	20·0
30	0·692	0·727	−0·050	16·7
40	0·885	0·830	−0·059	14·8
50	1·139	0·885	−0·072	14·4
60	1·451	0·918	−0·085	14·2
70	1·821	0·938	−0·098	14·0
80	2·248	0·952	−0·111	13·9
(c) Krypton				
20	0·245	0·647	−0·021	10·53
40	0·457	0·886	−0·038	9·45
60	0·827	0·946	−0·055	9·09
80	1·349	0·969	−0·072	9·05
100	2·020	0·979	−0·090	9·04
120	2·841	0·986	−0·108	9·03
(d) Xenon				
20	0·142	0·699	−0·014	7·02
40	0·288	0·907	−0·025	6·32
60	0·540	0·957	−0·037	6·16
80	0·895	0·975	−0·049	6·14
100	1·351	0·984	−0·061	6·13
120	1·908	0·988	−0·074	6·13
140	2·567	0·991	−0·086	6·13

Strictly we should include the static potential energy Φ of the lattice, and for quantities that are directly related to the free energy (e.g. latent heats) rather than through a temperature derivative, it is essential to do so (see, for example, Appendix A).

The zero-point-energy term in equation (4.60) may be obtained directly from the force constants and, as we have discussed in Section 2.12, is proportional to the first moment of the frequency spectrum; the values for the inert-gas solids are included in the tables of potential parameters in Appendix A.

4.6 Thermodynamics—thermal expansion

When the temperature of the lattice is raised, we know from observation that its volume (and hence the interatomic separation) increases. This is measured by the coefficient of thermal expansion (or expansivity):

$$\alpha_V(T) \equiv \frac{1}{V}\left(\frac{\partial V}{\partial T}\right)_P. \tag{4.61}$$

The thermal expansion of a solid is a property arising strictly from anharmonicity. However, without precise definition of terms, this statement can be misleading. Each atom of a crystal oscillates in a potential which, according to the way in which we have set up the dynamics of the lattice in Chapter 1, is the sum of pair interactions. For small amplitudes, it is a good approximation to consider the oscillations to be taking place in a parabolic potential well. We have made this approximation by terminating the potential-energy expansion at the squared terms. Thus the 'harmonic' approximation involves up to second-order derivatives of the potential-energy function. From this approximation we have derived an expression for the Helmholtz free energy F_0. We should include the static potential energy of the lattice (since this is strain dependent) and hence

$$F = N\Phi_0 + F_0 \tag{4.62}$$

F_0 being given by result (4.60); Φ_0 is the ground-state energy if all the atoms are in their equilibrium positions. The volume occupied by the crystal is that which makes F a minimum

$$-\left(\frac{\partial F}{\partial V}\right)_T = P = 0 \tag{4.63}$$

That is, the equation of state for the solid is characterized by no external pressure forces and the solid is free to move against internal stresses until they are balanced by intermolecular attractions. (Even if one takes account of the vapour pressure of the solid, the effect is negligible, and for thermal-expansion considerations it is valid to put $P = 0$ at all solid-state temperatures.) At $T = 0$ K equation (4.62) becomes

$$F = N\Phi_0 + \tfrac{1}{2}\sum_{\mathbf{k}j}\hbar\omega(\mathbf{k}j). \tag{4.64}$$

For the classical case, there is no zero point energy [i.e. the second term in equation (4.64) is absent] and, considering only nearest-neighbour interactions, the volume of the lattice would correspond to all atoms sitting at the minimum of the pair potential curve σ. (Since, for nearest neighbours only, the minima of all the pairs coincide.) For a face-centred cubic lattice, for

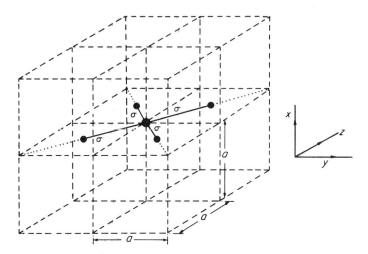

Figure 4.4   Showing nearest-neighbour atoms of face-centred cubic
crystal in the yz plane (there are eight more—four in the xy plane
and four in the xz plane)

example, we see from Figure 4.4 that $a = \sqrt{2}\sigma$ in the classical nearest-
neighbours-only approximation. Let us continue the discussion by particular
reference to the simplest crystals—the inert-gas solids; the principles
involved are perfectly general. The potential parameters ε and σ of Figure 1.3
may be found by using equation (4.64) and its derivative through the equation
(4.63). These are solved using experimental values of $F(T = 0)$ (the sublimation energy) and the lattice constant; see Appendix A. If we introduce the
zero point vibrations, the effect is to expand the lattice; however, since the
lattice constant at $T = 0$ K is included in the theory as a fixed quantity
(found by experiment), the effect is reflected by a decrease in σ.

   Similarly ε must decrease from that of the classical value (i.e. deeper well)
in order that the two-body potential be compatible with the experimental
quantities. The effect of the zero point energy on the parameterized two-body
potential is shown by the difference in the shape of lines (i) and (ii) in Figure
4.5. (For f.c.c. $\sigma_i = a/\sqrt{2}$ and $\varepsilon_i = -(2L_0)/(12N)$, where L_0/N is the latent
heat of sublimation per atom at $T = 0$ K and 12 is the number of nearest
neighbours.

   If we now consider the effect of including more distant neighbours in the
interaction, firstly without a zero point energy, we find a flatter two-body
curve [curve (iv) in Figure 4.5]. This too is physically intuitive; since there are
more contributions to the energy (fixed from experiment) each pair of atoms
contributes less, so that the sum over all pairs remains unchanged. The effect
of zero point energy [curve (iii) in Figure 4.5] is, again, to change the shape
(a deeper well nearer the origin) of the curve.

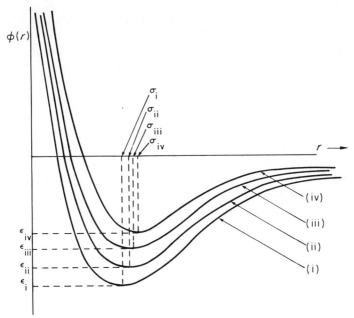

Figure 4.5 Showing the effect of zero point energy and the inclusion of more neighbours on the parameterized two-body potential: (i) nearest neighbour with zero point energy, (ii) nearest neighbour no zero point energy, (iii) all neighbours with zero point energy and (iv) all neighbours with no zero point energy

Thus the zero point vibrations effectively cause an expansion. If more energy is put into the lattice we would have to include the temperature-dependent terms of equation (4.60), and our equilibrium would be violated. Hence we would expect an expansion until equilibrium was again achieved. If we now regard the two-body potential-energy function as fixed, strains are induced to modify the frequencies so that the free energy is again a minimum. From equations (4.60), (4.62) and (4.63),

$$\frac{\partial E}{\partial V} = 0 = \frac{2N}{3a}\Phi_1 - \sum_{\mathbf{k}j}\left\{\frac{2\hbar}{a^3}\omega(\mathbf{k}j)\gamma(\mathbf{k}j)\coth\left[\frac{\beta\hbar\omega(\mathbf{k}j)}{2}\right]\right\} \tag{4.65}$$

where

$$\Phi_1 \equiv \frac{1}{2}\sum_l l_i^2 \frac{1}{r}\frac{\partial}{\partial r}\phi(r) \quad \left[\mathbf{r} = \frac{a}{2}(l_1, l_2, l_3)\right] \tag{4.66a}$$

$$\gamma(\mathbf{k}j) = -\frac{\partial \ln \omega(\mathbf{k}j)}{\partial \ln V} \tag{4.66b}$$

$$V = \frac{a^3}{4} \quad \text{(for a face-centred cubic structure)}.$$

Definition (4.66b) is a quantity of convenience known as Gruneisen's parameter and will be discussed later.

Now the expression for F [equations (4.62) and (4.60)] was deduced from the **harmonic** terms in the potential-energy expression, yet its derivative [equation (4.65)] very obviously predicts a thermal expansion. By an iterative self-consistency method we can solve the equilibrium condition (4.65) at any temperature and find the corresponding lattice spacing. (It is a simple matter[30] to increase the temperature stepwise from zero using the value of the lattice spacing obtained at the previous temperature as a first approximation, and to iterate systematically until self consistency is attained. Provided that the temperature increments are not too large, the convergence is very good.) Thermal expansions computed in this way are larger than those observed.[30] For example, in neon (all-neighbours model—Mie–Lennard Jones $m = 12$ potential) the method suggests a volume expansivity of $3 \times 10^{-3} \, K^{-1}$ (at 10 K) and $7 \cdot 2 \times 10^{-3} \, K^{-1}$ (at 20 K) while experiment (see Reference 69 in Chapter 2) finds values of $1 \times 10^{-3} \, K^{-1}$ (10 K) and $4 \cdot 1 \times 10^{-3} \, K^{-1}$ (20 K). Neon, being composed of light atoms, does not behave as a good harmonic solid, and clearly higher-order anharmonic terms are required; the third- and fourth-order terms in the expansion reduce the discrepancy by yielding $1 \cdot 5 \times 10^{-3} \, K^{-1}$ (10 K) and $5 \cdot 8 \times 10^{-3} \, K^{-1}$ (20 K). These figures were obtained by adding $\partial(F_3 + F_4)/\partial V$ to the right-hand side of equation (4.65) before solving to find the self consistent value of a. For the heavier atoms krypton and xenon, the thermal expansion is more accurately described by condition (4.65). The reason for the high values predicted by a quasiharmonic theory is found in considering phonon interactions. As the phonon density is increased, the energy required to create another phonon is modified by the existence of an energy of interaction between the one added and those already present. The total energy is not simply the sum of the individual phonon energies. The importance of anharmonicity rears again.

By differentiating the harmonic expression for F we have an implied third-order derivative even in the quasiharmonic approximation. In this sense anharmonicity is essential to account for thermal expansion. A 'rigorously' harmonic theory constrains the lattice to constant volume by rejecting third-order derivatives whenever they arise. This has led to differences in terminology; the terms we shall use here are as summarized by Leech and Reissland:[10]

$$F = \Phi \qquad (4.67a)$$

(classical, used at $T = 0$ K only)

$$F = N\Phi_0 + F_0 \qquad (4.67b)$$

[quasiharmonic; or harmonic if **all** third-order derivatives are rejected (i.e. no strain-dependent frequencies) or if no distinction with quasiharmonic is necessary]

$$F = N\Phi_0 + F_0 + F_3 + F_4 \qquad (4.67c)$$

(anharmonic).

Expression (4.67b) contains terms that arise purely from quadratic and zero-order terms in the potential energy. However the volume derivatives introduce third-order terms which lead some authors to use the term anharmonic. The terms F_3 and F_4 in equation (4.67c) arise directly from cubic and quartic terms in the potential-energy expansion. They contribute to Z_1 and Z_2 in equation (4.53) and, as we have seen, are of importance for other thermodynamical quantities. Thus non-harmonic effects appear in two ways; (i) the effect of the expansion of the lattice changing the energy of the modes but leaving them independent and (ii) the energy of interaction between modes. which is present even if the crystal is constrained to be at constant volume.

As was stated in Section 4.1, our policy is to avoid rigorous detail in this chapter. We have done this in this section at the risk of oversimplification, and hence a word of warning is required. For a proper treatment of thermal expansion it is necessary to consider finite-strain theory and to compute the effect of a strain on the crystal, taking non-linear effects into account. It is advantageous to delay this until we have an adequate formalism as a framework for discussion. Discussion of these effects appears in two reviews by Cowley.[31,32]

The Gruneisen parameter introduced earlier arose in the first instance from a theory of thermal expansion[33,34] based on the Debye approximation. The model was proposed so that when the lattice expanded, all the frequencies changed in the same way. In our notation this assumption means

$$\gamma_G = \frac{\partial \ln \omega(\mathbf{k}j)}{\partial \ln V} = \text{constant.} \qquad (4.68)$$

The significance is made clear by a simple thermodynamic argument. Noting the following standard results:

$$F = E - TS \qquad (4.69a)$$

$$S = -\left(\frac{\partial F}{\partial T}\right)_V \qquad (4.69b)$$

$$E = -T^2 \frac{\partial}{\partial T}\left(\frac{F}{T}\right) \qquad (4.69c)$$

$$P = -\left(\frac{\partial F}{\partial V}\right)_T \qquad (4.69d)$$

(S is the entropy; P, V, T and F we have used before), and applying them to the Debye expressions, the equation of state is

$$P = -\left(\frac{\partial}{\partial V} F_{\text{Debye}}\right)_T$$

$$= -\left(\frac{\partial F_{\text{Debye}}}{\partial \theta_D}\right)_T \cdot \left(\frac{\partial \theta_D}{\partial V}\right)_T \tag{4.70}$$

since F_{Debye} is specified at a given temperature by a single parameter $\theta_D (\equiv \hbar\omega_D/k_B)$.

Now we see from the expression (4.57a) for E_{Debye} that it is of the form $\theta_D f(\theta_D/T)$; thus F_{Debye} will also be of this form. We may write formally

$$-T\left\{\frac{\partial}{\partial T} f\left(\frac{\theta_D}{T}\right)\right\}_{\theta_D} \equiv \theta_D \left\{\frac{\partial}{\partial \theta_D} f\left(\frac{\theta_D}{T}\right)\right\}_T.$$

We see from equation (4.69c) that

$$E_{\text{Debye}} = -T^2 \frac{\partial}{\partial T}\left(\frac{F_{\text{Debye}}}{T}\right) = -T^2 \frac{\partial}{\partial T}\left[f\left(\frac{\theta_D}{T}\right)\right]$$

and thus from the above argument

$$E_{\text{Debye}} = T\theta_D \left\{\frac{\partial}{\partial \theta_D} f\left(\frac{\theta_D}{T}\right)\right\}_T = \theta_D \left(\frac{\partial F_{\text{Debye}}}{\partial \theta_D}\right)_T. \tag{4.71}$$

Equation (4.70) becomes

$$P = -\frac{E_{\text{Debye}}}{\theta_D} \frac{\partial \theta_D}{\partial V}$$

$$= \frac{E_{\text{Debye}}}{V}\gamma_G \tag{4.72a}$$

where

$$\gamma_G = -\frac{\partial \ln \theta_D}{\partial \ln V}. \tag{4.72b}$$

This dimensionless form is convenient, since it makes γ_G of order unity; the negative sign reflects the normal circumstance that the frequencies decrease as the lattice expands. Differentiating (4.72a) with respect to T (at constant volume)

$$\left(\frac{\partial P}{\partial T}\right)_V = \gamma_G \frac{C_V}{V} \tag{4.72c}$$

or using the relation

$$\left(\frac{\partial P}{\partial T}\right)_V = -\left(\frac{\partial P}{\partial V}\right)_T \left(\frac{\partial V}{\partial T}\right)_P$$

$$= \alpha/B \qquad (4.72\text{d})$$

where α is the volume expansivity $1/V(\partial V/\partial T)_P$ and B is the bulk modulus $-V(\partial P/\partial V)_T$, we see that

$$\gamma_G = \frac{\alpha V B}{C_V}. \qquad (4.72\text{e})$$

This expression for γ_G in terms of macroscopic thermodynamic quantities assumes that it is not temperature dependent. It thus relates the observable quantities and we have a means of testing the validity of the model. The theory accounts for the thermal expansion through this quantity γ_G; it allows the solid to expand but considers the vibrations about the new lattice positions to remain harmonic. In deriving equation (4.65), we have made the latter assumptions, but not that $\gamma(\mathbf{k}j)$ is a constant. The modified frequencies may be written

$$\omega(\mathbf{k}j) = \omega_{T=0}(\mathbf{k}j)[1 - \gamma(\mathbf{k}j)\Delta V] \qquad (4.73)$$

where ΔV is the change in volume from that at absolute zero. This effect may be treated as a two-phonon interaction process and analysed by the methods of the following chapter. The value of $\gamma(\mathbf{k}j)$ may be calculated for each frequency and the variation is usually found to be quite small.

Barron (Reference 85 of Chapter 2) and Blackman[35] extended the Gruneisen theory and define more general parameters. This, together with other work, has led to the use of γ_G as a parameter to characterize the thermal expansion just as the Debye temperature characterizes the specific heat. Averages of γ_G over all modes may be calculated as a function of temperature; thus it is computed as a comparative measure of the behaviour of a solid (Reference 15 of Chapter 2). The strain dependence of the frequencies,[13,36] and hence the Gruneisen parameter, is a measure of the deviation of the crystal from a rigorously harmonic model, i.e. it characterizes the quasiharmonic thermal expansion. The literature over the past five years contains so many references on thermal expansion, the Gruneisen parameter and elastic constants that it is not practicable to include a list here. The proceedings of a recent symposium on thermal expansion[37] provides a reasonably balanced view of current interests.

When the higher-order terms are included in the potential-energy expansion, it is no longer possible to describe the lattice vibrations as a set of independent normal modes. We shall see in detail in the next chapter that these non-harmonic terms are represented as interactions between the modes;

or, on the phonon gas model, that the gas is no longer ideal but that inter-phonon interactions occur. We may further the analogy between phonons and an ideal gas before formally introducing the higher-order terms. The phonon gas will have a 'radiation pressure' and we may postulate that this expands the lattice against the intermolecular binding forces when the pressure increases owing to a temperature rise. This means treating the surfaces as perfectly reflecting boundaries.

Table 4.8 Examples of the Gruneisen parameter for cubic crystals. These values are deduced from a number of sources, but primarily from Reference 15 in Chapter 2 and Reference 4 in this chapter.

Crystal	Temperature range	γ range
Ne	0–25	3·1 –3·5
Ar	0–50	2·8 – 3·1
Kr	0–50	2·75 – 3·05
Xe	0–50	2·75 – 3·0
Cu	0–600	1·7 – 1·95
Ag	0–300	2·7 – 2·8
Au	0–300	2·3 ±0·05
Al	0–400	2·3 – 2·7
Na	0–200	0·9 – 1·1
K	0–150	1·05 – 1·2

The radiation pressure of phonons differs from that of photons, since the velocities are not all the same; moreover, the velocities change as the lattice expands, since the forces are not strictly proportional to displacement. This deviation from Hooke's law leads to a larger effect than the photon-like radiation pressure ($= \frac{1}{3}u$, where u is the energy density). Brillouin[38] has discussed the radiation pressure of diffuse elastic waves and, from his results, we may write, for a cubic crystal

$$P_j = \frac{\overline{E_j}}{V}\left(\frac{1}{3} - \frac{a}{3v_j}\frac{dv_j}{da}\right) \qquad (4.74a)$$

where P_j is the pressure due to the elastic wave of polarization j (longitudinal or transverse) and v_j is the corresponding velocity. dv_j/da measures the change in velocity due to a change in the lattice spacing and reflects the anharmonic influence in interatomic forces. As an order-of-magnitude estimate, if we write $v_1 = v_{tr} \equiv v$ and $\overline{E} = \frac{1}{3}(\overline{E}_1 + 2\overline{E}_{tr})$, we find

$$P = \frac{\overline{E}}{V}\left(\frac{1}{3} - \frac{a}{3v}\frac{dv}{da}\right) \qquad (4.74b)$$

which, by comparison with equation (4.72a), suggests that

$$\gamma_G \approx \frac{1}{3} - \frac{a}{3v}\frac{dr}{da}.$$ (4.75)

For argon, $(a/3v)(dv/da)$ is approximately $-2\cdot7$, and hence values of γ_G of about 3 would seem to be indicated.

For metals, where there is an electronic contribution to the specific heat, we may define a corresponding electronic Gruneisen parameter. By this argument $\gamma_{electronic} = \frac{2}{3}$, since the pressure of a free electronic gas is $\frac{2}{3} \times$ (kinetic energy per unit volume). Most metals have values that are considerably higher than this (see examples in Table 4.8).

4.7 Thermodynamics—elastic constants

In Section 2.11 we have discussed the crystalline elastic constants and their relationships with the bulk elastic properties of a solid. Now anharmonic terms have been introduced into specific heat and thermal expansion, we can add to that discussion. Clearly, when the lattice expands, the elastic constants will change, since the forces between the atoms (or molecules) change. Thus there is a direct temperature dependence which may be found by computing the elastic constants by the method of Section 2.10 using the appropriate temperature-dependent lattice spacing. Table 4.9 shows this temperature dependence for argon; however, it must be noted that it is not the whole effect. There is also an effect due to the vibrations themselves. When the amplitudes become larger, these affect the elasticity directly as well as through the lattice expansion. Cowley and Cowley[39,40] have computed the temperature variation for alkali-halide crystals.

Table 4.9 An illustration of the effect of lattice expansion on the elastic constants of argon. The values are calculated using a 12-9-6 all-neighbour potential (see Appendix A). The numbers should not be taken as an accurate representation of the temperature variation of the quantities included, since (a) they are only part of the temperature effect and (b) they are computed by an empirical potential which is fitted to experiment only at absolute zero.

$T(K)$	C_{11} $(10^9 N/m^2)$	C_{12} $(10^9 N/m^2)$	C_{44} $(10^9 N/m^2)$	$V_l(100)$ $(10^3 m/s)$	$V_t(100)$ $(10^3 m/s)$	$V_t(100)$ $(10^3 m/s)$	S_{Hill}
0	4·104	2·152	2·404	1·521	1·163	0·741	1·675
10	4·104	2·152	2·404	1·521	1·163	0·741	1·675
20	3·964	2·063	2·330	1·500	1·150	0·734	1·626
30	3·708	1·898	2·206	1·456	1·123	0·719	1·543
40	3·499	1·764	2·104	1·419	1·101	0·707	1·475
50	3·140	1·534	1·930	1·353	1·060	0·684	1·358
60	2·753	1·289	1·739	1·276	1·014	0·658	1·229
70	2·328	1·021	1·529	1·184	0·959	0·627	1·087
80	1·953	0·786	1·341	1·094	0·906	0·598	0·960

Non-linear effects are described in elasticity theory by the introduction of third-order elastic constants. These appear when the energy due to a deformation includes third-order terms in the energy expansion in powers of the strain components (that is, the coefficients of products of three strain components). The significance, definitions, properties and measurements of third-order elastic constants are discussed by Brugger[9] and Thurston,[41] Cowley[31,32] and Blackman.[42] Very much work has been carried out in the past five years in this field (there are more than 1000 published papers on thermal expansion and elastic constants in this period) and it must be left to the reader to carry out his own literature search. No doubt by the time this book appears in print a new collection will have appeared, and more recent reviews than those already mentioned will be available. The most recent review to my knowledge at the time of writing is by Wallace.[43] An extensive list of the elastic moduli of single crystals and the corresponding isotropic moduli is given by Anderson.[44]

4.8 Thermodynamics—melting

When the amplitudes of the vibrations become large, it is necessary to include the anharmonic terms in the vibrations. Eventually a temperature is reached for which the amplitudes are too large to be contained by the intermolecular forces and the lattice breaks up. The point at which this breaking up or melting occurs is not uniquely associated by a well defined relation with the amplitudes. However, since the temperature is very well defined for each individual solid under given conditions, attempts have been made to establish such a general relation between lattice dynamical theories and macroscopic melting. The earliest and most famous is that of Lindemann.[45] Following his basic idea, we postulate that melting occurs when the root-mean-square amplitude becomes equal to some critical fraction of the distance between atoms. The displacement of an atom is due to the superposition of all the normal modes and is given by equation (1.4) together with equation (1.14). Thus the mean square amplitude is

$$\langle u^2(l\alpha) \rangle = \frac{1}{mN} \left\langle \left| \sum_{\mathbf{k}j} q(\mathbf{k}j) e_\alpha(\mathbf{k}j) \, e^{-i\mathbf{k}.\mathbf{r}^l} \right|^2 \right\rangle. \tag{4.76a}$$

The cross terms in this expression disappear and hence we may write

$$\langle u^2(l\alpha) \rangle = \frac{1}{mN} \sum_{\mathbf{k}j} \langle |q(\mathbf{k}j)|^2 \rangle. \tag{4.76b}$$

In terms of annihilation and creation operators [from equation (3.34)]

$$\langle u^2(l\alpha) \rangle = \frac{\hbar}{2mN} \sum_{\mathbf{k}j} \frac{1}{\omega(\mathbf{k}j)} \langle |a_{\mathbf{k}j}^+ + a_{\mathbf{k}j}|^2 \rangle. \tag{4.77a}$$

Since the averages of $a_{kj}^+ a_{kj}^+$ and $a_{kj} a_{kj}$ will be zero if the crystal is in an equilibrium state, equation (4.77a) reduces to

$$\langle u^2(l\alpha) \rangle = \frac{\hbar}{2mN} \sum_{kj} \frac{1}{\omega(kj)} (2\langle n(kj) \rangle + 1). \tag{4.77b}$$

This may be expressed in terms of the average energy associated with each mode, or, using the Bose–Einstein result for $\langle n(kj) \rangle$,

$$\langle u^2(l\alpha) \rangle = \frac{\hbar}{2mN} \sum_{kj} \frac{1}{\omega(kj)} \left\{ \frac{2}{e^{\beta\hbar\omega(kj)} - 1} + 1 \right\} \tag{4.78a}$$

$$= \frac{\hbar}{2mN} \sum_{kj} \frac{\coth\left[\frac{1}{2}\beta\hbar\omega(kj)\right]}{\omega(kj)}. \tag{4.78b}$$

Consider first the high-temperature approximation such that classical theory is valid, and thus that the average energy per mode is $k_B T$. From equation (4.78a), neglecting zero point energy and writing $e^{\beta\hbar\omega(kj)} = 1 + \beta\hbar\omega(kj)$

$$\langle u^2(l\alpha) \rangle = \frac{1}{mN} \sum_{kj} \frac{k_B T}{\omega(kj)^2}$$

$$= \frac{3k_B T}{m} \mu_{-2} \tag{4.79}$$

where [similarly to the definition (2.84)]

$$\mu_{-2} = \frac{1}{3N} \sum_{kj} \frac{1}{\omega(kj)^2} = \frac{1}{3N} \int_0^{\omega_{max}} \omega^{-2} Z(\omega)\, d\omega.$$

Clearly any attempt to apply the relation (4.79) directly runs into immediate difficulties, since the acoustic modes introduce singularities [where $\omega(kj)$ approaches zero at the Brillouin zone centre] if the density of states is not properly included in the average. However, since equation (4.79) is only applicable at high temperatures, and since also we know that, at high temperatures, Einstein averages and Debye averages become the same, we may use the Einstein model with reasonable confidence. Thus

$$\langle u^2(l\alpha) \rangle \approx \frac{3k_B T}{m\omega_E^2} = \frac{3\hbar^2 T}{mk_B \theta_E^2} \tag{4.80}$$

and, if we define a melting criterion by

$$\left. \frac{\langle u^2(l\alpha) \rangle}{r_s^2} \right|_{melting} \equiv C_{melt}^2 \tag{4.81a}$$

where $r_s^3 = v =$ atomic volume (e.g. $v_{(s.c.)} = a^3$, $v_{(f.c.c.)} = a^3/4$, $v_{(b.c.c.)} = a^3/2$), we see that

$$C_{\text{melt}}^2 = \frac{3\hbar^2 T_{\text{melt}}}{mk_B r_s^2 \omega_E^2} = \frac{3\hbar^2}{k_B} f_C^2 \frac{T_{\text{melt}}}{ma^2 \theta_E^2} \qquad (4.81b)$$

where T_{melt} is the melting point and f_C is a numerical factor dependent on the structure such that $r_s = a/f_C$. This expression is valid only if $T_{\text{melt}} > \theta_E$ (otherwise the high-temperature approximation invoked will not be valid at the melting point). We can find a value for ω_E for any solid by noting from relation (4.56) that when $T = \theta_E$, $x = 1$ and hence

$$C_{V(\text{Einstein}, T = \theta_E)} = 3Nk_B \frac{e}{(e-1)^2} = 0.921 \times 3Nk_B. \qquad (4.82)$$

Thus the equivalent Einstein temperature is that at which the actual C_V of the solid is equal to 0·921 of the classical value. As a rough indication of the validity of result (4.81b), consider solid xenon, $\theta_E \approx 50$ K (see Table 4.7), $T_{\text{melt}} = 161$ K (Table 4.6), $a_{(T=161)} = 6.35 \times 10^{-10}$ m, $m_{Xe} = 2.179 \times 10^{-25}$ kg and $f_C = 4^{1/3}$; these yield $C_{\text{melt}} = 0.067$. In xenon (a face-centred cubic structure) the nearest-neighbour distance is $a/\sqrt{2}$; thus this value of C_{melt} corresponds to vibrations with amplitude about $\frac{1}{16}$th of the nearest-neighbour separation. Rearranging equation (4.81b) we get

$$T_{\text{melt}} = K_{\text{melt}} ma^2 \theta_E^2 \qquad (4.83)$$

where $K_{\text{melt}} = \frac{1}{3}(k_B/\hbar^2 f_C^2) C_{\text{melt}}^2$. If we assume that C_{melt} is a constant equal to 0·067 as computed from xenon data, $K_{\text{melt}} = 7.33 \times 10^{41}$ J^{-1} K^{-1} s^{-2}. Applying this value through the relation (4.83) to krypton ($a \approx 5.820 \times 10^{-10}$ m, $m_{Kr} = 1.39 \times 10^{-25}$ kg, $\theta_E \approx 57$ K) we find a predicted melting point of 113 K compared with 116 K observed.

The Lindemann theory leads to a similar relation based on the Debye temperature. For a Debye solid we get, using equation (2.1) for $Z(\omega)$,

$$\mu_{-2(\text{Debye})} = \frac{1}{3N} \frac{V}{2\pi^2} \left(\frac{2}{v_t^3} + \frac{1}{v_l^3} \right) \int_0^{\omega_D} d\omega.$$

The integral is simply ω_D and, using equation (2.3), we see that

$$\mu_{-2(\text{Debye})} = 3\omega_D^{-2}. \qquad (4.84)$$

Hence the equation corresponding to equation (4.80) is

$$\langle u^2(l\alpha) \rangle = \frac{9\hbar^2 T}{mk_B \theta_D^2}. \qquad (4.85)$$

Defining a melting criterion as before leads to the Lindemann result, which he expressed in the form:

$$\theta_D = C_{Lind}\left(\frac{T_{melt}}{mNV^{2/3}}\right)^{1/2} \tag{4.86}$$

where N is Avogadro's number and V is the molar volume $= Nv$. In this form C_{Lind} is found to be about 200 for non-metals and about 137 for metals (see Zemansky,[2] p. 268 and p. 270). Since experiment confirms that relations of the form of equations (4.83) and (4.86) hold to within a few per cent for a given class of solids, it lends strong support to the premise that it is the relative magnitude of the amplitude of atomic vibrations that dominates the phenomena of melting.

For solids with $T_{melt} < \theta_D$, we must make more accurate calculations of equation (4.78b). These solids are highly anharmonic at their melting point and the problem becomes more complex.

At very low temperatures, the zero-point-energy term dominates the right-hand side of equation (4.78a) and we can get an estimate of the amplitudes of the zero point vibrations,

$$\langle u^2(l\alpha)\rangle_{z.p.e.} = \frac{\hbar}{2mN}\sum_{kj}\frac{1}{\omega(kj)} \tag{4.87a}$$

$$= \frac{3\hbar}{2m}\mu_{-1}. \tag{4.87b}$$

For the Debye model $\mu_{-1} = 3/2\omega_D$ and thus

$$\langle u^2(l\alpha)\rangle_{z.p.e.} = \frac{9}{4}\frac{\hbar}{m\omega_D} = \frac{9}{4}\frac{\hbar^2}{mk_B\theta_D} \tag{4.88a}$$

$$= \frac{1{\cdot}81 \times 10^{-45}}{m\theta_D}\ \text{metres}^2. \tag{4.88b}$$

Tables 4.10 gives examples of root-mean-square amplitudes evaluated using equation (4.88b). The magnitudes of these amplitudes indicate in which solids anharmonicity is likely to be of importance. As a working estimate it is reasonable to use the criterion that, if $(u_{rms}/d)_{z.p.e.} < 0{\cdot}015$, the quasi-harmonic approximation is adequate at temperatures below θ_D.

Another approach to describe melting is based on the Simon equation[46]

$$P - P_0 = a\left[\left(\frac{T}{T_0}\right)^c - 1\right] \tag{4.89}$$

where P_0 and T_0 are the pressure and temperature at the triple point and a and c are constants. Gilvarry[47-49] developed this, giving derivations of the constants a and c. The review by Babb[50] contains the vast bibliography of the work up to 1963 in this field.

It is tempting to try to set up a theory of melting based on the elastic constants. We see in Table 4.9 that all the elastic constants decrease as the lattice expands. We know that a liquid cannot support a shear stress ($S_{liquid} = 0$) so we could find the temperature at which $S_{solid} \to 0$. It is a simple matter to set up such a procedure, but it does not predict correct melting points. A solid retains solid-state properties right up to the temperature at which the lattice breaks up. The values of the thermodynamic quantities then take a discontinuous jump to those corresponding to a liquid. The general theory of phase transitions is discussed in detail elsewhere, for example Brout,[51] Fisher[52] (theoretical), Heller[53] (experimental) and melting in particular by Ubbelohde.[54]

Table 4.10 The amplitudes of zero point vibrations predicted by equation (4.88b). $u_{rms} = \langle u^2(l\alpha) \rangle^{\frac{1}{2}}_{z.p.e.}$, and d is the nearest-neighbour separation (the number in parentheses is the temperature at which the measurement was made). θ_0 are taken from Table 4.6.

Crystal	Mass $(10^{-27}kg)$	θ_D (K)	u_{rms} $(10^{-10}m)$	d $(10^{-10}m)$	u_{rms}/d
Ne	33·51	63	0·293	3·155 (4)	0·093
Ar	66·33	85	0·179	3·756 (4)	0·048
Kr	139·1	63	0·144	3·993 (4)	0·036
Xe	217·9	55	0·123	4·313 (4)	0·028
C (diamond)	19·92	2000	0·067	3·560 (298)	0·019
Si	46·63	570	0·082	3·420 (298)	0·023
Ge	120·53	300	0·071	2·450 (293)	0·029
Na	38·17	160	0·172	3·659 (4)	0·047
K	64·92	130	0·146	4·525 (4)	0·032
Rb	141·91	70	0·134	4·837 (4)	0·028
Cu	105·50	310	0·074	2·556 (293)	0·029
Au	327·0	170	0·057	2·884 (298)	0·020
Al	44·80	400	0·101	2·863 (294)	0·035

4.9 Summary

The behaviour of the phonon gas has been analysed in terms of **Bose–Einstein** statistics. We have seen that it is possible to treat the thermal energy of a solid in terms of **distinguishable atomic oscillators** and hence apply **classical statistical counting** or as a set of **number-unconserved indistinguishable** particles (phonons) and use **quantum-statistical** counting. In practice the latter is usually the most convenient, but both lead to the same results, provided that the atomic oscillators are treated with their correct quantized energy levels. The statistical behaviour of phonons emphasizes their analogy with **photons**, a **Debye solid** corresponding to a **black-body cavity**. **Fluctuations** in the **mean number** of **photons** with given energy are discussed, and the expressions presumed to be the same for phonons. Numerical tables are included to show the orders of magnitudes and the temperature variation of the quantities involved in the Einstein and Debye models.

Although we are primarily concerned with phonons, it is important to know how they fit into the general picture. To this end, we have considered the behaviour of **fermions** and found markedly different results. A striking distinction appears when **transition probabilities** are analysed. The **occupation** of the state to which a particle may make a transition plays a significant role; for fermions the transition probability is **zero** if the state is **occupied**, for bosons the probability of transition is **increased**. For the limiting classical case described by **Maxwell–Boltzmann statistics,** the transition probability is unaffected by the **occupancy** of the final state. **Phonon statistics** are characterized by putting the **chemical potential** to **zero** in the general Bose–Einstein expressions. This arises (as for photons) since their number is not conserved.

The **density matrix** is defined so as to provide a technique for performing **averages** and to lead from statistical properties to **macroscopic observables**. It is at this point that we first introduce terms **beyond** those of the **harmonic** model. To deal with these, **perturbation theory** is treated from a statistical foundation and the resulting expressions are couched in terms that relate **thermodynamic functions** to the **Hamiltonian** for the **atomic lattice**.

From the discussion of some observed and computed thermodynamic quantities, we begin to see when **anharmonicity** is of importance. The lighter atoms vibrate with **larger amplitudes** than do heavy atoms in order to take up a given amount of energy. Thus crystals made up of light atoms become anharmonic at relatively low temperatures. Another important factor is the strength of the **interatomic forces**; the **inert-gas solids** have fairly **weak** forces of interaction and hence the lighter inert-gas solids may be expected to be highly anharmonic. This is borne out by the representative results presented.

The amplitudes and frequencies of the atomic vibrations determine also the **stability** of the crystal. As the amplitudes increase by absorption of energy, **phase transitions** may occur to a **new crystal structure** which is energetically more favourable. The ultimate phase transition (for the solid) occurs when the lattice can no longer support vibrations with such large amplitudes; **melting** occurs and the long-range ordering is lost.

The thermodynamical quantities discussed in this chapter have not been treated exhaustively. It is intended as a shallow covering of the topics and problems for which the theoretical techniques in the following chapters are required. Properties which arise from non-equilibrium effects, such as thermal conduction and absorption of energy by the crystal, have not yet been introduced.

Chapter notes

[a] To carry out the integrations in equation (4.50d), change the variable q to $u \equiv p(1 - q)$ and hence the limits of the inner integration become $\int_p^0 \cdots du$; then change the order and perform the p integration first (whence the limits are $\int_1^u \cdots dp$ and $\int_0^1 \cdots du$).
[b] See, for example, equations (2.6) and (2.7) of Reference 10; these are also discussed in Section 5.4.

References

1. Wannier, G. H., *Statistical Physics*, Wiley, New York, 1966.
2. Zemansky, M., *Heat and Thermodynamics*, McGraw Hill, 1957.
3. Planck, M., *Ann. d. Physik*, **4**, 553–563 (1901).
4. Beattie, J. A., *Math. and Phys.*, **6**, 1–32 (1916).
5. ter Haar, D., *Fluctuations, Relaxation and Resonance in Magnetic Systems* (Ed. D. ter Haar), Oliver and Boyd, Edinburgh, 1962, pp. 109–117.
6. *Handbook of Mathematical Functions*, National Bureau of Standards, Abramowitz, M., and Stegun, I. A. (Eds.), Washington, 1965.
7. de Launay, J., *Solid State Physics*, **2**, 219–303 (1956).
8. Leech, J. W., and Reissland, J. A., *Phys. Letters*, **14**, 304–305 (1965).
9. Brugger, K., *Phys. Rev.*, **133**, A1611–A1612 (1964).
10. Leech, J. W., and Reissland, J. A., *J. Phys. C* (*Solid State Phys.*), **3**, 975–986, 987–1001 (1970).
11. Horton, G. K., *Am. J. Phys.*, **36**, 93–119 (1968).
12. Losee, D. L., and Simmons, R. O., *Phys. Rev.*, **172**, 944–957 (1968).
13. Davies, R. O., and Parke, S., *Phil. Mag.*, **4**, 341–358 (1959).
14. Davies, R. O., *Fluctuations, Relaxation and Resonance in Magnetic Systems* (Ed. D. ter Haar), Oliver and Boyd, Edinburgh, 1962, pp. 169–205.
15. Barron, T. H. K., *Lattice Dynamics* (Ed. R. F. Wallis), Pergamon, Oxford, 1964, pp. 247–254.
16. Domb, C., and Zucker, I. J., *Nature*, **178**, 484 (1956).
17. Feldman, J. L., and Horton, G. K., *Proc. Phys. Soc.*, **92**, 227–243 (1967).
18. Gillis, N. S., Werthamer, N. R., and Koehler, T. R., *Phys. Rev.*, **165**, 951–959 (1968).
19. Henkel, J. H., *J. Chem. Phys.*, **23**, 681–687 (1955).
20. Hooton, D. J., *Phil. Mag.*, **46**, 422–442 (1955).
21. Klein, M. L., and Reissland, J. A., *J. Chem. Phys.*, **41**, 2773–2776 (1964).
22. Koehler, T. R., *Phys. Rev.*, **165**, 942–950 (1968).
23. Kuebler, J., and Tosi, M. P., *Phys. Rev.*, **137**, A1617–A1620 (1965).
24. Nosanow, L. H., and Shaw, G. L., *Phys. Rev.*, **128**, 546–550 (1962).
25. Reissland, J. A., *Discuss. Faraday Soc.*, **40**, 123–125 (1966).
26. Wallace, D. C., *Phys. Rev.*, **131**, 2046–2056 (1963).
27. Wallace, D. C., *Phys. Rev.*, **133**, A153–A162 (1964).
28. Zucker, I. J., *Phil. Mag.*, **3**, 987–998 (1958).
29. Zucker, I. J., *Proc. Phys. Soc.* (*London*), **77**, 889–900 (1961).
30. Leech, J. W., Peachey, C. J., and Reissland, J. A., *Phys. Letters*, **10**, 69–70 (1964).
31. Cowley, R. A., *Rep. Prog. in Phys.*, **31**, 123–166 (1968).
32. Cowley, R. A., *Advances in Phys.*, **12**, 421–480 (1963).
33. Gruneisen, E., *Ann. Physik*, **58**, 753–758 (1919).
34. Gruneisen, E., *Handb. d. Phys.*, **10**, 21 *et seq.* (1926).
35. Blackman, M., *Phil. Mag.*, **3**, 831–838 (1958).

36. Barron, T. H. K., and Klein, M. L., *Proc. Phys. Soc.*, **82**, 161–173 (1963).
37. 'Symposium on thermal expansion', *J. Appl. Phys.*, **41**, 5043–5154 (1970).
38. Brillouin, L., *Tensors in Mechanics and Elasticity* (Tr. Brennon, R. O.), Academic Press, New York, 1964.
39. Cowley, E. R., and Cowley, R. A., *Proc. Roy. Soc.*, **A287**, 259–280 (1965).
40. Cowley, E. R., and Cowley, R. A., *Proc. Roy. Soc.*, **A292**, 209–223 (1966).
41. Thurston, R. N., and Brugger, K., *Phys. Rev.*, **133**, A1604–A1610 (1964).
42. Blackman, M., *Proc. Phys. Soc.*, **84**, 371–378 (1964).
43. Wallace, D. C., *Solid State Physics*, **25**, 302–404 (1970).
44. Anderson, O. L., *Physical Acoustics* (Ed. Mason, W. P.), Vol. IIIB, Academic Press, New York, 1965, pp. 43–95.
45. Lindemann, F., *Phys. Z.*, **11**, 609–612 (1910).
46. Simon, F., and Glatzel, G., *Z. Anorg. Allgem. Chem.*, **178**, 309 (1929).
47. Gilvarry, J. J., *Phys. Rev.*, **102**, 308–316, 317–325, 325–331, 331–340 (1956).
48. Gilvarry, J. J., *Phys. Rev.*, **103**, 1700–1704 (1956).
49. Gilvarry, J. J., *Phys. Rev.*, **104**, 908–913 (1956).
50. Babb, S. E., *Rev. Mod. Phys.*, **35**, 400–413 (1963).
51. Brout, R. H., *Phase Transitions*, Benjamin, New York, 1965.
52. Fisher, M. E., *Rep. Prog. Phys.*, **30**, 615–730 (1967).
53. Heller, P., *Rep. Prog. Phys.*, **30**, 731–826 (1967).
54. Ubbelohde, A. R., *Melting and Crystal Structure*, Oxford University Press, London, 1965.

5

Phonon–Phonon Interactions

5.1 Introduction

In the course of linking the thermodynamic properties of a crystal with the statistics of the phonons, we found effects that were not explicable on the ideal-gas model. These effects were embraced under the general term 'anharmonicity'. Quantum-statistical expressions were derived relating the lattice Hamiltonian to the partition function. The anharmonic parts were those involving higher than second-order terms in the atomic displacements.[1] We did not treat the mechanics of the anharmonic vibrations, only qualitatively discussing their significance and the evidence of their importance. Starting with a single anharmonic oscillator and building to a collection representing a solid, we shall introduce simple techniques that are the forerunners of more powerful and formal tools.

The existence of an interaction between phonons has numerous manifestations. Some of these become so complex that it is not possible, even with the sophisticated analytical techniques that have been developed, to deal with them in a satisfactory manner. However, recent work has made significant progress in some areas and in others the use of modern computing processes has pushed back the boundaries reached by analytical methods.

Considering them as quasiparticles, it seems quite natural to introduce an interaction between phonons, but this may also be understood as a wave concept. A normal mode is a standing wave in a crystal (there are no nodes, since standing waves of many wavelengths are superimposed) and hence causes instantaneous positions of high and low density. This, in effect, diffracts any other wave and modifies its wave vector. Thus the term 'interference condition' is sometimes used to describe the relation between the three wave vectors of the modes involved.

Interactions become more complex as the number of phonons taking part increases. Diagram techniques are used to describe the processes and, by defining a set of rules, they are also an aid to evaluating the effect of any process on the thermodynamical properties of the system. All diagram techniques are aimed at simplifying the description of the physics of the system. Very often, however, the introduction of diagrams creates more problems for the reader than it solves. This arises, in part, at least, because the author, knowing what the technique must include later, introduces diagrams that are more general than necessary. At the risk of criticism for using several different diagram techniques, this chapter starts with a very simple procedure and develops it to cover more complex processes.

The probability that a particular interaction will occur is governed by well defined selection rules. The rate at which a particular process occurs is dependent on the strength of the interaction and the numbers of the relevant phonons that are present. In equilibrium, the mean occupation number of each kind of phonon must be constant; so that all processes must leave the phonon states unchanged. If the crystal is in a non-equilibrium state, it will make transitions between phonon states that lead towards an equilibrium state. This is only possible if interactions between phonons occur; without phonon–phonon interactions a non-equilibrium state, once created, would persist.

We shall see that an anharmonic crystal cannot be represented by a set of non-interacting anharmonic oscillators. The coupling terms between displacements of different atoms cannot be eliminated as in the harmonic model. Thus the resulting expressions retain a mass of symbols and usually defy simple computation. We discuss the effects of phonon interactions on the thermal conductivity, the absorption of sound waves and on an equilibrium property not included in Chapter 4—the vapour-pressure ratio of different isotopes of the same solid.

Phonons interact with other crystal excitations, giving rise to interesting coupling problems; however this chapter is concerned solely with phonons interacting with other phonons, and the succeeding chapters will include other interactions.

5.2 Classical anharmonic oscillator

Since the effects of anharmonicity are more important at high temperatures, the classical approximation is adequate for many purposes. Consider a linear oscillator described by a Hamiltonian

$$H = \frac{p^2}{2m} + a_2 x^2 + H' \tag{5.1a}$$

where

$$H' = \sum_{s=3}^{\infty} a_s x^s \quad \text{and} \quad a_2 = \tfrac{1}{2} m \omega^2. \tag{5.1b}$$

In the classical region ($\hbar \omega \ll k_B T$), the partition function is

$$Z = \int\int_{\substack{\text{all phase} \\ \text{space}}} e^{-\beta H(x,p)} \, dx \, dp \tag{5.2}$$

and, using equation (5.1a), this becomes

$$Z = \int_{-\infty}^{+\infty} e^{-\beta p^2/2m} \, dp \int_{-\infty}^{+\infty} e^{-\beta a_2 x^2} e^{-\beta H'} \, dx. \tag{5.3}$$

(Note that there are no problems of commutation in classical theory as there were in Section 4.4.) Provided that $\beta H' \ll 1$, we may expand

$$e^{-\beta H'} - 1 - \beta H' + \tfrac{1}{2}\beta^2 H'^2 - \cdots$$

$$= 1 - \beta(a_3 x^3 + a_4 x^4) + \tfrac{1}{2}\beta^2 a_3^2 x^6 + \cdots \tag{5.4}$$

from equations (5.1b). Substituting this into equation (5.3) and carrying out the integrations^a, we get

$$Z = \frac{\pi}{\beta}\left(\frac{2m}{a_2}\right)^{1/2}\left(1 - \frac{3}{4}\frac{a_4}{\beta a_2^2} + \frac{15}{16}\frac{a_3^2}{\beta a_2^3} - \cdots\right). \tag{5.5}$$

We can now obtain the energy E and the specific heat C_V [for example, by using equations (4.52), (4.59) and (4.69c), or more simply by using equation (4.53) for E and differentiating with respect to T to find C_V], and these are

$$E = k_B T - \left[3\frac{a_4}{(m\omega^2)^2}k_B^2 - \frac{15}{2}\frac{a_3^2}{(m\omega^2)^3}k_B^2\right]T^2 \tag{5.6a}$$

$$C_V = k_B - \left[6\frac{a_4}{(m\omega^2)^2}k_B^2 - 15\frac{a_3^2}{(m\omega^2)^3}k_B^2\right]T \tag{5.6b}$$

where expression (5.1b) for a_2 has been inserted.

Thus we can see the origin of the linear temperature dependence of the specific heat at high temperatures, which was discussed in Section 4.5. Expressions (5.6) give the energy and specific heat of an oscillator described by

$$H = \frac{p^2}{2m} + \tfrac{1}{2}m\omega^2 x^2 + a_3 x^3 + a_4 x^4 \tag{5.7}$$

all higher terms having been neglected. If the potential-energy part of the Hamiltonian was expanded in terms of an order parameter α, such that α is the ratio of the magnitudes of successive terms, the quadratic part being of order unity, we see that a_3^2 and a_4 are of the same order, i.e. of order α^2. Thus the approximations we have made are consistent, both remaining terms having the same order of magnitude and all other terms being of higher order in α. Provided that $\alpha \ll 1$, approximation (5.7) is good and results (5.6) are an adequate description of a classical anharmonic oscillator. Before dealing with large numbers of oscillators, as in a solid, let us analyse the case of a single anharmonic quantum oscillator.

5.3 Quantum anharmonic oscillator

Although anharmonicity is of greatest importance at higher temperatures, we have seen that lighter solids (such as solid neon, as in Section 4.5, and to an even greater extent solid helium) may become highly anharmonic before they become classical. It is therefore more than an academic exercise to deduce the effect of anharmonicity on the energy levels of a quantum oscillator. We shall make use of this analysis to illustrate a simple diagram technique. Assuming a Hamiltonian of the same form as expression (5.7) and writing

$$H' \equiv a_3 x^3 + a_4 x^4 \qquad (5.8a)$$

and

$$H_0 \equiv -\frac{\hbar^2}{2m} \frac{\partial^2}{\partial x^2} + \frac{m\omega^2}{2} x^2 \qquad (5.8b)$$

we have from perturbation theory that, to second order, the anharmonic contribution to the energy level ε_n is

$$\Delta \varepsilon_n = H'_{nn} - \sum_{n' \neq n} \frac{H'_{nn'} H'_{n'n}}{\varepsilon^0_{n'} - \varepsilon^0_n} \qquad (5.9a)$$

where the matrix elements are defined in the usual way [for example, see equation (4.34)] and $\varepsilon^0_{n'}$ and ε^0_n are eigenvalues of H_0, given by equation (1.25a). Expression (5.9a) is valid, provided that the expectation values of H' are small compared with those of H_0. The resulting energy levels are

$$\varepsilon_n = \varepsilon^0_n + \Delta \varepsilon_n. \qquad (5.9b)$$

In order to find $\Delta \varepsilon_n$ corresponding to equation (5.8a) we have to evaluate $H'_{nn'}$ and H'_{nn} using the unperturbed (harmonic) wave functions. We know from section (3.3) that the transformation to the operators a^+ and a diagonalizes H_0; thus we apply these to H'. According to relations (3.10a), each x can raise or lower the quantum level of the oscillator by one step. If there is no transfer of energy to or from the oscillator, so that it is not making real transitions among its levels, it is in an equilibrium state and any raising or lowering must be accompanied by a 'simultaneous' lowering or raising, respectively. In other words, any creation of an excitation must be annihilated and vice versa, so that the intermediate states are virtual, not real. This suggests a simple method of enumerating contributions to $\Delta \varepsilon_n$ and, by defining suitable rules, it also enables us to express $\Delta \varepsilon_n$ in terms of n. However, before defining this procedure, let us briefly comment on the significance of the term 'simultaneous' and the use of time-independent perturbation theory. We are treating the oscillator as an isolated system, and thus the uncertainty in the energy is zero. Hence, according to Heisenberg's principle, the uncertainty in the time is infinite. Thus it is valid to use time-independent theory on any closed system.

Rules for evaluating the matrix elements $(x^p)_{n'n}$ for integer p

(1) Horizontal lines represent unperturbed states, labelled by quantum numbers of the oscillator.

(2) These states may be connected by sloping lines, representing creation ⟋ or annihilation ⟍ .

(3) Draw all possible diagrams consisting of p lines, such that the initial state is n and the final state is n'.

(4) Each diagram yields a term consisting of a product of p contributions, i.e. one for each line. The diagram ⟋$_n^{n+1}$ contributes $[(\hbar/2m\omega)(n+1)]^{1/2}$, while ⟍$_{n-1}^n$ contributes $[(\hbar/2m\omega)n]^{1/2}$.

(5) The value of $(x^p)_{n'n}$ for any allowed n' is given in terms of n by the sum over all diagrams.

The first rule arises from the approximation that we are evaluating the perturbed eigenvalues using the unperturbed states. The second rule represents transformation (3.10a), each x consisting of an annihilation and a creation. Rule 3 picks out the allowed combinations of a^+ and a from the term $(a^+ + a)^p$; for an equilibrium state only even values of p give non-zero contributions, since there must be an equal number of as and a^+s in order that $n' = n$. Rule 4 is a statement of the properties of a^+ and a as summarized by equations (3.24). Finally, Rule 5 takes into account that there may be many ways of making a transition from n to n' under the influence of the operator x^p, all intermediate states being virtual. This procedure is more straightforward in application than it sounds from the above formalization, so let us apply the rules to the evaluation of $\Delta\varepsilon_n$ (equation 5.9a).

First-order term H'_{nn}. We have the terms $(a_3x^3)_{nn}$ and $(a_4x^4)_{nn}$. Clearly, we cannot draw three lines (as in Rule 3) that begin and end in the state n; so we can say immediately that

$$(a_3x^3)_{nn} = 0$$

The diagrams representing $(a_4x^4)_{nn}$ are shown in Figure 5.1.

Thus, including the coefficient $a_4(\hbar/2m\omega)^2$, we have

$$\Delta\varepsilon_n(\text{quartic}) = (a_4x^4)_{nn} = \tfrac{3}{2}a_4\left(\frac{\hbar}{m\omega}\right)^2 (n^2 + n + \tfrac{1}{2}). \qquad (5.10a)$$

With an increased familiarity of the method, some of the steps may be omitted, for example, it is unnecessary to draw in the horizontal lines.

Table 5.1 Diagrammatic method of evaluating H'_{nn}. The right-hand column is included as an aid to the summation required by Rule 5

Diagram	Represents	Contribution [Rule 4, omitting common factor $(\hbar/2m\omega)^2$]	Number of powers of n		
			n^2	n^1	n^0
1 $n+2$ / $n+1$ / n	aaa^+a^+	$(n+1)(n+2)$	1	3	2
2 $n+1$ / n	aa^+aa^+	$(n+1)^2$	1	2	1
3* $n+1$ / n / $n-1$	a^+aaa^+	$(n+1)n$	1	1	0
4* $n+1$ / n / $n-1$	aa^+a^+a	$n(n+1)$	1	1	0
5 n / $n-1$	a^+aa^+a	n^2	1	0	0
6 n / $n-1$ / $n-2$	a^+a^+aa	$n(n-1)$	1	-1	0
		Sum	$6n^2 + 6n + 3$		

* The equivalence of diagrams that can be made identical by changing the directions of all the arrows follows from invariance under time reversal.

Second-order term $H'_{nn'}H'_{n'n}$. The second-order perturbation term involving $a_4 x^4$ is of higher order than $\Delta\varepsilon_n$(quartic) in equation (5.10a), whereas the corresponding term from $a_3 x^3$ is of the same order as $\Delta\varepsilon_n$(quartic). The order parameter argument in Section 5.2 still holds; moreover, the following analysis shows that $(a_3 x^3)_{nn'}(a_3 x^3)_{n'n}$ does not yield any higher powers of n than are contained in result (5.10a). Constructing the diagrams for this second-order cubic term, we see that the intermediate (virtual) state n' may take only four values; $n' = n \pm 1$ or $n' = n \pm 3$. The diagrams are grouped accordingly. To find $\Delta\varepsilon_n$(cubic) using expression (5.9a), we must sum over all allowed intermediate states weighted with a factor $(\varepsilon_{n'}^0 - \varepsilon_n^0)^{-1}$.

Table 5.2   Diagrammatic method of evaluating $\displaystyle\sum_{n' \neq n} \frac{H'_{nn'}H'_{n'n}}{\varepsilon_{n'}^0 - \varepsilon_n^0}$

Diagram	n'	$\varepsilon_{n'}^0 - \varepsilon_n^0$	Contribution [each term is to be multiplied by $\dfrac{1}{\hbar\omega}\left(\dfrac{\hbar}{2m\omega}\right)^3$]	Powers of n			
				n^3	n^2	n^1	n^0
[i]	$n+3$	$3\hbar\omega$	$\frac{1}{3}(n+1)(n+2)(n+3)$	$\frac{1}{3}$	2	$\frac{11}{3}$	2
[ii(a)]	$n+1$		$(n+1)(n+2)^2$	1	5	8	4
[ii(b)]	$n+1$	$\hbar\omega$	$(n+1)^2(n+2)$	1	4	5	2
[ii(c)]	$n+1$		$n(n+1)(n+2)$	1	3	2	0
[iii(a)]	$n+1$		$(n+1)^3$	1	3	3	1
[iii(b)]	$n+1$	$\hbar\omega$	$(n+2)(n+1)^2$	1	4	5	2
[iii(c)]	$n+1$		$(n+1)^2 n$	1	2	1	0
[iv(a)]	$n+1$		$n^2(n+1)$	Cancels with diagram [v(a)]			
[iv(b)]	$n+1$	$\hbar\omega$	$n(n+1)(n+2)$	1	3	2	0

$x_{nn'}^3 \qquad x_{n'n}^3$

Table 5.2 continued

Diagram	n'	$\varepsilon_{n'}^0 - \varepsilon_n^0$	Contribution [each term is to be multiplied by $\dfrac{1}{\hbar\omega}\left(\dfrac{\hbar}{2m\omega}\right)^3$]	Powers of n n^3 n^2 n^1 n^0
[iv(c)]	$n+1$	$\hbar\omega$	$n(n+1)^2$	Cancels with diagram [v(b)]
[v(a)]	$n-1$		$-(n+1)n^2$	Cancels with diagram [iv(a)]
[v(b)]	$n-1$	$-\hbar\omega$	$-(n+1)^2n$	Cancels with diagram [iv(c)]
[v(c)]	$n+1$		$-(n+1)n(n-1)$	$-1 \quad 0 \quad 1 \quad 0$
[vi(a)]	$n-1$		$-n^3$	$-1 \quad 0 \quad 0 \quad 0$
[vi(b)]	$n-1$	$-\hbar\omega$	$-n^2(n+1)$	$-1 \quad -1 \quad 0 \quad 0$
[vi(c)]	$n-1$		$-n^2(n-1)$	$-1 \quad 1 \quad 0 \quad 0$
[vii(a)]	$n-1$		$-n(n-1)^2$	$-1 \quad 2 \quad -1 \quad 0$
[vii(b)]	$n-1$	$-\hbar\omega$	$-(n-1)n^2$	$-1 \quad 1 \quad 0 \quad 0$
[vii(c)]	$n-1$		$-(n-1)n(n+1)$	$-1 \quad 0 \quad 1 \quad 0$
[viii]	$n-3$	$-3\hbar\omega$	$-\tfrac{1}{3}n(n-1)(n-2)$	$-\tfrac{1}{3} \quad 1 \quad -\tfrac{2}{3} \quad 0$

Sum $\quad 30n^2 + 30n + 11$

Thus taking into account the $a_3^2(\hbar/2m\omega)^3/\hbar\omega$ and the sign in equation (5.9a), the cubic contribution to the energy levels of the oscillator is

$$\Delta\varepsilon_{n(\text{cubic})} = -\frac{15}{4}\frac{a_3^2}{\hbar\omega}\left(\frac{\hbar}{m\omega}\right)^3(n^2 + n + \tfrac{11}{30}). \tag{5.10b}$$

Collecting these two terms together, we find that the energy levels of an anharmonic oscillator are given by

$$\varepsilon_n = (n + \tfrac{1}{2})\hbar\omega + A(n^2 + n) + A_0 \tag{5.11a}$$

where

$$A \equiv \left(\frac{3a_4}{2} - \frac{15}{4}\frac{a_3^2}{m\omega^2}\right)\left(\frac{\hbar}{m\omega}\right)^2 \tag{5.11b}$$

and

$$A_0 \equiv \left(\frac{3a_4}{4} - \frac{11}{8}\frac{a_3^2}{m\omega^2}\right)\left(\frac{\hbar}{m\omega}\right)^2 \tag{5.11c}$$

which is the contribution of anharmonicity to the zero point energy.

To find the expectation value of the energy of an oscillator with energy levels given by equations (5.11), we must apply the averaging procedure of Section 4.4. We have, from equation (4.53b)

$$\overline{\Delta\varepsilon_n} = -\frac{\partial}{\partial\beta}\left(\frac{Z_1}{Z_0} + \frac{Z_2}{Z_0}\right) \tag{5.12}$$

where Z_0, Z_1 and Z_2 are given by equations (4.51). Hence, from results (5.10):

$$\frac{Z_1}{Z_0} = -\beta \cdot \frac{3}{2}a_4\left(\frac{\hbar}{m\omega}\right)^2(\overline{n^2} + \bar{n} + \tfrac{1}{2}) \tag{5.13a}$$

and

$$\frac{Z_2}{Z_0} = \beta\frac{15}{4}\frac{a_3^2}{m\omega^2}\left(\frac{\hbar}{m\omega}\right)^2(\overline{n^2} + \bar{n} + \tfrac{11}{30}). \tag{5.13b}$$

Substituting these into equation (5.12), noting that, as in equation (4.16), $\overline{n^2} = 2\bar{n}^2 + \bar{n}$;

$$\overline{\Delta\varepsilon} = 2A(\bar{n}^2 + \bar{n}) + 2\beta A(2\bar{n} + 1)\frac{\partial\bar{n}}{\partial\beta} + A_0. \tag{5.14}$$

Now

$$\frac{\partial\bar{n}}{\partial\beta} = \frac{\partial}{\partial\beta}(e^{\beta\hbar\omega} - 1)^{-1} = -\hbar\omega\, e^{\beta\hbar\omega}\bar{n}^2 = -\hbar\omega(1 + \bar{n})\bar{n} \tag{5.15}$$

since $e^{\beta\hbar\omega} = (1 + \bar{n})/\bar{n}$, and thus

$$\Delta\varepsilon = 2A(\bar{n}^2 + \bar{n})(1 - \beta\hbar\omega) - 4\beta\hbar\omega A\bar{n}^3 + A_0. \tag{5.16}$$

In the classical limit $\bar{n} \to 1/\beta\hbar\omega(= k_B T/\hbar\omega)$ and equation (5.16) becomes

$$\overline{\Delta\varepsilon}_{\text{(classical approx)}} = -2A\left(\frac{k_B T}{\hbar\omega}\right)^2 + A_0 - 2A. \tag{5.17}$$

Dropping the zero-point-energy terms from this, since it has no classical counterpart, equation (5.17) is identical with the energy [equation (5.6a)] deduced classically.

From the foregoing analysis we see that, if A is positive, the energy levels of the anharmonic oscillator (equation 5.11a) are higher than those of a harmonic oscillator with the same frequency, but the expectation value of the energy at a given (high) temperature is less. Physically this arises from the occupations of the higher anharmonic levels being slightly less than those of the corresponding harmonic levels at a given temperature. For a harmonic oscillator $\bar{\varepsilon} = \varepsilon/(e^{\beta\varepsilon} - 1)$, where $\varepsilon = \hbar\omega$. If ε is increased slightly, the effect on $\bar{\varepsilon}$ is given by

$$\frac{\partial\bar{\varepsilon}}{\partial\varepsilon} = \frac{e^{\beta\varepsilon}(1 - \beta\varepsilon) - 1}{(e^{\beta\varepsilon} - 1)^2}. \tag{5.18}$$

This is negative for all ε, since the numerator[b] has the sign of $e^x(1 - x) - 1$. Thus an increase in ε gives a decrease in $\bar{\varepsilon}$.

5.4 Collection of anharmonic oscillators

We saw in Section 1.5 that the motions of a set of harmonic oscillators could be uncoupled and expressed in terms of a set of independent (normal) modes. In Section 3.5 the Hamiltonian was written in terms of annihilation and creation operators defined in terms of the complex normal coordinates and momenta [equations (3.34)]. Since the corresponding modes are independent, the expectation value of the energy of a set of harmonic oscillators is a sum of the mean energies of each mode [as in equation (4.54)]. The problem now facing us is more complicated. Although in the previous two sections we have analysed the mechanics of a single anharmonic oscillator without difficulty, a collection of them cannot be transformed to a set of independent modes. Thus cross terms, which we were able to eliminate in the harmonic case, remain and introduce interactions. The energy of a collection of coupled anharmonic oscillators cannot be written as the sum of a set of independent energy terms.

The Hamiltonian for a set of anharmonic oscillators is

$$H = H_0 + H' \tag{5.19a}$$

where H_0 is given by equation (1.3) and

$$H' = \frac{1}{3!}\Phi_{\alpha\alpha'\alpha''}^{ll'l''}u_\alpha^l u_{\alpha'}^{l'} u_{\alpha''}^{l''} + \frac{1}{4!}\Phi_{\alpha\alpha'\alpha''\alpha'''}^{ll'l''l'''}u_\alpha^l u_{\alpha'}^{l'} u_{\alpha''}^{l''} u_{\alpha'''}^{l'''} \qquad (5.19b)$$

namely the continuation of the Taylor-series expansion (1.1).

The Einstein summation convention (Section 1.4) is used in this and succeeding expressions in this section.

We cannot diagonalize the Hamiltonian (5.19a) exactly, but provided that the effect of H' on the system satisfies the conditions of validity of perturbation theory, it is worthwhile applying the transformation to uncouple the largest terms—those in H_0. Thus using equations (3.26), H_0 is given by equation (1.7) or equation (3.39),

$$H' = H_3 + H_4 \qquad (5.20a)$$

with

$$H_3 = \frac{1}{6(mN)^{3/2}}\Phi_{\alpha\alpha'\alpha''}^{ll'l''}e_\alpha(1)e_{\alpha'}(2)e_{\alpha''}(3)q(1)q(2)q(3)\,e^{-i(\mathbf{k}_1.\mathbf{r}^l + \mathbf{k}_2.\mathbf{r}^{l'} + \mathbf{k}_3.\mathbf{r}^{l''})}. \qquad (5.20b)$$

$$H_4 = \frac{1}{24(mN)^2}\Phi_{\alpha\alpha'\alpha''\alpha'''}^{ll'l''l'''}e_\alpha(1)e_{\alpha'}(2)e_{\alpha''}(3)e_{\alpha'''}(4)q(1)q(2)q(3)q(4) \qquad (5.20c)$$
$$\times\,e^{-i(\mathbf{k}_1.\mathbf{r}^l + \mathbf{k}_2.\mathbf{r}^{l'} + \mathbf{k}_3.\mathbf{r}^{l''} + \mathbf{k}_4.\mathbf{r}^{l'''})}$$

where $e_\alpha(i) \equiv e_\alpha(\mathbf{k}_i j_i)$, etc., and $q(i) \equiv q(\mathbf{k}_i j_i)$ are convenient abbreviations, and where the implied summations are now over the cartesian components (α, etc.), the direct lattice (l, etc.) and the modes ($\mathbf{k}_i j_i$, etc.). Now these expressions must be invariant under translation by a lattice vector, say $\mathbf{r}^l$. Thus subtracting $\mathbf{r}^l$ from $\mathbf{r}^l$, $\mathbf{r}^{l'}$ and $\mathbf{r}^{l''}$ in the cubic term introduces factor $e^{+i(\mathbf{k}_1 + \mathbf{k}_2 + \mathbf{k}_3).\mathbf{r}^l}$. If the argument (of the implied summations) is to remain unchanged, this factor must be unity, since $\Phi_{\alpha\alpha'\alpha''}^{ll'l''}$ depends only on the relative positions of the three atoms. This imposes the condition (3.29),

$$\mathbf{k}_1 + \mathbf{k}_2 + \mathbf{k}_3 = \mathbf{K} \quad \text{(including } \mathbf{K} = 0) \qquad (5.21a)$$

where $\mathbf{K}$ is a reciprocal lattice vector [see equation (1.44)]. Similarly, in equation (5.20c):

$$\mathbf{k}_1 + \mathbf{k}_2 + \mathbf{k}_3 + \mathbf{k}_4 = \mathbf{K} \quad \text{(including } \mathbf{K} = 0). \qquad (5.21b)$$

Thus the translational symmetry introduces a restriction on the values of $\mathbf{k}$ vectors which give non-zero contributions to the cubic and quartic terms of the Hamiltonian. The functions $\Delta(\mathbf{k}_1 + \mathbf{k}_2 + \mathbf{k}_3)$ and $\Delta(\mathbf{k}_1 + \mathbf{k}_2 + \mathbf{k}_3 + \mathbf{k}_4)$ are usually introduced to emphasize this where $\Delta(\mathbf{k})$ has the properties as in the result (3.29):

$$\Delta(\mathbf{k}) \equiv \begin{array}{l} 1 \text{ if } \mathbf{k} = \mathbf{K} \text{ a reciprocal lattice vector (including zero)} \\ 0 \text{ otherwise.} \end{array} \qquad (5.22)$$

These cubic and quartic terms are three-phonon and four-phonon processes, respectively. The conditions (5.21) correspond to conservation of momentum, the **K** part being the amounts that may be transferred to the lattice. On a wave picture these are the various orders of Bragg reflections from the periodic structure.

The interaction terms (5.20b) and (5.20c) may be written in terms of phonon creation and annihilation operators by application of the transformation (3.34). Suppose now we consider the case of an equilibrium state—as in Section 5.3 for a single oscillator—and find the contributions of H_3 and H_4 to the thermodynamic properties of the anharmonic crystal. We have a suitable statistical formalism in Section 4.4 and, just as for the single oscillator, we may use equations (4.51) and evaluate $H'_{nn}[=(H_4)_{nn}]$ and $H'_{n'n}[=(H_3)_{n'n}]$ by the diagram method. However, it is important to remember that there are now many different modes, and hence the description of the excited states requires the specification of the $3sN$ values[c] $n(\mathbf{k}j)$. For this reason it is advisable to label each transition line with the relevant phonon; Figure 5.1 shows examples of terms in $(H_3)_{n'n}$.

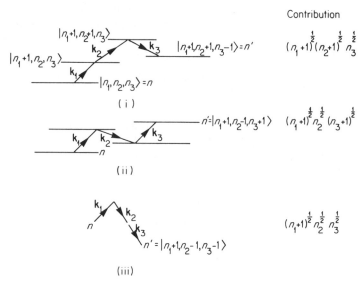

Contribution

(i)

(ii)

(iii)

Figure 5.1   Examples of contributions to $(H_3)_{n'n}$, illustrating that the full details need not be included. The initial phonon state $|n\rangle$ is $|n_1, n_2, n_3\rangle$ and the final state $|n'\rangle$ is shown for each case, $n(\mathbf{k}_1 j_1) \equiv n_1$, etc. In diagram (ii) the labels on the intermediate phonon states have been omitted, and in diagram (iii) the horizontal lines are omitted

From these examples, a number of features become clear. If a process (one diagram) is to contribute to an equilibrium property of the crystal, there must be an even number of lines with labels equal in pairs of annihilation and creation. For example, in the quartic term the phonon state $|n_1 + 1,$ $n_2 + 1, n_3 - 1, n_4 - 1\rangle$ is not equivalent to the state $|n_1 n_2 n_3 n_4\rangle$ unless $\mathbf{k}_1 = -\mathbf{k}_3$ and $\mathbf{k}_2 = -\mathbf{k}_4$. There are three ways of choosing four variables to be equal in pairs; thus we take one of them (say $\mathbf{k}_1 = -\mathbf{k}_3, \mathbf{k}_2 = -\mathbf{k}_4$) and multiply by a factor 3:

$$\sum_{\substack{k_1 k_2 k_3 k_4 \\ j_1 j_2 j_3 j_4}} f(\mathbf{k}_1, \mathbf{k}_2, \mathbf{k}_3, \mathbf{k}_4) \to 3 \sum_{\substack{k_1 k_2 \\ j_1 j_2}} f(\mathbf{k}_1, \mathbf{k}_2, \mathbf{k}_3 \equiv -\mathbf{k}_1, \mathbf{k}_4 \equiv -\mathbf{k}_2) \qquad (5.23a)$$

Thus the condition (5.21b) is automatically included by taking diagrams that begin and end in the same state.

$|H_3|^2_{nn}$ has six $q(\mathbf{k}j)$ involved, namely the product $q_1^* q_2^* q_3^* q_4 q_5 q_6$. Again we require these to group into pairs to describe an equilibrium-state process. The symmetry of expression (5.20b) is such that there are only two kinds of groupings. Either a pair from $\mathbf{k}_1, \mathbf{k}_2$ and $\mathbf{k}_3$ and a pair from $\mathbf{k}_4, \mathbf{k}_5$ and $\mathbf{k}_6$ must be (i) equal and opposite, e.g. $\mathbf{k}_1 = -\mathbf{k}_2$ and $\mathbf{k}_4 = -\mathbf{k}_5$, and then $\mathbf{k}_3 = \mathbf{k}_6 = 0$ [since $\Delta(\mathbf{k}_1 + \mathbf{k}_2 + \mathbf{k}_3) = 0$ if $\mathbf{k}_1 + \mathbf{k}_2 + \mathbf{k}_3 \neq 0$]; or (ii) equal in pairs, one from each group, e.g. $\mathbf{k}_1 = \mathbf{k}_4, \mathbf{k}_2 = \mathbf{k}_5$ and $\mathbf{k}_3 = \mathbf{k}_6$. The former arrangements contribute zero. They are a special case of the harmonic term (two virtual phonons $\mathbf{k}$ and $-\mathbf{k}$) and correspond to a translation of the whole lattice $\mathbf{k} = 0$. Thus $\mathbf{k}_1, \mathbf{k}_2$ and $\mathbf{k}_3$ are to be equal in pairs with $\mathbf{k}_4, \mathbf{k}_5$ and $\mathbf{k}_6$. There are 3! equivalent ways of choosing the pairs, and therefore

$$\sum_{k_1 \to k_6} f(\mathbf{k}_1 \cdots \mathbf{k}_6) \to 3! \sum_{k_1 \to k_3} f(\mathbf{k}_1, \mathbf{k}_2, \mathbf{k}_3, \mathbf{k}_4 = \mathbf{k}_1, \mathbf{k}_5 = \mathbf{k}_2, \mathbf{k}_6 = \mathbf{k}_3).$$
$$(5.23b)$$

Although we have not written it explicitly, it follows that wherever $\mathbf{k}_i = \pm \mathbf{k}_{i'}$ that $j_i = j_{i'}$; both $\mathbf{k}$ and j are required to specify a phonon state.

Taking account of all the above features, the thermal averaging according to equation (4.51) and the summation over all diagrams, the contributions of H' to the free energy may be evaluated. As general expressions, these look complicated. They are included here so as to avoid leaving the discussion in mid air and for the enthusiast who wishes to carry out the analysis and check the result.

Cubic term:

$$F_3 = -\frac{1}{\beta} \frac{Z_2}{Z_0} = \frac{3!}{(3!)^2} \left(\frac{\hbar}{2mN}\right)^3 \sum_{\substack{k_1 k_2 k_3 \\ j_1 j_2 j_3}} \Delta(\mathbf{k}_1 + \mathbf{k}_2 + \mathbf{k}_3) \qquad (5.24a)$$

$$\times |f_3(\mathbf{k}_1 \mathbf{k}_2 \mathbf{k}_3)|^2 g_3(\mathbf{k}_1 \mathbf{k}_2 \mathbf{k}_3, T)$$

where

$$f_3(\mathbf{k}_1 \mathbf{k}_2 \mathbf{k}_3) \equiv \sum_{\substack{ll'l'' \\ \alpha\alpha'\alpha''}} \Phi_{\alpha\alpha'\alpha''}^{ll'l''} \frac{e_\alpha(1)}{\sqrt{\omega_1}} \frac{e_{\alpha'}(2)}{\sqrt{\omega_2}} \frac{e_{\alpha''}(3)}{\sqrt{\omega_3}} e^{-i(\mathbf{k}_1 \cdot \mathbf{r}^l + \mathbf{k}_2 \cdot \mathbf{r}^{l'} + \mathbf{k}_3 \cdot \mathbf{r}^{l''})}$$

and

$$g_3(\mathbf{k}_1, \mathbf{k}_2, \mathbf{k}_3, T) = \left\{ \frac{(1 + \bar{n}_1)(1 + \bar{n}_2)(1 + \bar{n}_3) - \bar{n}_1\bar{n}_2\bar{n}_3}{\omega_1 + \omega_2 + \omega_3} \right.$$

$$\left. + 3\frac{(1 + \bar{n}_1)(1 + \bar{n}_2)\bar{n}_3 - \bar{n}_1\bar{n}_2(1 + \bar{n}_3)}{\omega_1 + \omega_2 - \omega_3} \right\}$$

in which

$$e_\alpha(1) \equiv e_\alpha(\mathbf{k}_1 j_1), \omega_1 \equiv \omega(\mathbf{k}_1 j_1) \text{ and } \bar{n}_1 \equiv \overline{n(\mathbf{k}_1 j_1)} = (e^{\beta\hbar\omega(\mathbf{k}_1 j_1)} - 1)^{-1},$$

etc.

Quartic term:

$$F_4 = -\frac{1}{\beta}\frac{Z_1}{Z_0} = \frac{3}{4!}\left(\frac{\hbar}{2mN}\right)^2 \sum_{\substack{\mathbf{k}_1\mathbf{k}_2 \\ j_1 j_2}} f_4(\mathbf{k}_1\mathbf{k}_2) \cdot g_4(\mathbf{k}_1\mathbf{k}_2, T) \qquad (5.24b)$$

where

$$f_4(\mathbf{k}_1\mathbf{k}_2) = \sum_{\substack{l'l''l''' \\ \alpha\alpha'\alpha''\alpha'''}} \Phi^{ll'l''l'''}_{\alpha\alpha'\alpha''\alpha'''} \frac{e_\alpha(1)}{\sqrt{\omega_1}}\frac{e_{\alpha'}(2)}{\sqrt{\omega_2}}\frac{e_{\alpha''}(1)}{\sqrt{\omega_1}}\frac{e_{\alpha'''}(2)}{\sqrt{\omega_2}} e^{-i\mathbf{k}_1.(\mathbf{r}^l - \mathbf{r}^{l''}) - i\mathbf{k}_2(\mathbf{r}^{l'} - \mathbf{r}^{l'''})}$$

and

$$g_4(\mathbf{k}_1\mathbf{k}_2, T) = (1 + 2\bar{n}_1)(1 + 2\bar{n}_2).$$

As a further check for the reader to evaluate (5.24b) by the steps outlined, the diagrams for g_4 are shown in Figure 5.2, including all the pair permutations [i.e. the factor of 3 in equation (5.25a)]. The cubic term is of second order

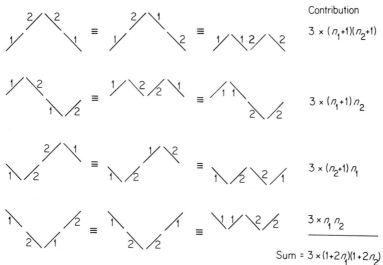

Figure 5.2 The diagrammatic representation of the processes contributing to g_4 in equation (5.24b). The numbers on the transition lines represent the $\mathbf{k}$ values. n_1 becomes $\bar{n}_1$ in g_4 by virtue of the averaging carried out by equation (4.51)

and hence involves a sum over allowed intermediate states. There are eight such states; $(n_1 \pm 1), (n_2 \pm 1), (n_3 \pm 1)$, but since the remaining terms in F_3 are symmetric in $\mathbf{k}_1, \mathbf{k}_2$ and $\mathbf{k}_3$ and there is a sum over each of them, there are only four distinct cases: (i) $n' = n_1 + 1$, $n_2 + 1, n_3 + 1$; (ii) $n' = n_1 - 1$, $n_2 - 1, n_3 - 1$; (iii) $n' = n_1 + 1, n_2 + 1, n_3 - 1$; (iv) $n' = n_1 - 1, n_2 - 1, n_3 + 1$. There are three equivalent intermediate states to cases (iii) and (iv); hence the weighting factor 3 in g_3. Each of these intermediate states may be connected to the initial state, (n_1, n_2, n_3), in 3! ways.

We could effect minor simplifications of equations (5.24) by invoking the equivalence of $\Phi^{ll'l''}_{\alpha\alpha'\alpha''}$ and of $\Phi^{ll'l''l'''}_{\alpha\alpha'\alpha''\alpha'''}$ at all lattice sites; however this does not have much value. In order to progress further towards the evaluation of the anharmonic free energy, some explicit assumptions about the interatomic interactions must be made. Equations (5.24) may be considerably simplified by the assumption of central, two-body forces between atoms.[2-4] Appendix J gives details of the third- and fourth-order force constants for such atoms.

The quartic term is considerably simpler than the cubic term, since the interference condition may be explicitly written into the expression which then neatly factorizes into two independent $\mathbf{k}j$ summations. A property which depends only on this and not on the cubic term would provide a very valuable link between theory and experiment. References 5 and 6 show that the effect of the cubic anharmonicity on the vapour-pressure ratio of two isotopes of a solid is negligible provided that $T_{\text{melt}} > \theta_D$. The quartic term makes a significant contribution which for $Ar_{36}:Ar_{40}$[6] is as large as the quasiharmonic part. The agreement with experiment[7,8] is within any uncertainty due to the potential function, but the conclusions are limited by this uncertainty.

In the previous chapter we have seen some of the effects of H_3 and H_4 on the equilibrium properties of a crystal, and we shall now go on to consider non-equilibrium effects arising from them.

5.5   Selection rules

A system in any non-equilibrim state will, left to its own devices, relax towards the equilibrium state corresponding to the total amount of energy that must be distributed among the components. The phonon interaction terms are a mechanism for this to take place. If energy is put into a crystal that was previously in equilibrium, by the creation of a number of extra phonons of a particular $(\mathbf{k}j)$, this energy must become redistributed until the Bose distribution corresponding to a new temperature is reached. Similarly, if one end of a crystal is heated, some energy travels to the cooler regions and is absorbed so that the phonon distribution approaches equilibrium in all parts of the crystal. On a harmonic model, there is no mechanism for such effects; we can consider only equilibrium phenomena. The thermal resistance of a harmonic solid is zero; since there are no interactions between phonons, an extra phonon cannot share its energy and hence it would not heat the crystal but would pass through until the energy was emitted from one of the surfaces. A harmonic solid would not absorb radiation, since the radiation could not couple to the modes. Thus the inclusion of higher-order terms is qualitatively essential, as well as being necessary to explain quantitative discrepancies.

The range of phenomena now open to discussion is much wider. The concept of selection rules to indicate allowed and forbidden transitions comes into all such phenomena. We shall illustrate most of the discussions by reference to three-phonon processes. Higher-order processes follow, although with more manipulative problems, since there are more ways of satisfying selection rules. The expression for $(H_3)_{n'n}$ describes a three-phonon process that takes the crystal from state n to state n'. We have seen in Section 5.4 that there is a restriction [equation (5.21a), $\mathbf{k}_1 + \mathbf{k}_2 + \mathbf{k}_3 = \mathbf{K}$], corresponding to conservation of momentum. By analogy with optics, this is sometimes called the condition of interference. In addition, energy must be conserved; hence we have

$$\omega(\mathbf{k}_1 j_1) + \omega(\mathbf{k}_2 j_2) - \omega(\mathbf{k}_3 j_3) = 0 \qquad (5.25)$$

since the only possibilities for a three-phonon process are (i) one phonon $(\mathbf{k}_3 j_3)$ decays into two $(\mathbf{k}_1 j_1)$ and $(\mathbf{k}_2 j_2)$, or (ii) two phonons $(\mathbf{k}_1 j_1)$ and $(\mathbf{k}_2 j_2)$ combine to form one $(\mathbf{k}_3 j_3)$. Figure 5.3 shows these diagrammatically.

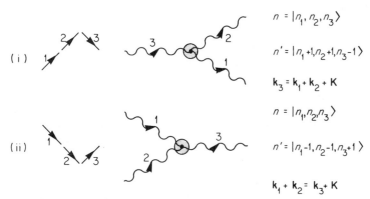

$$n = |n_1, n_2, n_3\rangle$$

$$n' = |n_1+1, n_2+1, n_3-1\rangle$$

$$k_3 = k_1 + k_2 + K$$

$$n = |n_1, n_2, n_3\rangle$$

$$n' = |n_1-1, n_2-1, n_3+1\rangle$$

$$k_1 + k_2 = k_3 + K$$

Figure 5.3 Diagrammatic representation of allowed three-phonon processes. The left-hand diagrams are those used earlier in this chapter; the others are often used to depict interactions. Lines going into an interaction (shown by the circle) represent annihilation, lines coming out represent creation. The wavy lines signify phonons (we shall be concerned with interactions between different kinds of excitation in later chapters). Both processes (i) and (ii) are subject to the selection rules (5.21a) and (5.25)

The requirement (5.21a) leads to two classes of processes; ones in which $\mathbf{K} = 0$ (called normal processes) and ones in which $\mathbf{K} \neq 0$ (called umklapp processes, a term introduced by Peierls[9,10] in 1929). The latter result from the periodic structure and have no counterpart in a continuum. We have already discussed in Section 1.10 the problems which arise if phonon momentum ($\hbar\mathbf{k}$) is treated as an ordinary particle momentum. Momentum conservation arises from the invariance of the laws of nature under the Lorentz transformation. Crudely, space may be uniformly displaced (at constant velocity) relative to the particle without affecting any physical property. The same is true for the relative displacement of a continuum and any excitation in that continuum. However, for a periodic structure only uniform displacements of an integer number of lattice spacings leave the 'space' unchanged. Thus excitations in a continuum obey strict momentum conservation, while those in a periodic structure are less constrained. The selection rule (5.21a) allows a unique combination of wave vectors since given $\mathbf{k}_1$ and $\mathbf{k}_2$ specifies one and only one value for $\mathbf{k}_3$ in the first Brillouin zone; this combination must also satisfy equation (5.25) if the process is to be allowed. Clearly higher-order processes involving more than three phonons will be more numerous, since there is more freedom to satisfy the selection rules. In taking only three-phonon processes, one hopes that the numbers of allowed higher-order processes do not compensate for their lower magnitude. There are techniques for formally including all phonon processes, which we shall explain later in Chapter 6.

5.6   Transition probabilities

Consider now the probability of any particular transition taking place by a multiphonon process H'. For equilibrium properties, we used time-independent perturbation theory, since we were dealing with a closed system and virtual processes in which time was indeterminate. Now that we are concerned with real transitions between levels, the procedure of time-dependent perturbation theory is appropriate. We are interested in the probability of the crystal making a transition between the unperturbed (harmonic) states under the influence of a perturbation H'. We have the time-dependent Schrodinger equation

$$(H_0 + H')\Psi(n, t) = i\hbar\dot{\Psi}(n, t) \tag{5.26a}$$

and the standard solution of this written in terms of our phonon states is

$$\Psi(n, t) = \sum_n C_n(t)|n\rangle \, e^{-i\omega_n t} \tag{5.26b}$$

(omitting zero point energy in the exponential, since it will not affect transitions between phonon states) where $\omega_n \equiv \sum_{\mathbf{k}j} n(\mathbf{k}j)\omega(\mathbf{k}j)$ and $C_n(t)$ are the time-dependent coefficients of the linear combination of eigenstates $|n\rangle$. These states (of the whole crystal) are specified by a set of $n(\mathbf{k}j)$, one for each phonon, and the summation is over all possible sets (i.e. over all allowed n-phonon states). If we substitute equation (5.26b) into equation (5.26a), we see that

$$(H_0 + H') \sum_n C_n(t)|n\rangle \, e^{-i\omega_n t}$$

$$= \sum_n \left[C_n(t)|n\rangle \sum_{\mathbf{k}j} n(\mathbf{k}j)\hbar\omega(\mathbf{k}j) \, e^{-i\omega_n t} + i\hbar\dot{C}_n(t)|n\rangle \, e^{-i\omega_n t} \right]. \quad (5.27)$$

Since $H_0 = \sum_{\mathbf{k}j} \hbar\omega(\mathbf{k}j)a^+(\mathbf{k}j)a(\mathbf{k}j)$ (neglecting zero point energy again), the first terms on each side are identical and cancel. Taking the Dirac bracket (Section 3.4) of the remaining terms in equation (5.27) with $\langle n'|$ (a bra vector for a particular n-phonon state) we see that:

$$\sum_n \langle n'|H'|n\rangle C_n(t) \, e^{-i\omega_n t} = i\hbar \sum_n \dot{C}_n(t)\langle n'|n\rangle \, e^{-i\omega_n t}$$

$$= i\hbar\dot{C}_{n'}(t) \, e^{-i\omega_{n'} t} \quad (5.28a)$$

where $\omega_{n'} \equiv \sum_{\mathbf{k}j} n'(\mathbf{k}j)\omega(\mathbf{k}j)$. This may be rearranged to

$$\dot{C}_{n'}(t) = \frac{1}{i\hbar} \sum_n H'_{n'n}C_n(t) \, e^{i\omega_{n'n} t} \quad (5.28b)$$

with $\omega_{n'n} \equiv \omega_{n'} - \omega_n$.

The probability of finding the crystal in a state $|n'\rangle$ at time t when it was initially in a state $|n\rangle$ is $|C_{n'}(t)|^2$, from the expansion (5.26b). Consideration of the physics provides the boundary conditions that, long before the interaction operates, we may write $C_{n'}(-\infty) = 0$ and $C_n(-\infty) = 1$. For times shortly after the perturbation H' acts, i.e. while $C_n(t)$ does not differ appreciably from unity, we see that

$$\dot{C}_{n'}(t) = \frac{1}{i\hbar}H'_{n'n} \, e^{i\omega_{n'n} t}. \quad (5.29)$$

Thus if $H'_{n'n}$ is 'switched on' at $t = 0$,

$$C_{n'}(t) = \frac{1}{i\hbar} \int_0^t H'_{n'n} \, e^{i\omega_{n'n} t} \, \mathrm{d}t. \quad (5.30)$$

The form of this expression should provoke a mental gulp, since if energy is to be conserved, $\omega_{n'n} = 0$. However, a more careful look at its range of validity gives a clue to the resolution of this difficulty. Since t is very small, we must consider an uncertainty in the energy of the order $\hbar/t$. This is closely related to the theory of transition linewidths and will be treated by more formal methods in the next chapter. For our present purposes it is convenient to be less formal. Carrying out the integration in equation (5.30),

$$C_{n'}(t) = -\frac{1}{\hbar}H'_{n'n}\frac{(e^{i\omega_{n'n} t} - 1)}{\omega_{n'n}} \quad (5.31)$$

and taking the square modulus

$$|C_{n'}(t)|^2 = \frac{2}{\hbar^2} \frac{|H'_{n'n}|^2}{\omega_{n'n}^2}(1 - \cos \omega_{n'n}t) \tag{5.32}$$

we have an expression that gives the probability of finding the crystal in a state described by $|n'\rangle$ at a short time $t(\ll 1/\omega_{n'n})$ after it was known to be in the state $|n\rangle$.

Before proceeding to find the rate at which transitions occur, let us briefly consider the physics corresponding to this analysis. The crystal is in a non-equilibrium state specified by $|n\rangle$, and there is a mechanism H' by which it proceeds towards the equilibrium distribution of the values of $n(\mathbf{k}j)$. The state is not necessarily the equilibrium state, but it is one of the states through which the system passes during the relaxation. States $|n'\rangle$, $|n\rangle$ and the ultimate equilibrium state all have the same energy to within the uncertainty corresponding to the state having a finite lifetime, $\omega_{n'n}$ in the denominator being a resonance factor. The crystal may make many transitions of the kind described by the result (5.32) before equilibrium is achieved. We have not yet said how the non-equilibrium state came about—this is discussed in succeeding chapters and is, of course, of paramount interest, since it is the process by which energy can be absorbed by the solid. Here we are concerned only that a non-equilibrium state exists at $t = 0$, and we treat the basic processes by which the state changes. Of course our description of 'switching on' H' at $t = 0$ is unphysical. The multiphonon processes are present all the time; when the crystal is in an equilibrium state they contribute only virtual processes, but their existence gives stability to the equilibrium state, since they come into action to oppose any tendency for equilibrium to be destroyed. If the crystal is put into a non-equilibrium state, it immediately relaxes towards the equilibrium state that has the same total energy. So, realistically, it is the non-equilibrium state $|n\rangle$ that is created at $t = 0$ for the purposes of our derivation.

The 'transition probability' Ω is the rate at which transitions occur out of $|n\rangle$, or the probability $\sum_{n'} |C_{n'}(t)|^2$ per unit time.

$$\Omega = \frac{\mathrm{d}}{\mathrm{d}t} \sum_{n'} |C_{n'}(t)|^2. \tag{5.33}$$

It is the rate at which transitions occur from the state $|n\rangle$ to any other state. It is customary to express this in terms of the density of states since it takes on a simple form. $\rho_{n'}(E_{n'})\,\mathrm{d}E_{n'}$ is the number of n-phonon states in the energy range from $E_{n'}$ to $E_{n'} + \mathrm{d}E_{n'}$, where $E_{n'} = \hbar \sum_{\mathbf{k}j} n'(\mathbf{k}j)\omega(\mathbf{k}j)$. Thus we may replace the summation in equation (5.33) by an integral and write

$$\Omega = \frac{2}{\hbar} \int_{\substack{\text{allowed final} \\ \text{states } |n'\rangle}} \frac{|H'_{n'n}|^2}{\omega_{n'n}} \sin \omega_{n'n}t\, \rho_{n'}(E_{n'})\,\mathrm{d}E_{n'}. \tag{5.34}$$

Provided that $|H'_{n'n}|^2$ and $\rho_{n'}(E_{n'})$ are both well behaved functions, they will not vary much in the range covered by the integral and they may be taken outside the integral. Also $dE_{n'} = \hbar \, d\omega_{n'n}$ and since t is always positive, equation (5.34) becomes

$$\Omega = \frac{2}{\hbar}|H'_{n'n}|^2 \rho_{n'}(E_n) \int \frac{\sin x}{x} \, dx. \tag{5.35}$$

The range of the integration is over $x(\equiv \omega_{n'n}t)$ corresponding to allowed final states $|n'\rangle$. However this integrand has significant magnitude only in the region $x \approx 0$. Thus we may take the limits to be $-\infty$ to $+\infty$ to a good approximation. Hence[d]

$$\Omega = \frac{2\pi}{\hbar}|H'_{n'n}|^2 \rho_{n'}(E_n) \tag{5.36}$$

and the only significant contribution is from the transitions that link states with nearly the same energies.

If a given non-equilibrium state may change only by decay processes and is not replenished, it is easy to show that the probability that it has not decayed in a time t is

$$P_n(t) = e^{-\Omega t}. \tag{5.37}$$

Just as in the time-independent case, where we developed perturbative series that could be extended to any order (equation 4.50), we may do so for this time-dependent system. We have introduced only first-order terms here. Later we shall extend this to the 'interaction representation' in which formal expressions include all orders of the interaction Hamiltonian.

The analysis that leads to result (5.36) makes two assumptions concerning the magnitude of the time period involved. To get equation (5.29), we say t must be small so that $C_n(t)$ is still very close to unity; to be able to extend the limits of equation (5.34) to infinity requires that $t \gg 1/\omega_{n'n}$. The process under discussion is a transition through an intermediate state whose lifetime[11] is related to the uncertainty in its energy. Since $\hbar\omega_{n'n}$ is the amount by which energy is 'temporarily unconserved', the lifetime of the state $|n'\rangle$ is $\sim \omega_{n'n}^{-1}$. Thus the requirement $t \gg 1/\omega_{n'n}$ is that the time in which the transition to the state $|n'\rangle$ has significant probability is very much longer than the lifetime of $|n'\rangle$. If the uncertainty in the energy is of the order of the energy of a mode (say $\sim 10^{13}$ s^{-1}), then $\Delta t \sim 10^{-13}$ s. If the characteristic relaxation time is longer than this, we may expect equation (5.32) and (5.36) to be a reasonable representation of one step in the relaxation process. From the relation (5.37), we see that this is equivalent to saying the theory is valid if

$$\Omega \ll \omega_{n'n}^{-1}.$$

For a fuller discussion of stochastic processes reference must be made to the relevant literature.[12,13]

5.7 Selection rules and transition probabilities

Returning to the question of selection rules, we see from the time derivative of $|C_{n'}(t)|^2$ [equation (5.32)] that two states will be closely coupled if

$$\Omega_{n'n} = \frac{2}{\hbar^2}|H'_{n'n}|^2\frac{\sin \omega_{n'n}t}{\omega_{n'n}} \tag{5.38a}$$

is significant. Making use of the properties of the Dirac delta function,[e] this may be expressed in the form

$$\Omega_{n'n} = \frac{2\pi}{\hbar^2}|H'_{n'n}|^2\delta(\omega_{n'n}). \tag{5.38b}$$

The simplest contribution to the first-order transition probability $\Omega_{n'n}$ is a three-phonon process, i.e. one of those of Figure 5.3. From expression (5.20b), the definition of $f_3(\mathbf{k}_1, \mathbf{k}_2, \mathbf{k}_3)$ used in expression (5.24a) and the transformation (3.34a), we see that for three specific phonons, $\mathbf{k}_1 j_1$, $\mathbf{k}_2 j_2$ and $\mathbf{k}_3 j_3$ (i.e. **no** implied $\mathbf{k}_i j_i$ sums):

$$H' = H_3 = \left(\frac{\hbar}{2mN}\right)^{3/2} f_3(\mathbf{k}_1\mathbf{k}_2\mathbf{k}_3)\Delta(\mathbf{k}_1 + \mathbf{k}_2 + \mathbf{k}_3) \prod_{i=1}^{3} (a_i^+ + a_{-i}) \tag{5.39}$$

where for convenience $a_i^+ \equiv a^+(\mathbf{k}_i j_i)$ and $a_{-i} \equiv a(-\mathbf{k}_i j_i)$ and the expression includes the 3! equivalent terms from the summation over $\mathbf{k}_1 j_1$, $\mathbf{k}_2 j_2$ and $\mathbf{k}_3 j_3$ implied in equation (5.20b).

For the two processes of Figure 5.3 we get

$$\left\langle n' \left| \prod_{i=1}^{3} (a_i^+ + a_{-i}) \right| n \right\rangle = (n_1 + 1)^{1/2}(n_2 + 1)^{1/2}n_3^{1/2} \tag{5.40a}$$

and

$$\left\langle n'' \left| \prod_{i=1}^{3} (a_i^+ + a_{-i}) \right| n \right\rangle = n_1^{1/2}n_2^{1/2}(n_3 + 1)^{1/2}. \tag{5.40b}$$

Thus using results (5.38b), (5.39) and (5.40), the transition probabilities for the two processes are

$$\Omega_{n'n} = \frac{2\pi}{\hbar^2}\left(\frac{\hbar}{2mN}\right)^3 |f_3(\mathbf{k}_1\mathbf{k}_2\mathbf{k}_3)|^2(n_1 + 1)(n_2 + 1)n_3\Delta(\mathbf{k}_1 + \mathbf{k}_2 - \mathbf{k}_3)$$

$$\times \delta(\omega_1 + \omega_2 - \omega_3) \tag{5.41a}$$

$$\Omega_{n''n} = \frac{2\pi}{\hbar^2}\left(\frac{\hbar}{2mN}\right)^3 |f_3(\mathbf{k}_1\mathbf{k}_2\mathbf{k}_3)|^2 n_1 n_2(n_3 + 1)\Delta(\mathbf{k}_1 + \mathbf{k}_2 - \mathbf{k}_3)$$

$$\times \delta(\omega_1 + \omega_2 - \omega_3). \tag{5.41b}$$

If we consider the number of phonons of a particular kind $\mathbf{k}_1 j_1$ and wish to know how the number of them changes with time—i.e. the difference in the rates at which three-phonon processes create and destroy phonons of the kind $\mathbf{k}_1 j_1$—we must include all processes involving $\mathbf{k}_1 j_1$. These are shown in Figure 5.4. Now $\mathbf{k}_1 j_1$ is fixed, since it is a phonon that we have singled out for

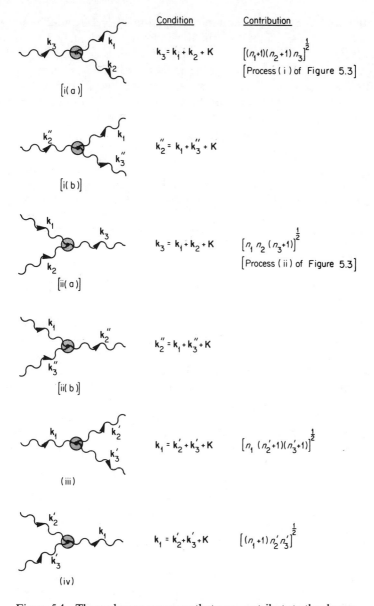

	Condition	Contribution
[i(a)]	$k_3 = k_1 + k_2 + K$	$[(n_1+1)(n_2+1)n_3]^{\frac{1}{2}}$ [Process (i) of Figure 5.3]
[i(b)]	$k_2'' = k_1 + k_3'' + K$	
[ii(a)]	$k_3 = k_1 + k_2 + K$	$[n_1 n_2 (n_3+1)]^{\frac{1}{2}}$ [Process (ii) of Figure 5.3]
[ii(b)]	$k_2'' = k_1 + k_3'' + K$	
(iii)	$k_1 = k_2' + k_3' + K$	$[n_1 (n_2'+1)(n_3'+1)]^{\frac{1}{2}}$
(iv)	$k_1 = k_2' + k_3' + K$	$[(n_1+1) n_2' n_3']^{\frac{1}{2}}$

Figure 5.4　Three-phonon processes that may contribute to the change of $n(\mathbf{k}_1 j_1)$. $\mathbf{K} = 0$ or a reciprocal lattice vector [i(b)] and [ii(b)] are not distinct from [i(a)] and [ii(a)], respectively; when the sum over $\mathbf{k}_2$ is taken all terms like this are included. Care is necessary with processes (iii) and (iv) to ensure that they are not included twice when summing over $\mathbf{k}_2$. Processes (i) and (iv) increase $n(\mathbf{k}_1 j_1)$, while processes (ii) and (iii) decrease it

investigation. The total effect on the occupation $n(\mathbf{k}_1 j_1)$ is found by summing over all values of $\mathbf{k}_2$, since then the third phonon is uniquely defined by the interference condition. In this summation, processes [i(a)] and [i(b)] in Figure 5.4 will both appear; so we include only one of them explicitly; similarly for [ii(a)] and [ii(b)]. Processes (iii) and (iv) in Figure 5.4 will be counted twice, and hence we introduce the factor of $\frac{1}{2}$. Thus the total rate of change of $n(\mathbf{k}_1 j_1) \equiv n_1$ due to three-phonon processes is

$$\dot{n}_1(\text{3-ph}) = \sum_{\mathbf{k}_2} (\Omega_{(i)} - \Omega_{(ii)}) + \frac{1}{2} \sum_{\mathbf{k}_2'} (\Omega_{(iv)} - \Omega_{(iii)}) \qquad (5.42)$$

since processes (i) and (iv) cause n_1 to increase and processes (ii) and (iii) cause it to decrease. These four transitions are of the form (5.41a) or (5.41b); hence we have

$$\dot{n}_1(\text{3-ph}) = \frac{\pi\hbar}{4Nm^3} \sum_{\mathbf{k}_2} \{|f_3(\mathbf{k}_1\mathbf{k}_2\mathbf{k}_3)|^2[(n_1 + 1)(n_2 + 1)n_3 - n_1 n_2(n_3 +)]$$

$$\times \delta(\omega_1 + \omega_2 - \omega_3) + \frac{1}{2}|f_3(\mathbf{k}_1\mathbf{k}_2\mathbf{k}_3')|^2$$

$$\times [(n_1 + 1)n_2 n_3' - n_1(n_2 + 1)(n_3' + 1)]\delta(\omega_1 - \omega_2 - \omega_3')\} \qquad (5.43)$$

where $\mathbf{k}_3 = \mathbf{k}_1 + \mathbf{k}_2 + \mathbf{K}$ and $\mathbf{k}_3' = \mathbf{k}_1 - \mathbf{k}_2 - \mathbf{K}$.

Alternatively, this could have been expressed in terms of an integral over surfaces defined by the selection rules. In Section 5.9 we shall introduce another term contributing to a change in n_1, representing the net drift of $\mathbf{k}_1 j_1$ phonons away from a region of higher temperature.

By considering the general structure of energy surfaces in $\mathbf{k}$-space or, for special cases, by considering the dispersion curves along lines in $\mathbf{k}$ space, we can be more explicit about the kinds of three-phonon processes that have a possibility of satisfying the selection rules. Peierls[14] summarizes these as follows: the only allowed three-phonon processes involving the acoustic modes l (longitudinal), t_1 and t_2 (transverse) where $t_2 > t_1$ are (a) $t_1 + t_1 \rightleftharpoons t_2$, (b) $t_1 + t_2 \rightleftharpoons l$, (c) $t_1 + t_2 \rightleftharpoons t_2$, (d) $t_1 + t_1 \rightleftharpoons l$, (e) $t_1 + l \rightleftharpoons l$ and (f) $t_2 + l \rightleftharpoons l$. These hold for the case of an isotropic crystal. For a strongly anisotropic crystal, more processes become possible.[15] These have been discussed by Pomeranchuk[16] and by Herring.[17] The optic modes are included in the analysis of Sections 5.4–5.7 if suitable suffices, κ, are added and $\sum_l$ is replaced by $\sum_l \sum_\kappa$. In particular, there may be different masses involved so that m^3 becomes $m_\kappa m_{\kappa'} m_{\kappa''}$; also the j summation (over branches) must be extended. We have not separated normal from umklapp processes in the above expressions; an important distinction between these will appear when thermal conductivity is discussed in Section 5.9.

5.8 Higher-order processes

The expressions we have derived and applied to three-phonon processes are of first order in the perturbation Hamiltonian H'. Multiphonon processes involving more than three phonons can arise in two ways: (i) through first order perturbations (of which that involving three phonons is the simplest) or (ii) through higher orders in the perturbation series [of which equation (5.38) is the lowest]. A development of our second kind of diagram technique serves to classify the possibilities.

Figure 5.3 shows the only kinds of first-order three-phonon processes. Four-phonon processes may arise (i) through $\langle n'|H_4|n\rangle$ or (ii) through second-order terms such as

$$\sum_{n'' \neq n \,\text{or}\, n'} \frac{\langle n'|H_3|n''\rangle \langle n''|H_3|n\rangle}{E_n - E'_n} \tag{5.44}$$

where n'' is an intermediate virtual state and does not require energy conservation. Figure 5.5 shows these processes.

The effect of these processes on the transition probabilities is easily written down from the diagrams of Figure 5.5, by the adaption of Rule 4 of Section 5.3. The contributions shown beside the corresponding diagram in Figure 5.5 were evaluated using the following rule.

Adapted Rule 4: To evaluate the contribution of multiphonon process (see Section 5.3) to $\langle n'|H'|n\rangle$, $\langle n'|H'|n''\rangle \langle n''|H'|n\rangle$, etc.

(i) Each phonon line $\mathbf{k}j$ going **into** an interaction point contributes

$$\left[\frac{\hbar}{2\omega(\mathbf{k}j)} n(\mathbf{k}j)\right]^{1/2} ;$$

those coming **out** contribute

$$\left\{\frac{\hbar}{2\omega(\mathbf{k}j)}[n(\mathbf{k}j) + 1]\right\}^{1/2} ,$$

where $n(\mathbf{k}j)$ is the number of phonons $(\mathbf{k}j)$ before the interaction.[f]
(ii) Take the product of **all** lines (real and virtual) associated with a given enclosure (process).

Clearly there are an infinite number of possible processes. In first-order processes an n-phonon process involves H_n; for higher orders, there are many possibilities for an n-phonon process. In the Figure 5.6, we illustrate some of the terms which, in principle, contribute. The examples are not a complete list but only an indication of how an n-phonon process may arise. The classification is by interaction order (i.e. diagrams involving s interactions are of order s), but, of course, the magnitudes are not necessarily of the same order. Some indication is obtained of the relative magnitude of terms of the type shown by expanding $H' = \alpha H_3 + \alpha^2 H_4 + \alpha^3 H_5$ where α is an order parameter. If the perturbation approximation is valid $\alpha \ll 1$.

A pattern emerges from these and the multiplicity of the terms coupled with the duo-classification [in terms of (i) the interaction order and (ii) the relative magnitudes, measured in powers of α], and suggests the setting up of a

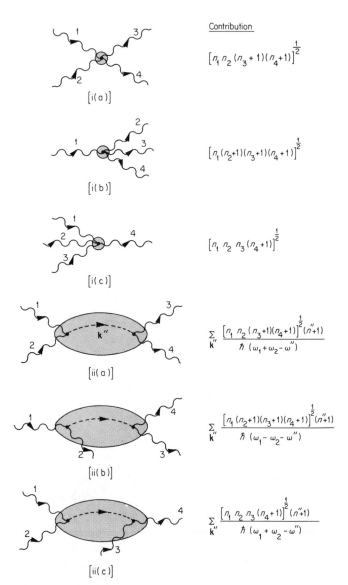

Figure 5.5 Some of the possible kinds of four-phonon processes. An interaction is represented by a heavy point •. The interactions giving rise to a particular n-phonon process are enclosed and the n real phonons involved are shown by n lines entering and leaving the enclosure. The order of the process is shown by the number of interaction points enclosed. Within the enclosure, energy need not be conserved, but the interference condition must be satisfied at every interaction point. Energy must be conserved in the overall process. In [ii(a)], [ii(b)] and [ii(c)], $\mathbf{k}''$ may go either way; as shown it is for $\mathbf{k}''$ created in the first interaction. If $\mathbf{k}''$ is annihilated in the first interaction $n'' + 1 \to n''$ and $\omega'' \to -\omega''$ in the contribution shown

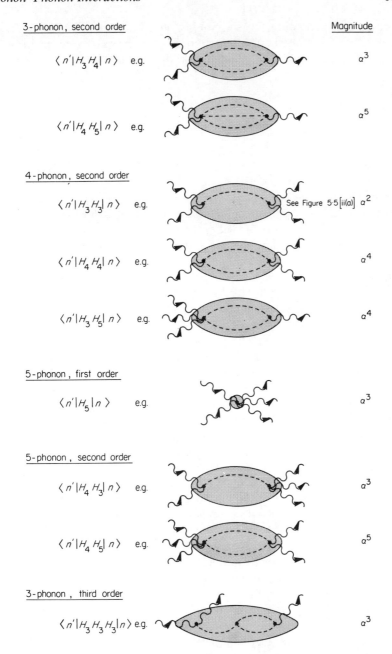

3-phonon, second order   Magnitude

$\langle n'|H_3 H_4| n \rangle$ e.g. α^3

$\langle n'|H_4 H_5| n \rangle$ e.g. α^5

4-phonon, second order

$\langle n'|H_3 H_3| n \rangle$ e.g.   See Figure 5·5[ii(a)] α^2

$\langle n'|H_4 H_4| n \rangle$ e.g. α^4

$\langle n'|H_3 H_5| n \rangle$ e.g. α^4

5-phonon, first order

$\langle n'|H_5| n \rangle$ e.g. α^3

5-phonon, second order

$\langle n'|H_4 H_3| n \rangle$ e.g. α^3

$\langle n'|H_4 H_5| n \rangle$ e.g. α^5

3-phonon, third order

$\langle n'|H_3 H_3 H_3| n \rangle$ e.g. α^3

Figure 5.6   Examples of higher order *n*-phonon processes where (in these cases) *n* is the number of **external** (real) phonons involved. 5-phonon first-order processes are important in the theory of liquid helium[18–20]

more formal procedure for summing over both n (number of phonons involved) and the orders of interaction. This is necessary if terms of order higher than α are important. Such a procedure is outlined in Chapter 6.

5.9   Thermal conductivity

On a harmonic or quasiharmonic model of a solid there would be no impedance to resist the flow of heat. If one end of a crystal was heated the extra phonons would travel away from the region of higher temperature. The energy $\hbar\omega(\mathbf{k}j)$ of creation of a phonon would be carried with the phonon velocity in a straight path until it reached a surface. Our theory of a harmonic solid has been developed so as to avoid the need to consider surface effects; we postulated an infinite crystal or cyclic boundary conditions. To discuss the effects at the surface when the phonon reaches it requires additional knowledge or assumptions. The two extremes are that the phonon would be totally reflected and thus remain permanently in the crystal or that it would be thermally radiated from the surface and thus be lost to the crystal. Leaving aside the problem at the surface (we can calculate the total energy radiated from the surface without great difficulty), the model is still inadequate.

From observation we know that a crystal heated at one end approaches equilibrium slowly. On the harmonic model, a fire poker (made of any crystalline solid) would burn the operator's hand almost immediately it was used. Conveniently this does not happen. Clearly some mechanism resists the travel of phonons that are supernumerary to the equilibrium distribution corresponding to the temperature of that part of the crystal. If a part of the crystal (away from the part in contact with the source of heat) is in thermal equilibrium and then a phonon attempts to travel through the region,[g] the distribution is then non-equilibrium and it begins relaxing towards equilibrium corresponding to a slightly higher temperature. The extra phonon has a finite lifetime in that region of the crystal, and it decays into others by processes of the kind discussed in Sections 5.7 and 5.8. This mechanism accounts for the slow spreading of the input energy; it is the source of thermal resistance, although, as we shall see, not all phonon interactions resist the flow. In the following we shall be concerned with the conduction of heat only by phonons, usually termed the 'lattice conductivity'. In metals the conduction of heat by mobile electrons usually dominates, and consequently our treatment is primarily the theory of heat conduction in an insulator or a semiconductor at low temperatures.

Thermodynamics is not concerned with the microscopic origins of the phenomena it seeks to describe. Thermal conduction is summarized by the differential equation

$$\frac{\mathrm{d}E}{\mathrm{d}t} = -\sigma\frac{\mathrm{d}T}{\mathrm{d}x} \tag{5.45}$$

where dE/dt is the rate of flow of thermal energy across unit area (in the plane yz) under the action of a temperature gradient dT/dx; the constant of proportionality σ is the coefficient of thermal conductivity. We are interested in the fundamental processes that determine σ for a particular crystal.

The kinetic theory of gases yields the well known result (e.g. Kittel[21]):

$$\sigma = AC_V\bar{c}l \qquad (5.46a)$$

where A is a numerical factor which takes account of the resolution of the flow to a given direction, $\bar{c}$ is the mean velocity of an energy-carrying particle which has a mean free path l.

In a dispersive medium σ must be a sum of terms like equation (5.46a) over all phonons:

$$\sigma = A \sum_{kj} C(\mathbf{k}j)\mathbf{V}(\mathbf{k}j) \cdot \mathbf{l}(\mathbf{k}j) \qquad (5.46b)$$

where $C(\mathbf{k}j)$ is the contribution of the mode $(\mathbf{k}j)$ to the specific heat $[= \hbar\omega(\mathbf{k}j)\,d\bar{n}(\mathbf{k}j)/dT]$. Unless the medium is isotropic, the flow of heat will not, in general, be parallel to the temperature gradient. The conductivity is thus a tensor, and may be expressed in the form [since $\mathbf{l}(\mathbf{k}j) = \mathbf{V}(\mathbf{k}j)\tau(\mathbf{k}j)$ where τ is the relaxation time]

$$\sigma_{\alpha\alpha'} = A \sum_{kj} V_\alpha(\mathbf{k}j)V_{\alpha'}(\mathbf{k}j)C(\mathbf{k}j)\tau(\mathbf{k}j) \qquad (5.46c)$$

where α and α' are cartesian components and $\sigma_{\alpha\alpha'}$ is the conductivity in a direction α due to a temperature gradient in the α' direction.

The mean free path of a phonon is infinite in a harmonic solid; hence $\sigma_{harm} \to \infty$ as we have already deduced. Any effect that decreases l contributes to the thermal resistance. At this stage we shall consider phonon interactions to be the only contribution to the impedance; other effects such as crystal defects and boundary scattering, although they are important, would confuse the issue.

The simplest phonon processes contributing to the thermal resistance are those involving three phonons. By the arguments of Section 5.5, the only relevant three-phonon processes are those shown in Figure 5.3. Furthermore, the part played by umklapp processes (Section 5.5) in establishing equilibrium is of special importance. In order for energy to flow from one part of the crystal to another there must be a nett imbalance of phonon momenta between these two parts. Without the umklapp processes, this nett momentum would persist and energy could flow with or without a temperature gradient once the flow was initiated. (Peierls draws the analogy with an infinite frictionless tube containing a gas that has a nett drift velocity.) The normal processes [$\mathbf{K} = 0$ in the selection rule (5.21a)] conserve the total momentum of the phonons and distribute the energy into other phonons which still transport the energy without checking the flow. Thus the only processes contributing to the impedance are umklapp processes.[9,10] The relevant mean free path in relation (5.46) is the mean distance that a phonon will travel between two umklapp processes.[22,23]

From the interference condition (5.21a), we see that unless at least one of the phonons involved has a value of $\mathbf{k} > \frac{1}{4}\mathbf{K}$ (i.e. is more than halfway to the zone boundary), an umklapp process cannot occur. At low temperatures the thermal resistance will be closely proportional to the number of phonons with $\mathbf{k} > \frac{1}{4}\mathbf{K}$. The lowest energy of phonons whose presence is essential to make umklapp processes possible is thus

$$\hbar\omega_L \approx \tfrac{1}{4}\hbar\mathbf{V}\cdot\mathbf{K}.$$

Along the axis of a cubic crystal this becomes

$$\hbar\omega_L \approx \tfrac{1}{4}\hbar\frac{2\pi V}{a}.$$

If we write ω_L as a fraction α of the Debye frequency, the mean number of phonons with energy $\hbar\omega_L$ present in a crystal of $3N$ atoms at temperature T is

$$\overline{N(\omega_L)} = 3N(e^{\alpha\theta_D/T} - 1)^{-1}$$

$$\approx 3N\,e^{-\alpha\theta_D/T}$$

at low temperatures. Thus the scattering due to umklapp processes rises exponentially at low temperatures.

Bearing these considerations in mind, the temperature variation of the thermal conductivity may be expected to exhibit the following properties. At absolute zero, with no phonons present, the mean free path is the size of the crystal, C_V in equation (5.46) is zero and hence σ is zero. At very low temperatures $C_V \propto T^3$ [see equation (4.57b), l is approximately a constant (the size of the crystal—this is boundary scattering)] and so $\sigma \propto T^3$. As the temperature is increased, the number of phonons with large enough $\mathbf{k}$ to take part in an umklapp process rises exponentially and the increase in σ through increasing C_V has a competing effect. A maximum is reached and the thermal conductivity falls rapidly. In the high-temperature region we may expect a T^{-1} dependence, since C_V becomes the classical $3Nk_B$ and $l \propto 1/\rho \propto 1/T$ (ρ is the number density of phonons with which an energy-transporting phonon may interact). The measurements of Berman[24] on Al_2O_3 exhibit the broad features that we have just discussed.

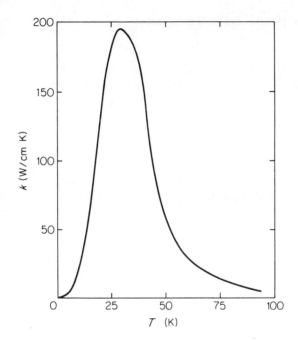

Figure 5.7 The temperature dependence of the thermal conductivity measured by Berman. Reproduced with permission, from Berman, R., *Z. f. Phys. Chem (Neue Folge)*, **16**, 145–157 (1958)

These arguments apply to a perfect crystal insulator.

The expressions deduced in Section 5.7 provide the analysis of these three-phonon processes necessary to derive the corresponding thermal conductivity. Equation (5.43) gives the rate of change of the number of phonons $n(\mathbf{k}_1 j_1)$ due to three-phonon processes. The other term to be included is the rate of change due to phonons moving out of the region, viz.

$$\dot{n}_{1\,(\text{drift})} = -\frac{\partial n_1}{\partial x} v_x(1) = -\frac{\partial n_1}{\partial T}\frac{\partial T}{\partial x} v_x(1) \qquad (5.47)$$

where $v_x(1) = (\partial\omega(\mathbf{k}_1 j_1)/\partial k_x)_{\mathbf{k}_1 j_1}$, the group velocity. The total rate of change of the number of phonons $n(\mathbf{k}_1 j_1)$ is

$$\dot{n}_{1\,(\text{total})} = \dot{n}_{1\,(\text{drift})} + \dot{n}_{1\,(3\text{-ph})}. \qquad (5.48)$$

Equation (5.48) is the Boltzmann form of the transport equation. We shall apply it under the conditions pertaining to gentle heat flow. Following the usual linearization procedure for transport problems, the equilibrium distribution is modified by a small term

$$n_i = \bar{n}_i + \Delta n_i \tag{5.49}$$

where $\bar{n}_i = (e^{\beta\hbar\omega_i} - 1)^{-1}$, the equilibrium state.

In the steady state—i.e. the heat flow through the crystal is a constant and the temperature is a function of position but not time—we have

$$\dot{n}_{1\,(\text{total})} = 0. \tag{5.50}$$

The local phonon distributions are time-independent in all parts of the crystal. Substituting equation (5.49) into equation (5.43) we get the equation describing the state of the crystal under the conditions of a constant temperature gradient. The result is considerably simplified by the following:

(i) $$\bar{n}_1\bar{n}_2(\bar{n}_3 + 1) \equiv (\bar{n}_1 + 1)(\bar{n}_2 + 1)\bar{n}_3. \tag{5.51}$$

This is easily verified by substituting the expressions for $\bar{n}_i$.

(ii) Drop the term involving the derivative of Δn_1 from equation (5.47); this is of second order.

(iii) Drop all terms higher than first order.

Hence

$$\frac{\partial \bar{n}_1}{\partial T}\frac{\partial T}{\partial x}v_x(1) = \frac{\pi\hbar}{4Nm^3}\sum_{\mathbf{k}_2}\{|f_3(\mathbf{k}_1\mathbf{k}_2\mathbf{k}_3)|^2\delta(\omega_1 + \omega_2 - \omega_3)[\Delta n_1(\bar{n}_3 - \bar{n}_2)$$

$$+ \Delta n_2(\bar{n}_3 - \bar{n}_1) + \Delta n_3(\bar{n}_1 + \bar{n}_2 + 1)]$$

$$+ \tfrac{1}{2}|f_3(\mathbf{k}_1\mathbf{k}_2\mathbf{k}'_3)|^2\delta(\omega_1 - \omega_2 - \omega'_3)[-\Delta n_1(\bar{n}'_3 + \bar{n}_2 + 1)$$

$$+ \Delta n_2(\bar{n}'_3 - \bar{n}_1) + \Delta n'_3(\bar{n}_2 - \bar{n}_1)]\} \tag{5.52}$$

(where $\mathbf{k}_3 = \mathbf{k}_1 + \mathbf{k}_2 + \mathbf{K}$ and $\mathbf{k}'_3 = \mathbf{k}_1 - \mathbf{k}_2 + \mathbf{K}$ and $\mathbf{K} \neq 0$).

This may be written in an alternative form by noting that

$$\frac{d\bar{n}_1}{dT} = \bar{n}_1(\bar{n}_1 + 1)\frac{\hbar\omega}{k_B T^2} \tag{5.53}$$

and writing

$$\Delta n_i = \bar{n}_i(\bar{n}_i + 1)\delta n_i. \tag{5.54}$$

Thus the first term in equation (5.52) becomes

$$\Delta n_1(\bar{n}_3 - \bar{n}_2) = \bar{n}_1(\bar{n}_1 + 1)(\bar{n}_3 - \bar{n}_2)\,\delta n_1. \tag{5.55}$$

Rearranging the identity (5.51), we find that

$$\bar{n}_3 - \bar{n}_2 \equiv \bar{n}_3(\bar{n}_2 + 1)/\bar{n}_1 \tag{5.56}$$

whence the term (5.55) becomes

$$(\bar{n}_1 + 1)(\bar{n}_2 + 1)\bar{n}_3\,\delta n_1. \tag{5.57}$$

By a similar procedure on each of the other terms in (5.52), we may write

$$\bar{n}_1(\bar{n}_1 + 1)\frac{\hbar\omega}{k_B T^2}\frac{\partial T}{\partial x}v_x(1) = \frac{\pi\hbar}{4Nm^3}\sum_{\mathbf{k}_2}\{|f_3(\mathbf{k}_1\mathbf{k}_2\mathbf{k}_3)|^2\delta(\omega_1 + \omega_2 - \omega_3)$$

$$\times [(\bar{n}_1 + 1)(\bar{n}_2 + 1)\bar{n}_3(\delta n_3 - \delta n_1 - \delta n_2)]$$

$$+ \tfrac{1}{2}|f_3(\mathbf{k}_1\mathbf{k}_2\mathbf{k}_3')|^2\delta(\omega_1 - \omega_2 - \omega_3')$$

$$\times [(\bar{n}_1 + 1)\bar{n}_2\bar{n}_3'(\delta n_2 + \delta n_3' - \delta n_1)]\} \qquad (5.58)$$

with the same restraint on $\mathbf{k}_3$ and $\mathbf{k}_3'$ as in equation (5.52).

There is no conceptual problem in extending this treatment to include higher-order phonon processes, but obviously there are enormous manipulative problems. Even the simplest term, equation (5.58), requires a fairly detailed knowledge of the forces of interaction between the atoms making up the crystal. As we have seen in Chapter 2, such knowledge is not available for the majority of crystals. This leads us to the unsatisfactory situation that we have an analytical expression that neatly accounts for an observable effect in terms of fundamental processes, but which, in practice, is of little more use than an empirical law based on general arguments. Detailed discussions on the conduction of heat by phonons are given by Peierls[14] (who did much of the original work around 1929) and Ziman.[15] An excellent review of the historical background and the work up to 1958 has been made by Klemens.[25] The thermal conductivity of metals at low temperatures has been reviewed by Mendelssohn and Rosenberg.[26]

Experimentally one is faced with the problem of isolating one effect from others. In real crystals various imperfections contribute to a scattering that is not included in our scheme. There is also impurity scattering, boundary scattering (already mentioned as being dominant at very low temperatures) and scattering from free electrons. By a suitable choice of a sample and a temperature range, it is possible to make observations of conduction properties so that one scattering effect dominates under those conditions. The general conclusions are summarized in Table 5.3, which is a rearrangement of the table due to Klemens.[25]

An alternative method of formulating the lattice conduction problem is discussed in the next chapter.

When more than one scattering process is operative it is sometimes possible to compute the total effect on the thermal resistance by means of Matthiessen's law. This proposes that the total resistance is the sum of resistances due to each of the scattering processes. The rule is more closely obeyed by the electrical resistance originating from various processes which scatter conduction electrons. For lattice thermal conductivity the rule becomes violated rather often, and its use demands careful consideration. Ziman[15] discusses the various circumstances in some detail.

Table 5.3 The effect of various scattering mechanisms on the thermal resistance $1/\sigma(T)$ of a solid and mean free path $l(\omega)$ of a phonon.

Scattering mechanism	$\dfrac{1}{l(\omega)}$ (frequency variation)	$\dfrac{1}{\sigma(T)}$ (temperature variation)	
		Low temperature $(T < \theta_D)$	High temperature $(T > \theta_D)$
Finite size of crystal	ω^0	T^{-3}	T^0
Imperfections:			
Grain boundaries	ω^0	T^{-3}	T^0
Stacking faults	ω^2	T^{-1}	
Dislocations (strain field)	ω	T^{-2}	
Dislocations (core)	ω^3	T^0	
Point defects	ω^4	T	
Umklapp processes	ω	$T^{-3}e^{-\alpha\theta_D/T}$	T
Free electrons (metals)	ω	T^{-2}	

We have been concerned with the direct contribution of phonon umklapp processes to the thermal resistance and have rejected normal processes as being non-contributory. However they do have an indirect effect. The lifetimes of phonons are not all the same. Normal processes involving those phonons that also take part in umklapp processes contribute to the rate of change of the number of these phonons. Hence, indirectly, normal processes play a minor role in affecting the conduction properties. They play a more significant role when isotopic scattering is considered [this is due to 'impurities' of the same element (as the atoms forming the lattice) but a different isotope].

5.10 The absorption of sound

Phonons may take part in the absorption of sound in three ways (not including effects involving interactions with other kinds of crystal excitations or electrons):

(i) Sound waves have maximum frequencies of about 10^9 Hz. (10^{10} Hz may be induced in some crystals, see Dunn and Breyer.[27]) Although this represents the highest frequency that ultrasonic techniques can achieve, it is still low compared with a typical phonon frequency. It corresponds to a wavelength extending over about 20,000 atoms. By comparison with the phonons, a longitudinal sound wave is a static arrangement of compressions and rarefactions. The temperature in the compressed regions is higher than it was before the wave appeared, and the temperature is lower than before in the rarefied regions. Thus heat may be conducted between these regions converting some of the elastic energy into heat energy and resulting in a loss of intensity of the sound wave. Transverse waves are not attenuated in this way, as there are no local volume changes.

(ii) The sound wave behaves as a beam of phonons which interacts directly with the thermal phonons and hence becomes scattered.

(iii) The phonon gas through which the sound wave passes is strained in local regions and the equilibrium is perturbed by the modification of the phonon frequencies. Thus it relaxes towards a new equilibrium. The resulting increase in entropy is accompanied by dissipation of energy from the sound wave.

The latter two mechanisms of absorption involve phonons in a more direct manner, and hence these are of greater interest than the first. The first results in the relevant elastic constants lying between their adiabatic and the isothermal values. Since there are a large number of mechanisms contributing to thermal conductivity besides the phonon part, we shall restrict our discussion to absorption by mechanisms (ii) and (iii). Mechanism (i) is discussed in phenomenological terms in many textbooks.

Consider first the direct interactions of mechanism (ii). An ultrasonic or hypersonic[h] wave induced in a crystal is the same kind of excitation as a phonon or lattice wave. For a distinction we must look to their origins and magnitudes. For clarity we shall use the term **wave** to mean the induced sound wave (i.e. the elastic wave in the solid) and the term **phonon** for the lattice wave present by virtue of the thermal energy of the solid. We shall assume the thermal energy of the crystal to be distributed over the phonons according to the equilibrium law, and the sound wave to be (initially) superimposed on this equilibrium distribution. The sound waves are induced as a coherent train with a well defined wave vector and polarization. Any scattering mechanism contributes to the attenuation of this beam, and a similarity with thermal resistivity is apparent. Conductivity does not provide much information about fundamental phonon processes—the effects are complex and veiled. However, observations on the attenuation of a wave of a particular frequency passing through a crystal have more to offer. The drawback is that only waves of relatively low frequency can be satisfactorily induced. The phonons have energies of order of magnitude $k_B T$; the highest-frequency hypersonic wave has an energy about two orders of magnitude less than this. Nevertheless, measurements of the temperature and frequency dependence of the attenuation of sound waves provide useful information about the crystal excitations and imperfections.

For energy to be removed from the sound wave and taken into the phonon distribution there must be at least two other phonons involved. The simplest process, then, is a three-phonon process in which one of the phonons is replaced by the induced wave. The other two phonons involved must have very nearly the same energy, since, by the conservation laws,

$$\omega_s = \omega - \omega' \tag{5.59}$$

(ω_s is the angular frequency of the induced sound wave, ω and ω' are those of the two phonons). Also

$$\mathbf{k}_s = \mathbf{k} - \mathbf{k}' \tag{5.60}$$

from the interference condition. Here we need consider only normal processes ($\mathbf{K} = 0$), since the conditions for umklapp processes are not met. Thus it is exactly those processes that are not effective in the theory of thermal resistance that attenuate an ultrasonic wave.

The phonons have a finite lifetime owing to the interactions with other phonons; this results in an effective mean free path $l(\mathbf{k}j)$. If the ultrasonic wavelength λ_s is much less than $l(\mathbf{k}j)$ for the phonon involved, it may interact with that phonon. (On a wave picture the two waves coexist in space over a distance such that they are both well defined waves; hence they can interfere.) However, if $\lambda_s \approx l(\mathbf{k}j)$ the problem is very complex. For $\lambda_s \gg l(\mathbf{k}j)$, the wave interacts simultaneously with the whole phonon system. Hence the condition for interaction with individual phonons to be meaningful is

$$\omega_s \tau > 1 \tag{5.61}$$

where τ is the mean lifetime of the phonon. Without this condition the energy uncertainty ($\sim \hbar/\tau$) would be large enough to violate the conservation equation (5.59). Thus for small ω_s or for small τ (high temperature), equation (5.59) may be satisfied by most of the phonons simultaneously, and the concept of individual processes is invalid.

Clearly the interaction with individual phonons will be significant only for high frequencies and in a certain temperature range. At very low temperatures the scattering of the wave will be dominated by imperfections (not necessarily the same imperfections as are important in the thermal resistivity, since the frequencies of the transporting waves differ so widely); anharmonic coupling is small. As the temperature is increased, the phonon interactions become more pronounced and, while $l(\mathbf{k}j) > \lambda_s$, fundamental three-phonon processes contribute to the attenuation. λ_s increases rapidly with temperature until $\lambda_s \approx l(\mathbf{k}j)$, when the wave is no longer adequately characterized by the atomic displacements (due to the induced wave) that take place during the phonon lifetime.

Since $\omega_s \ll \omega$ in equation (5.59), it is reasonable to assume that ω and ω' come from the same branch of the frequency spectrum. Writing $\omega' = \omega - \Delta\omega$

$$\Delta\omega = \frac{\partial\omega}{\partial\mathbf{k}} \cdot \Delta\mathbf{k}. \tag{5.62}$$

This has a maximum value

$$\Delta\omega_{max} = |\mathbf{v}_g(\mathbf{k}j)| \, |\Delta\mathbf{k}| \tag{5.63}$$

where $\mathbf{v}_g(\mathbf{k}j)$ is the group velocity.

Now

$$\omega_s = |v_{phase}(s)| \, |\mathbf{k}_s| \tag{5.64}$$

and, according to condition (5.59), $\Delta\omega = \omega_s$. Thus by comparing equations (5.62) and (5.64):

$$|v_{phase}(s)| \, |\mathbf{k}_s| = v_g(kj) \cdot \Delta\mathbf{k} \leq |v_g(kj)| \, |\Delta\mathbf{k}|. \tag{5.65}$$

The condition (5.60) gives $\mathbf{k}_s = \Delta\mathbf{k}$; hence, from the result (5.65), an interaction between a sound wave and a phonon (kj) can only occur if

$$v_g(kj) \geq v_{phase}(s) \tag{5.66}$$

Except in special cases, expression (5.66) restricts this attenuation mechanism to transverse waves. Longitudinal waves interact with phonons of comparable frequency where the necessary conditions may be satisfied. Since the number of thermal phonons with frequencies comparable to the induced wave is negligible, longitudinal waves are of less interest in the present context. The special cases are for isotropic crystals, in which the degeneracy permits other solutions for longitudinal waves of low frequency (Herring[17]).

Suppose then we are in a region in which a direct interaction involving a transverse elastic wave and two thermal phonons occurs. This requires that the conditions (5.61) and (5.66) are satisfied. The problem is clearly defined; we have a beam of low-frequency 'phonons' (the sound wave) with well defined $\mathbf{k}_s$. This is the only mode which departs from the equilibrium distribution, and we are interested in its energy loss by three-phonon processes as in Figure 5.8.

Figure 5.8 Three-phonon absorption process. $\mathbf{k}_s$ = wave vector of sound wave; $\mathbf{k}'$ and $\mathbf{k}$ are wave vectors of the two thermal phonons involved

The rate of loss of energy from the sound wave due to these processes is

$$\left(\frac{dE}{dt}\right)_{3\text{-ph}} = \hbar\omega_s \frac{dn_s}{dt} \tag{5.67}$$

where n_s is the number of sound-wave 'phonons'. In the previous section we dealt with a similar problem, but there we were interested only in umklapp processes. Now we must include only normal processes; also, since only one phonon state has a non-equilibrium occupancy, there is only a contribution which decreases n_s. Thus the rate of loss of energy due to three-phonon processes will be given by the first term on the right hand side of equation equation (5.52) with the following identifications:

$$\omega_1 \Rightarrow \omega_s, \qquad \omega_2 \Rightarrow \omega', \qquad \omega_3 \Rightarrow \omega \tag{5.68a}$$

$$\Delta n_1 \Rightarrow n_s, \qquad \Delta n_2 = \Delta n_3 = 0 \tag{5.68b}$$

$$\bar{n}_2 \Rightarrow \bar{n}', \qquad \bar{n}_3 \Rightarrow \bar{n} \tag{5.68c}$$

$$\mathbf{k}_1 \Rightarrow \mathbf{k}_s, \qquad \mathbf{k}_2 \Rightarrow \mathbf{k}', \qquad \mathbf{k}_3 \Rightarrow \mathbf{k}. \tag{5.68d}$$

Thus, using this modification of equation (5.52) and the interference condition (5.60), the attenuation given by equation (5.67) is

$$\left(\frac{dE}{dt}\right)_{3\text{-ph}} = \frac{\pi\hbar^2 \omega_s}{4Nm^3} \sum_{\mathbf{k}'} \{|f_3(\mathbf{k}_s, \mathbf{k}, \mathbf{k}')|^2 \delta(\omega_s + \omega' - \omega)$$

$$\times \, n_s(\bar{n} - \bar{n}')\Delta(\mathbf{k}_s + \mathbf{k}' - \mathbf{k}). \tag{5.69}$$

This may be simplified for the conditions under which it is valid

$$n_s(\bar{n} - \bar{n}') = n_s \frac{e^{\beta\hbar\omega'} - e^{\beta\hbar\omega}}{(e^{\beta\hbar\omega} - 1)(e^{\beta\hbar\omega'} - 1)}$$

$$\approx n_s \frac{e^{\beta\hbar\omega}(\omega' - \omega)\beta\hbar}{(e^{\beta\hbar\omega} - 1)^2}$$

$$= -\frac{n_s \omega_s \beta\hbar \, e^{\beta\hbar\omega}}{(e^{\beta\hbar\omega} - 1)^2} \tag{5.70}$$

since

$$\omega' \approx \omega \quad \text{and} \quad \omega_s = \omega - \omega'.$$

Thus

$$\left(\frac{dE}{dt}\right)_{3\text{-ph}} = \frac{\pi\beta\hbar^3 \omega_s^2}{4Nm^3} \sum_{\mathbf{k}'} \left[|f_3(\mathbf{k}_s, \mathbf{k}, \mathbf{k}')|^2 \frac{e^{\beta\hbar\omega}}{(e^{\beta\hbar\omega} - 1)^2} \right.$$

$$\left. \times \, \delta(\omega_s + \omega' - \omega)\Delta(\mathbf{k}_s + \mathbf{k}' - \mathbf{k}) \right] \tag{5.71}$$

which again requires a knowledge of the interatomic forces before it may be evaluated. An estimate of the magnitude of this effect may be obtained by using the Gruneisen parameter as a measure of the strength of the anharmonicity. This verifies that the mechanism is plausible but has no other value.

The experimental work of Bömmel and Dransfield[28] on quartz provides useful evidence to support the above theory, but unfortunately they also found that the longitudinal waves were absorbed almost as much as the transverse waves. The measurements were carried out over a range of temperatures for a sound wave of 10^9 Hz travelling in different crystalline directions. At 140 K the attenuation of longitudinal waves due to thermal conduction between parts of the crystal [mechanism (i) on p. 172] is negligible and evidence suggests that the longitudinal waves interact with the phonons. According to our previous arguments this should not be the case; however, various simple explanations have been proposed. The most convincing explanation is that the low-frequency phonon (high-frequency sound wave) decays into low-frequency longitudinal and transverse phonons. The latter may then interact with a thermal phonon as above. Thus, via an intermediate process, the absorption still occurs. Simons[29] suggests that even if $\omega_s\tau > 1$ the uncertainty in the phonon energy may still allow a direct interaction between the longitudinal wave and the phonons.

Suppose now we consider the absorption of low-frequency sound waves in the region

$$\omega_s\tau \ll 1. \tag{5.72}$$

Now the uncertainty in the energy of the phonon $(\sim \hbar/\tau)$ is much greater than the quanta of elastic energy $(\hbar\omega_s)$. Thus the energy conservation that characterizes the individual interactions [equation (5.59)] is no longer a restriction. Instead of the δ function in the result (5.69), we must go back to the expression (5.34). Now, provided that t is large enough for all processes to be completed, energy is exactly conserved, and we saw that the integral in equation (5.34) could be safely extended to infinity. Thus we found (in the notation of this section) that

$$\lim_{t\to\infty} \int \frac{\sin(\omega - \omega')t}{\omega - \omega'}\,\mathrm{d}(\omega - \omega') = \pi \tag{5.73a}$$

However, the maximum value of t is τ; so when $\omega_s\tau$ is small, the upper limit of the integration is ω_s. Also $\sin \omega_s\tau \approx \omega_s\tau$, and therefore

$$\lim_{\omega_s t \ll 1} \int_0^{\omega_s} \frac{\sin(\omega - \omega')t}{(\omega - \omega')}\,\mathrm{d}(\omega - \omega') \to \omega_s\tau. \tag{5.73b}$$

(The lower limit is zero because the processes we have included require $\omega > \omega'$). Thus the attenuation of low-frequency sound is less than the expression (5.71) by the ratio of term (5.73b) to term (5.73a)—a factor $\omega_s\tau(\mathbf{k}j)/\pi$ should be included in the high-frequency expression to give the attenuation when condition (5.72) pertains. This region corresponds to the mechanism (iii) on p. 173, in which phonons take part in the absorption of sound. The uncertainty argument yields substantially the same result as an analysis based on the effect of the periodic strains on the phonon distribution. In the latter, the dissipation of energy from the elastic wave is governed by the relaxation of the induced non-equilibrium distribution.

This arises because the equilibrium distribution is described in terms of occupation numbers [equation (4.7)] that are frequency dependent. The frequencies are strain dependent, and thus if, before the sound wave appears, there are n phonons of a particular frequency, when that frequency is modified locally n is no longer the correct equilibrium value. Application of the expressions is severely hampered by the lack of any suitable potential function, and one can usually resort to only order-of-magnitude estimates.

5.11 Summary

When the amplitude of an oscillator is such that the condition for harmonicity is violated, the energy expression involves additional terms. In the **classical** region the lowest-order additional terms contribute a **linearly temperature dependent** term to the specific heat. The explicit form of the energy of a **single** anharmonic oscillator is simple in both the quantum and classical forms; however the expressions for a **set** of anharmonic oscillators representing a solid is complex because they cannot be **uncoupled**. **Diagram techniques** are used to break down the effects into **fundamental phonon processes**. For equilibrium situations these fundamental processes are **virtual**.

If the anharmonicity is not too large, **perturbation theory** provides a good description of the effect. The thermodynamic expressions deduced in Section 4.4 are appropriate for **equilibrium properties**, but it is necessary to use **time-dependent perturbation theory** when **real transitions** between phonon states are involved. **Transition probabilities** depend on the strength of the anharmonic coupling between the modes taking part in the **interaction**. The simplest interaction of interest is a **three-phonon process**. **Selection rules** restrict which phonons are allowed to interact; these arise from **conservation** of **energy** and of **'momentum'**. The latter is not conserved for all processes, since transfers occur to the lattice in units of $\hbar K$, where K is any reciprocal lattice vector. Such processes (where $K \neq 0$) are called **umklapp processes**; when phonon momentum is conserved it is called a **normal process**.

Higher-order phonon processes, involving four or more phonons, are more **numerous** and arise from different orders of the perturbation theory. **Three-phonon** processes arise only from **first**-order terms in the perturbation expansion; **four-phonon** processes arise from **first**- and **second**-order terms. For some effects, **five-phonon** processes are the simplest contributors.

Phonon interactions provide a mechanism for a crystal to relax from a **non-equilibrium state** towards an **equilibrium state**. Umklapp processes enable a net momentum imbalance to be dissipated and hence account for a **resistance** to **thermal flow** in a perfect infinite crystal. The phenomenon, under conditions such that this effect dominates the flow of heat, is usually called **'lattice conductivity'**. Even in some metals there are temperature regions in which the lattice conduction is more important than the **electron conduc-tion**. Since phonons interact with each other to create other phonons, a phonon has a **finite lifetime**. Thus, through the energy–time uncertainty relationship, the selection rule arising from the conservation of energy becomes relaxed when lifetimes are small (at **high** temperatures). So long as the phonon lifetime is long compared with the **reciprocal** of the angular frequencies involved, energy is conserved in individual processes; if one of the frequencies is very small, energy conservation is not rigid.

The **absorption** of **sound** by a solid is an interesting effect. Since the induced sound wave has a well defined **frequency** and **intensity** and represents the only non-equilibrium 'phonon state', a particular mode may be singled out for investigation. The decay of these extra phonons into the thermal distribution is measured by the **attenuation** of the beam. **Transverse** waves of high frequency ($\sim 10^9$ Hz) interact directly with individual thermal phonons, and expressions may be deduced to describe this contribution to the attenuation. **Longitudinal** waves are also absorbed, but by a **less direct** interaction. **Lower-frequency** elastic waves interact with the whole phonon spectrum simultaneously, because of the relaxation of the energy-conservation law as applied to individual processes. The drawbacks are twofold: **experimentally** the highest frequencies that can be induced are considerably smaller than those of a typical thermal phonon, and **theoretically** too little is known about the **interatomic potential** to carry out accurate calculations.

Chapter notes

[a] Standard integrals of the form required in equation (5.3) when the expansion (5.4) is made are:

$$\int_{-\infty}^{+\infty} e^{-ax^2}\,dx = \left(\frac{\pi}{a}\right)^{1/2}, \qquad \int_{-\infty}^{+\infty} e^{-ax^2}x^2\,dx = \frac{1}{2}\left(\frac{\pi}{a^3}\right)^{1/2}$$

$$\int_{-\infty}^{+\infty} e^{-ax^2}x^4\,dx = \frac{3}{4}\left(\frac{\pi}{a^5}\right)^{1/2}, \qquad \int_{-\infty}^{+\infty} e^{-ax^2}x^6\,dx = \frac{15}{8}\left(\frac{\pi}{a^7}\right)^{1/2}$$

$$\int_{-\infty}^{+\infty} e^{-ax^2}x^{2s-1}\,dx = 0 \quad \text{for } s = \text{integer.}$$

[b] Rearranging, this is negative if $1 > e^x(1-x)$, which holds for $x > 0$ to the limit at $x = 0$.

[c] We have not explicitly written the indices required for $s > 1$ (i.e. more than one atom in each unit cell) since this adds further to an already overburdened list. The inclusion of the more general unit cell is achieved by writing κ (taking values $1 \rightarrow s$) wherever there is an l. This is necessary to include the optic modes in the interactions.

[d] The integral in equation (5.35) may be evaluated as follows:

$$\int_{-\infty}^{+\infty} \frac{\sin x}{x}\,dx = 2\int_0^\infty \frac{\sin x}{x}\,dx$$

$$= 2\int_0^\infty dx \int_0^\infty d\alpha\, e^{-\alpha x}\sin x = 2\int_0^\infty d\alpha \frac{1}{\alpha^2 + 1}$$

$$= 2|\tan^{-1}\alpha|_0^\infty = \pi.$$

^{e} A 'function' with the property $\int_{-\infty}^{+\infty} \delta(x)\,dx = 1$, but that $\delta(x) = 0$ everywhere except in a small region around $x = 0$; see pages 82–84 of Reference 2 of Chapter 1.
^{f} If lines appear more than once, care is necessary to observe the correct time ordering of interactions. Earlier times are those on the left in our diagrams. See Chapter 6 for more detail on this point.
^{g} This concept is not invalid. Although a phonon is associated with the whole crystal and is localized only in **k** space, here we are treating each section of the crystal as a crystal in its own right. The part of the crystal under consideration must be small enough to be able to neglect temperature gradients but large enough to have the same properties as an 'infinite' crystal. These criteria may be simultaneously satisfied for macroscopic size samples.
^{h} Recently a new term for an even higher frequency range has crept into use—'praetersonic'.

References

1. Born, M., and Blackman, M., Z. *Physik*, **82**, 551–558 (1933).
2. Liebfried, G., and Ludwig, W., *Solid State Physics*, **12**, 275–444 (1961).
3. Maradudin, A. A., and Flinn, P. A., *Ann. Phys. (New York)*, **22**, 223–238 (1963).
4. Maradudin, A. A., Flinn, P. A., and Cordwell-Horsefall, R. A., *Ann. Phys. (New York)*, **15**, 337–386 (1961).
5. Klein, M. L., *J. Chem. Phys.*, **41**, 749–755 (1964).
6. Klein, M. L., and Reissland, J. A., *J. Chem. Phys.*, **41**, 2773–2776 (1964).
7. Boato, G., Scoles, G., and Vallauri, M. E., *Nuovo Cimento*, **23**, 1041–1053 (1962).
8. Boato, G., Casanova, G., and Levi, J., *J. Chem. Phys.*, **37**, 201–202 (1962).
9. Peierls, R. E., *Ann. Phys.*, **3**, 1055–1102 (1929).
10. Peierls, R. E., *Ann. Phys.*, **4**, 121–148 (1930).
11. Weisskopf, V. F., and Wigner, E. P., Z. *Physik*, **63**, 54 (1930).
12. Feller, W., *An Introduction to Probability Theory and its Applications*, Vol. 1, 3rd ed., 1968; Vol. 2, 2nd ed., 1971, Wiley, New York.
13. Kubo, R., *Fluctuation, Relaxation and Resonance in Magnetic Systems*, Oliver and Boyd, London, 1961, pp. 23–68.
14. Peierls, R. E., *Quantum Theory of Solids*, Oxford University Press, London, 1955.
15. Ziman, J. M., *Electrons and Phonons*, Oxford University Press, London, 1960, pp. 137–147.
16. Pomeranchuk, I., *J. Phys. U.S.S.R.*, **7**, 197 (1943).
17. Herring, C., *Phys. Rev.*, **95**, 954–965 (1954).
18. Landau, L. D., and Khalatnikov, I. M., *J.E.T.P.*, **19**, 637–650, 709–726 (1949).
19. Khalatnikov, I. M., *J.E.T.P.*, **20**, 243–266 (1950).
20. Khalatnikov, I. M., *Zh. eksper. teor. Fiz.*, **23**, 21–34 (1952).
21. Kittel, C., *Thermal Physics*, Wiley, New York, 1969, p. 215.
22. Herpin, A., *Ann. de Phys. (Paris)*, **7**, 91–140 (1952).
23. Herpin, A., *Bull. Soc. Franc. Mineral. Crist.*, **77**, 228–235 (1954).
24. Berman, R., Z. f. *Phys. Chem. (Neue Folge)*, **16**, 145–157 (1958).
25. Klemens, P. G., *Solid State Physics*, **7**, 1–98 (1958).
26. Mendelssohn, K., and Rosenberg, H. M., *Solid State Physics*, **12**, 223–274 (1961).
27. Dunn, F., and Breyer, J. E., *J. Acoust. Soc. Am.*, **34**, 775–778 (1962).
28. Bömmel, H. E., and Dransfield, K., *Phys. Rev.*, **117**, 1245–1252 (1960).
29. Simons, S., *Proc. Phys. Soc (London)*, **83**, 749–754 (1964).

6

The Green's-function Formulation

6.1 Introduction

When a physical system, previously in equilibrium, is subjected to an external influence, its reaction to the influence is known as the response. Response theory seeks to predict the behaviour of the system to a given disturbance and this clearly depends on the nature of the disturbance. Perturbation theory is adequate under conditions corresponding to small disturbances, but may become invalid (or at least too slowly convergent) in many cases of real physical interest. A formalism is required that will extend the validity over a wider range and that may be related to the conceptually simpler perturbation results where they are valid. Such a formalism has developed from the application of quantum-field theoretical techniques to many-body problems. The use of Green's functions (which have been known to mathematicians for over a hundred years) represents a great step forward in the theory of solids.

Theoretically it is easy to isolate the different contributions to an observed effect, but it is difficult to combine them to predict the nett effect; experimentally it is easy to observe the combined effects of various contributions but it is difficult to separate them. Theorists must start with idealized non-interacting systems and work towards real systems by allowing the interactions to become larger and more numerous; experimentalists must start with a real system and modify the conditions (temperature, pressure, purity, etc.) until only a small number of factors (preferably only one) contribute to an observed property. The aim is to overlap before experimental difficulties prevail or the theory becomes invalid; the problem arises from both parties working at their limits and comparing results which neither of them would regard as the best representation of their method. (The absorption of ultrasonic waves is a good illustration of this.)

In this chapter the aim is a formal representation of the lattice dynamical problem. Applications of the relations developed appear in following chapters. To avoid unnecessary complications, the discussions and derivations are limited to boson systems and further specialized to systems with $\mu = 0$ (chemical potential), in particular phonons. The Green's-function technique is used in many different branches of theoretical physics for both Fermi and Bose systems. Although the majority of the results that we will obtain explicitly may be obtained by conventional methods (as in Chapters 4 and 5), it is instructive to deduce known results and then be able to use the same method to obtain more complex contributions or to formulate a problem for which ordinary perturbation methods are inadequate.

It is necessary to introduce the general properties and definitions of Green's functions before applying the ideas to phonons. However this is tackled from a physical standpoint rather than a rigorous mathematical one. Sections 6.2–6.5 develop the general concept of correlation and Green's functions, but only so far as is required for the purposes of this book. Readers wishing to obtain a fuller understanding of the wide range of problems to which Green's functions have been applied should consult one of the general references given.

6.2   Response

We have some interest in the properties of a physical system that is in equilibrium and in isolation from the rest of the universe, but sooner or later we cannot contain the urge to poke at it. We poke at it for a good clear reason; we want to see how it reacts. In order to build up a store of coherent information about the system, the 'poke' must be controlled and the reaction carefully analysed to ensure that the observed effect is due strictly to the poke.

Perturbation theory has been applied with great success. When the poke is gentle and does not have a violent effect, the theory of small perturbations provides a valuable and fairly simple description of the response of the system. However the merit of perturbation theory relies on rapid convergence of a series expansion; without this the expressions are manipulatively impossible. Later in this chapter we develop a general formalism for handling higher-order terms, but first it is helpful to say a few words to bridge the gap between the 'direct equation of motion method' and the formal procedures that follow.

A simple system, and one that is a very suitable example for our interests, is a driven oscillator. The oscillator has a natural (angular) frequency ω_0 and we 'poke' it with a force that varies harmonically with a frequency ω. The equation of motion of the oscillator is

$$\ddot{x} + \omega_0^2 x = \frac{F_0}{m} e^{i\omega t} \tag{6.1}$$

whose solution once the transient has decayed (i.e. once the complementary function becomes negligible) is the particular integral that yields

$$x = \frac{F_0}{m}\left(\frac{1}{\omega_0^2 - \omega^2}\right) e^{i\omega t}. \tag{6.2}$$

The part of this solution determined by the relation between the properties of the system (ω_0) and the character of the external influence (ω) is known as the response function $R_0(\omega)$ (labelled zero to indicate no damping):

$$R_0(\omega) = \frac{1}{\omega_0^2 - \omega^2}. \tag{6.3}$$

Immediately we see an important property of the response function; when $\omega = \omega_0$, $R_0(\omega)$ becomes infinite. Thus, if we can find the response function for one of the dynamical variables of a system, its infinities (singularities) will yield the normal modes of that system. Physically this is the resonance condition and accounts for the observed frequency dependence of the absorption of energy by the lattice modes. (This is discussed in some detail in Chapter 8.)

An interaction between normal modes allows energy to transfer to other modes, and this introduces a damping term. The equation of motion of a single, damped, driven oscillator is

$$\ddot{x} + \gamma\dot{x} + \omega_0^2 x = \frac{F_0}{m} e^{i\omega t} \tag{6.4}$$

which has the solution

$$x = \frac{F_0}{m} \left(\frac{1}{\omega_0^2 - \omega^2 - i\gamma\omega} \right) e^{i\omega t}. \tag{6.5}$$

Thus

$$R(\omega) = \frac{1}{(\omega_0^2 - \omega^2 - i\gamma\omega)}. \tag{6.6}$$

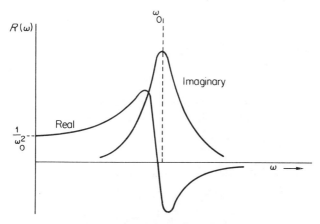

Figure 6.1 The real and imaginary parts of the response function of a driven damped harmonic oscillator; ω is the angular frequency of the driving force and ω_0 is the resonance (or natural) frequency of the oscillator

We shall leave equation (6.6) in its present form, but we shall recognize it again in a later chapter. Figure 6.1 indicates the behaviour of the real and imaginary parts of $R(\omega)$.

In a solid a large number of dynamical variables are required to specify the complex motions. For a harmonic solid we have shown that the vibrational properties of the system are those of a gas of non-interacting phonons. These were defined in terms of the quantum-field operators (second quantization) $a^+(\mathbf{k}j)$ and $a(\mathbf{k}j)$. The time development of the motion of a system depends on the response of the expectation values of the operators which couple to the disturbance. If the disturbance $F(\mathbf{r}, t)$ couples with an operator O where

$$F(\mathbf{r}, t) = F_0(e^{i(\mathbf{k}\cdot\mathbf{r} - \omega t)} + e^{-i(\mathbf{k}\cdot\mathbf{r} - \omega t)}) = F(k, \omega) \tag{6.7}$$

and we take the Fourier transform of $\langle O \rangle_{\mathbf{r},t}$ with respect to $\mathbf{k}$ and ω

$$O(\mathbf{k}\omega) \equiv \int e^{i(\mathbf{k}\cdot\mathbf{r} + \omega t)}\langle O \rangle_{\mathbf{r},t} \, d\mathbf{r} \, dt$$

$$= R(\mathbf{k}, \omega)F(\mathbf{k}, \omega) \tag{6.8}$$

we see that the time development may be written in terms of the response of individual modes (provided that the modes are non-interacting). The response function has singularities where $\omega = \omega(\mathbf{k}j)$. The introduction of interactions between the crystalline excitations modifies the response function.

The quantum-mechanical equation of motion is the Schrödinger time-dependent equation

$$i\hbar\dot{\Psi}(\mathbf{r}, t) = H\Psi(\mathbf{r}, t) \tag{6.9}$$

or the Heisenberg expression for the operator $O(t)$

$$i\hbar\dot{O}(t) = [O(t), H(t)]. \tag{6.10}$$

The time-dependent Heisenberg operators are related to the time-independent operators of wave mechanics by the transformation

$$O(t) = e^{iHt/\hbar}O(t = 0)e^{-iHt/\hbar}. \tag{6.11}$$

The time-dependent solution of equation (6.9) is

$$\Psi(\mathbf{r}, t) = \sum_j C_j(t)\psi_j(\mathbf{r})e^{-i\varepsilon_j t/\hbar} \tag{6.12}$$

where $H\psi_j(\mathbf{r}) = \varepsilon_j\psi_j(\mathbf{r})$ and where $C_j(t)$ are time independent if the Hamiltonian does not contain time explicitly. (Solution (6.12) is written explicitly for phonons in equation (5.26b), but it is convenient to retain the more general form for the moment.) The value of $C_j(t)$ is given by

$$C_j(t) = \int \psi_j^*(\mathbf{r}')\Psi(\mathbf{r}', t)\, e^{i\varepsilon_j t/\hbar}\, d\mathbf{r}' \qquad (6.13)$$

and if $\partial H/\partial t = 0$

$$C_j(t) = C_j(0) = \int \psi_j^*(\mathbf{r}')\Psi(\mathbf{r}', 0)\, d\mathbf{r}'. \qquad (6.14)$$

For this case we may write, using equations (6.12) and (6.14), that the time development of the state of the system is

$$\Psi(\mathbf{r}, t) = \int g(\mathbf{r}', 0; \mathbf{r}, t)\Psi(\mathbf{r}', 0)\, d\mathbf{r}' \qquad (6.15)$$

where

$$g(\mathbf{r}', 0; \mathbf{r}, t) \equiv \sum_j \psi_j^*(\mathbf{r}')\psi_j(\mathbf{r})\, e^{-i\varepsilon_j t/\hbar} \qquad (6.16)$$

The function $g(\mathbf{r}', 0; \mathbf{r}, t)$ correlates the initial state $\psi_j(\mathbf{r}')$ at $t = 0$ to the state $\psi_j(\mathbf{r})$ at time t. Physically it is the probability of finding the system in a state $\psi_j(\mathbf{r})$ at a time t after it was known to be in a state $\psi_j(\mathbf{r}')$ at $t = 0$. It is easy to see that $g(\mathbf{r}', 0; \mathbf{r}, t)$ is a solution of the equation of motion (6.9). For the special case $t = 0$, equation (6.16) becomes

$$g(\mathbf{r}', 0; \mathbf{r}, 0) = \sum_j \psi_j^*(\mathbf{r}')\psi_j(\mathbf{r})$$

$$= \delta(\mathbf{r}' - \mathbf{r}) \qquad (6.17)$$

by the closure property of eigenfunctions. Physically this means that there is no correlation between the probability amplitudes at different points in space unless sufficient time elapses for a flow of probability density between these two points.

If the Hamiltonian does include time explicitly, we must use equation (6.13) instead of equation (6.14) in equation (6.12). By using first-order time-dependent perturbation theory as in Section 5.5, we find a function

$$g(\mathbf{r}', t'; \mathbf{r}, t) \equiv \sum_j \psi_j^*(\mathbf{r}')\psi_j(\mathbf{r})\, e^{-i\varepsilon_j(t - t')/\hbar}. \qquad (6.18)$$

This correlates a disturbance on a state $\psi(\mathbf{r}')$ at time t' with an effect which results in the system being in the state $\psi(\mathbf{r})$ at time t; clearly t must be greater (later) than t'.

These g functions all trace the time development of the state of a system, and hence the response of that system to a perturbation. They are Green's functions, but, for reasons based on simplifying the boundary conditions that will emerge later, it is customary to work in terms of modified forms of g.

Following this custom, we shall consider the function

$$G(\mathbf{r}, t; \mathbf{r}', t') = -i\eta(t - t')g(\mathbf{r}', t'; \mathbf{r}, t) \tag{6.19}$$

where $\eta(t - t')$ is a step function such that

$$\eta(t - t') = 0 \qquad t < t' \tag{6.20a}$$

$$= 1 \qquad t > t'. \tag{6.20b}$$

6.3   One-particle Green's functions—equations of motion

If we now apply the ideas of the preceding section to a collection of boson[a] particles (later we shall consider phonons explicitly), the physical significance of the functions introduced becomes clear. If the effect of a perturbation $H'(t)$ is to create a particle at position $\mathbf{r}'$ at time t', the function (6.19) traces the propagation of that particle until it is removed at $\mathbf{r}$ at a time t. Hence the term 'propagator' for the one-particle Green's function

$$G(\mathbf{r}, t; \mathbf{r}', t') \equiv i\eta(t - t')\langle a(\mathbf{r}, t)a^+(\mathbf{r}', t')\rangle \tag{6.21}$$

where $a^+(\mathbf{r}', t')$ creates a particle at $(\mathbf{r}', t')$ and $a(\mathbf{r}, t)$ destroys it at $(\mathbf{r}, t)$. For $t' > t$ the right-hand side of equation (6.21) is zero, but a related function, which describes the destruction of a particle at $(\mathbf{r}, t)$ later to be created at $(\mathbf{r}', t')$, is non-zero. This leads us to define three basic Green's functions, known as retarded, advanced and causal, respectively,

$$G_R(A_t; B_{t'}) \equiv -i\eta(t - t')(\langle A_t B_{t'}\rangle - \langle B_{t'}A_t\rangle)$$

$$= -i\eta(t - t')\langle [A_t, B_{t'}]\rangle \tag{6.22a}$$

$$G_A(A_t; B_{t'}) \equiv i\eta(t' - t)\langle [A_t, B_{t'}]\rangle \tag{6.22b}$$

$$G_C(A_t; B_{t'}) \equiv -i\eta(t - t')\langle A_t B_{t'}\rangle - i\eta(t' - t)\langle B_{t'}A_t\rangle$$

$$= -i\langle T\{A_t B_{t'}\}\rangle \tag{6.22c}$$

For brevity, we have written the Heisenberg operators $A(\mathbf{r}, t) \equiv A_t$ and $B(\mathbf{r}', t') \equiv B_{t'}$; the $\langle \cdots \rangle$ in the definitions (6.22) are thermodynamic averages given as in Section 4.4 by equations (4.35) and (4.37). The operator $T\{\cdots\}$ time orders operators so that those with earlier times operate first (i.e. appear to the right). For example

$$T\{A_{t_1}B_{t_2}C_{t_3}\} = C_{t_3}A_{t_1}B_{t_2} \quad \text{for } t_3 > t_1 > t_2.$$

It is very easily shown that all three functions (6.22) depend only on the difference $t - t'$ and not independently on t or t': using equation (4.35)

$$\langle A_t B_{t'}\rangle = \text{Tr}\{A_t B_{t'}\rho\} \tag{6.23}$$

and, from relation (6.11), this may be written

$$\langle A_t B_{t'} \rangle = \text{Tr} \{ e^{iHt/\hbar} A_0 \, e^{-iH(t-t')/\hbar} B_0 \, e^{-iHt'/\hbar} \rho \}. \tag{6.24}$$

Using the cyclic theorem of traces, and noting from equation (4.37) that ρ commutes with $e^{iHt'/\hbar}$, the expression (6.24) becomes

$$\langle A_t B_{t'} \rangle = \text{Tr} \{ A_0 \, e^{-iH(t-t')/\hbar} B_0 \, e^{iH(t-t')/\hbar} \rho \} \tag{6.25}$$

which depends on time only through $t - t'$.

In our applications we shall be interested primarily in the causal Green's function (6.22c), and therefore we drop the suffix unless we wish to emphasize some distinction with G_R and G_A.

The equations of motion of these quantities may be found as follows. The time derivative of G (with respect to t) is

$$\dot{G} = -i \langle A_t B_{t'} \rangle \dot{\eta}(t - t') - i \langle B_{t'} A_t \rangle \dot{\eta}(t' - t) - i\eta(t - t') \tfrac{d}{dt} \langle A_t B_{t'} \rangle$$

$$- i\eta(t' - t) \tfrac{d}{dt} \langle B_{t'} A_t \rangle. \tag{6.26}$$

From the definition of the step function (6.20)

$$\dot{\eta}(t - t') = -\dot{\eta}(t' - t) = \delta(t - t') \tag{6.27}$$

and from the Heisenberg equation of motion (6.10)

$$i\hbar \tfrac{d}{dt} \langle A_t B_{t'} \rangle = \langle [A_t B_{t'}, H_t] \rangle = \langle [A_t, H_t] B_{t'} \rangle \tag{6.28a}$$

and

$$i\hbar \tfrac{d}{dt} \langle B_{t'} A_t \rangle = \langle B_{t'} [A_t, H_t] \rangle. \tag{6.28b}$$

Using the relations (6.27) and (6.28), the equation of motion (6.26) becomes

$$i\hbar \dot{G}(A_t; B_{t'}) = \hbar \langle [A_t, B_{t'}] \rangle \delta(t - t') + G([A_t, H]; B_{t'}). \tag{6.29}$$

By a similar process we can show that the equations of motion of G_R and G_A are the same as equation (6.29) with the relevant subscripts on the $\dot{G}$ and G. The second term on the right-hand side of equation (6.29) is a higher-order Green's function, the significance of which will become more clear as our discussion progresses.

We shall be interested in Green's functions in which the operators are (or are closely related to) the boson annihilation and creation operators. Thus we shall write

$$A_t \to a(\mathbf{r}t) \tag{6.30a}$$

$$B_{t'} \to a^+(\mathbf{r}'t'). \tag{6.30b}$$

6.4   One-particle Green's functions—boundary conditions

The form of the definitions (6.22) are chosen to make best use of the boundary conditions. The functions G_R, G_A and G_C are not defined at $t = 0$, but

$$G_R(t < t') = 0 \qquad (6.31a)$$

$$G_A(t > t') = 0. \qquad (6.31b)$$

Consider the boundary conditions for G_C at $t = 0$. The time correlation functions appearing in the Green's functions are not independent:

$$\langle A_t B_{t'} \rangle = \mathrm{Tr}\,\{A_t B_{t'} \rho\}$$

where ρ is the density matrix. Applying the transformation (6.11) to A_t:

$$\langle A_t B_{t'} \rangle = \mathrm{Tr}\,\{e^{iHt/\hbar} A_0\, e^{-iHt/\hbar} B_{t'} \rho\}. \qquad (6.32)$$

Now consider

$$\langle B_{t'} A_t \rangle = \mathrm{Tr}\,\{B_{t'} A_t \rho\}$$

$$= \mathrm{Tr}\,\{A_t \rho B_{t'}\}.$$

In particular, at $t = 0$

$$\langle B_{t'} A_0 \rangle = \mathrm{Tr}\,\{A_0 \rho B_{t'}\}$$

and using the explicit form (4.37) for ρ,

$$\langle B_{t'} A_0 \rangle = Z^{-1}\,\mathrm{Tr}\,\{A_0\, e^{-\beta(H - \mu N)} B_{t'}\}$$

$$= Z^{-1}\,\mathrm{Tr}\,\{e^{-\beta(H - \mu N)}\, e^{+\beta(H - \mu N)} A_0\, e^{-\beta(H - \mu N)} B_{t'}\}$$

$$= \mathrm{Tr}\,\{\rho\, e^{\beta(H - \mu N)} A_0\, e^{-\beta(H - \mu N)} B_{t'}\}. \qquad (6.33)$$

For the operators (6.30)

$$e^{-\beta \mu N} a(\mathbf{r}, t)\, e^{\beta \mu N} = e^{\beta \mu} a(\mathbf{r}, t). \qquad (6.34)^b$$

Noting this, equations (6.32) and (6.33) are very similar, and if we put $it = \beta\hbar$ in equation (6.32) and compare it with equation (6.33), we see that

$$\langle a^+(\mathbf{r}', t') a(\mathbf{r}, 0) \rangle = e^{\beta \mu} \langle a(\mathbf{r}, t) a^+(\mathbf{r}', t') \rangle_{it = \beta\hbar}. \qquad (6.35)$$

We have arrived at this result by exploiting the similarity between temperature and imaginary time (for phonons $\mu = 0$). Now, from definition (6.22c)

$$G^{t > t'}[a(\mathbf{r}, t); a^+(\mathbf{r}', t')] = -i\langle a(\mathbf{r}, t) a^+(\mathbf{r}', t') \rangle \qquad (6.36a)$$

$$G^{t < t'}[a(\mathbf{r}, t); a^+(\mathbf{r}', t')] = -i\langle a^+(\mathbf{r}', t') a(\mathbf{r}, t) \rangle. \qquad (6.36b)$$

At $t = 0$ we may write

$$G[a(\mathbf{r}, 0); a^+(\mathbf{r}', t')] = -i\langle a^+(\mathbf{r}', t') a(\mathbf{r}, 0) \rangle$$

$$= -i\, e^{\beta \mu} \langle a(\mathbf{r}, t) a^+(\mathbf{r}', t') \rangle_{it = \beta\hbar}$$

from relation (6.35). The right-hand side of this may be rewritten using equation (6.36a), and we then see that

$$G[a(\mathbf{r}, 0); a^+(\mathbf{r}', t')] = e^{\beta\mu}G[a(\mathbf{r}, \beta\hbar/i); a^+(\mathbf{r}', t')] \qquad (6.37)$$

which is a relation between the values of G at the boundaries of the imaginary time domain. Thus we have made use of the formal equivalence of temperatures to an imaginary time. This will enable us to evaluate the thermodynamic Green's functions that are of interest.

6.5 One-particle Green's functions—spectral representation

We have seen that the time correlation functions (6.36) depend only on $t - t'$ and not on t or t' separately [see equation (6.25)]; similarly, they depend only on $|\mathbf{r} - \mathbf{r}'|$ and not on $\mathbf{r}$ or $\mathbf{r}'$ separately. Thus if we write $t - t'$ as t and $\mathbf{r} - \mathbf{r}'$ as $\mathbf{r}$, the one-particle Green's functions may be written more economically as $G(\mathbf{r}, t)$—the operators being those of convention (6.30) unless otherwise specified. Consider now the Fourier transforms of $G^{t>0}(\mathbf{r}, t)$ and $G^{t<0}(\mathbf{r}, t)$:

$$G^{t>0}(\mathbf{k}\omega) = i \int \int_{-\infty}^{+\infty} e^{-i(\mathbf{k}.\mathbf{r} - \omega t)}G^{t>0}(\mathbf{r}, t)\, d\mathbf{r}\, dt \qquad (6.38a)$$

$$G^{t<0}(\mathbf{k}\omega) = i \int \int_{-\infty}^{+\infty} e^{-i(\mathbf{k}.\mathbf{r} - \omega t)}G^{t<0}(\mathbf{r}, t)\, d\mathbf{r}\, dt. \qquad (6.38b)$$

Substituting $it = it - \beta\hbar$ in equation (6.38a), from the condition (6.35) we see that

$$G^{t<0}(\mathbf{k}\omega) = e^{\beta(-\hbar\omega + \mu)}G^{t>0}(\mathbf{k}\omega). \qquad (6.39)$$

If we define a function

$$J(\mathbf{k}\omega) = G^{t>0}(\mathbf{k}\omega) - G^{t<0}(\mathbf{k}\omega) \qquad (6.40)$$

equation (6.39) may be rewritten in the form

$$G^{t<0}(\mathbf{k}\omega) = e^{\beta(-\hbar\omega + \mu)}[J(\mathbf{k}\omega) + G^{t<0}(\mathbf{k}\omega)]$$

or, by rearranging $G^{t<0}(\mathbf{k}\omega)$ to be on the left-hand side,

$$G^{t<0}(\mathbf{k}\omega) = \overline{n(\omega)}J(\mathbf{k}\omega) \qquad (6.41a)$$

where

$$\overline{n(\omega)} = \frac{e^{-\beta(\hbar\omega - \mu)}}{1 - e^{-\beta(\hbar\omega - \mu)}} = (e^{\beta(\hbar\omega - \mu)} - 1)^{-1}.$$

Similarly

$$G^{t>0}(\mathbf{k}\omega) = e^{\beta(\hbar\omega - \mu)}[G^{t>0}(\mathbf{k}\omega) - J(\mathbf{k}, \omega)]$$

$$= [1 + \overline{n(\omega)}]J(\mathbf{k}\omega). \qquad (6.41b)$$

$\overline{n(\omega)}$ is the Bose–Einstein mean occupation of the state with energy $\hbar\omega$ and $J(\mathbf{k}\omega)$ is known as the spectral distribution function.

The expressions we have introduced so far are valid for any boson system. We shall now consider systems for which $\mu = 0$ and, in particular, address our remarks to a phonon gas. The operators $a(\mathbf{r}, t)$ are transformed to Fourier space, and we recognize the familiar annihilation and creation operators $a(\mathbf{k}j)$ and $a^+(\mathbf{k}j)$ of Chapter 3; but now they are time-dependent Heisenberg operators. It is convenient to drop the j label and to remember that a label $\mathbf{k}$ also implies a label j. Thus we use the notation $a_\mathbf{k}(t) =$ annihilation of a phonon $\mathbf{k}j$ at time t and $a_\mathbf{k}^+(t) =$ creation of a phonon $\mathbf{k}j$ at time t. In the Schrödinger representation [i.e. if we wish to use equations (6.9) and (6.12) rather than equations (6.10) and (6.11)], $|n_1, \cdots, n_\mathbf{k}, \cdots, t\rangle$ describes the state of a phonon gas at time t.

Thus we may follow the time-dependent state (Schrödinger) after a perturbation acts on a known state at $t = 0$ or we may follow the time development of the operator (Heisenberg) through equation (6.11). The latter is often called the interaction representation. For example, suppose that a phonon $\mathbf{k}j$ is destroyed at $t = 0$ in a solid where there are no interactions between phonons. From equation (6.11), we have

$$a_k(t) = e^{iHt/\hbar} a_k(0) e^{-iHt/\hbar} \tag{6.42}$$

where

$$H = \sum_{\mathbf{k}'} (a_{\mathbf{k}'}^+ a_{\mathbf{k}'} + \tfrac{1}{2})\hbar\omega_{\mathbf{k}'}. \tag{6.43}$$

Thus

$$a_k(t) = e^{-i\omega_\kappa t} a_k(0). \tag{6.44}^c$$

Now, from equation (6.36a), and carrying out the spatial Fourier transform in equation (6.38a)

$$G_0^{t>0}(\mathbf{k}\omega) = 2\pi \int_{-\infty}^{+\infty} e^{i\omega t} \langle a_k(t) a_k^+(0) \rangle \, dt \tag{6.45}$$

and using the result (6.44)

$$G_0^{t>0}(\mathbf{k}\omega) = 2\pi \langle a_k(0) a_k^+(0) \rangle \int_{-\infty}^{+\infty} e^{i(\omega - \omega_k)t} \, dt$$

$$= 2\pi \langle 1 + a_k^+(0) a_k(0) \rangle \int_{-\infty}^{+\infty} e^{i(\omega - \omega_k)t} \, dt$$

$$= 2\pi[1 + \overline{n(\omega_k)}]\delta(\omega - \omega_k). \tag{6.46}$$

The subscript zero on the propagator signifies non-interacting phonons. Comparing equations (6.46) and (6.41b)

$$J_0(\mathbf{k}\omega) = 2\pi\delta(\omega - \omega_\mathbf{k}).$$ (6.47)

This trivial example of finding the spectral distribution function explains the origin of the name; it is a function of frequency which has Dirac-delta-function peaks at values corresponding to the normal modes of the system. The Green's functions in real space may be found by taking the inverse Fourier transform of equation (6.46) and the corresponding equation for $G_0^{t<0}$. For our purposes it is usually sufficient to work entirely in Fourier space, where the phonons are localized. The Fourier transforms of the Green's functions of interest may be evaluated most easily by a diagram technique.

Now consider the effect of interactions between the phonons. The similarity between the response function discussed in Section 6.2 and the spectral distribution function is now becoming apparent, in particular the singularities of the response function (6.3) of the undamped oscillators and those of the spectral function (6.47). When the modes are coupled the delta functions smooth away to a continuous function with some peaks where the modes behave more freely than others.

6.6   One-phonon Green's functions

In the preceding three sections, we have introduced the idea of Green's functions to describe the dynamics of a system. It is couched in terms of operators that create or annihilate a single excitation. In practice, phonon Green's functions are best defined in terms of the normal coordinates [transformation (3.34a)]. This is convenient, since the Hamiltonian is usually a power series of normal coordinates, and it also effects some analytical simplifications, since both positive and negative $\mathbf{k}$ appear. The response function of Section 6.2 and the spectral function of Section 6.5 bear strong similarities, which we shall exploit.

We define the following one-phonon Green's function:

$$G(\mathbf{k}jt; \mathbf{k}'j't') \equiv i\langle T\{A_{\mathbf{k}j}(t)A^*_{\mathbf{k}'j'}(t')\}\rangle$$ (6.48)

where we have followed the procedure of Maradudin and Fein[1] and used the operator $A_{\mathbf{k}j}$ which is dimensionless and is given by

$$q(\mathbf{k}jt) = \left(\frac{\hbar}{2\omega(\mathbf{k}j)}\right)^{1/2} A_{\mathbf{k}j}(t)$$ (6.49a)

i.e.

$$A_{\mathbf{k}j}(t) = a^+_{-\mathbf{k}j}(t) + a_{\mathbf{k}j}(t)$$ (6.49b)

(see Section 3.5).

The use of $A_{kj}(t)$ instead of a and a^+ reduces the number of terms, and since $\mathbf{k}$ and $-\mathbf{k}$ appear in each term, it is not necessary to assign a direction to each line in a diagram. As before, we shall drop the j suffix and remember that every label $\mathbf{k}$ implies a j also.

The application of Green's functions as a technique in the theory of solids has been well documented over the past ten years. The methods described in outline here derive mainly from Alekseev,[2] Cowley,[3] Maradudin and Fein,[1] Kwok,[4] Parry and Turner,[5] Kadanoff and Baym,[6] Matsubara[7] and Zubarev.[8] In particular, the review of Alekseev gives a detailed development of the application of the techniques that we cannot go into here.

From the results of Section 6.3, the Green's function in equation (6.48) may be written (since $t - t' \to t$)

$$G_{kk'}(t) \equiv i\langle T\{A_k(t)A_{k'}^*(0)\}\rangle. \tag{6.50}$$

In Section 6.4 we noted a correspondence between temperature and imaginary time. The idea was exploited by Alekseev.[2] Following the most usual notation we shall write $it/\hbar \equiv u$ which then has the same dimensions as β (i.e. inverse energy). Thus adapting equation (6.32) to the present case (namely $A_t \to A_k(t)$, $B_{t'} \to A_{k'}(0)$, ρ being given by equation (4.37) with $\mu = 0$) we have, for $u > 0$:

$$G_{kk'}(u) \equiv \frac{1}{Z}\mathrm{Tr}\,\{e^{uH}A_k(0)\,e^{-uH}A_{k'}(0)\,e^{-\beta H}\} \tag{6.51a}$$

and, for $u < 0$:

$$G_{kk'}(u) \equiv \frac{1}{Z}\mathrm{Tr}\,\{A_{k'}(0)\,e^{uH}A_k(0)\,e^{-uH}\,e^{-\beta H}\}. \tag{6.51b}$$

For $u < 0$, $G_{kk'}(u)$ is given by (6.51b), but, provided that $u + \beta > 0$, $G_{kk'}(u + \beta)$ is given by (6.51a). Rearranging the latter inside the trace, we see that for $u < 0$ but $u + \beta > 0$:

$$G_{kk'}(u + \beta) = G_{kk'}(u) \tag{6.52}$$

[This relation also follows from result (6.37) with $\mu = 0$.]

Equation (6.52) describes the periodicity of the phonon Green's function along the u axis (imaginary time). Thus, if we arrange for all our expressions to fall in the region so that u lies between $-\beta$ and 0 $(0 > u > -\beta)$, we may express $G_{kk'}(u)$ as a Fourier sum with periodicity β:

$$G_{kk'}(u) = \sum_p G_{kk'}^p\, e^{2\pi i p u/\beta} \tag{6.53a}$$

or, defining a quantity

$$\hbar\omega_p = \frac{2\pi}{\beta}p \tag{6.53b}$$

$$G_{kk'}(u) = \sum_p G_{kk'}(\omega_p)\, e^{i\hbar\omega_p u} \tag{6.53c}$$

where the Fourier coefficients in the series are

$$G_{kk'}(\omega_p) \equiv \frac{1}{\beta}\int_0^\beta G_{kk'}(u)\, e^{-i\hbar\omega_p u}\, du. \tag{6.53d}$$

This function is defined only where ω_p is given by the values (6.53b); however we may analytically continue it so that

$$G_{kk'}(\omega) \equiv G_{kk'}(\omega_p) \tag{6.54}$$

when $\omega = \omega_p$ and where $G_{kk'}(\omega)$ is a function of a continuous variable ω. A complete discussion of the mathematics of these functions has been given by Baym and Mermin.[9]

It now becomes possible to see the relation between the retarded Green's functions [equation (6.22a) with $B_{t'} \to A_{k'}(0)$ and $A_t \to A_k(t)$] and the causal or thermodynamic Green's function [equation (6.53c)]. Consider the Fourier transform of equation (6.22a):

$$G_R(\Omega) = -\frac{i}{2\pi}\int_{-\infty}^{+\infty} e^{-i\Omega t}\eta(t)\langle[A_k(t)A_{k'}(0)]\rangle\, dt. \tag{6.55}$$

According to equations (6.36), (6.38) and (6.41)

$$\langle[A_k(t)A_{k'}(0)]\rangle = \int_{-\infty}^{+\infty} J(\omega)\, e^{i\omega t}\, d\omega \tag{6.56}$$

and hence we have

$$G_R(\Omega) = \frac{1}{2\pi}\int_{-\infty}^{+\infty} J(\omega)\frac{d\omega}{\Omega - \omega - i\varepsilon}. \tag{6.57}$$

The ε is a positive infinitesimal (i.e. $\varepsilon \to +0$) and arises from the integration of the step function $\eta(t)$.

From equation (6.41), and noting equation (6.52), we may write

$$G_{kk'}(u) = \int_{-\infty}^{+\infty} \overline{n(\omega)J(\omega)}\, e^{i\omega t}\, d\omega \tag{6.58}$$

and, substituting this into equation (6.53d), we see that

$$G_{kk'}(\omega_p) = \frac{1}{\beta}\int_{-\infty}^{+\infty}\int_0^\beta \overline{n(\omega)J(\omega)}\, e^{\hbar\omega u - i\hbar\omega_p u}\, du\, d\omega \tag{6.59}$$

where it in equation (6.58) is replaced by $\hbar u$. Carrying out the imaginary time integration,

$$G_{kk'}(\omega_p) = \frac{1}{\beta}\int_{-\infty}^{+\infty} \overline{n(\omega)J(\omega)}\frac{e^{\beta(\hbar\omega - i\hbar\omega_p)}}{\hbar(\omega - i\omega_p)}\, d\omega \tag{6.60}$$

but since $e^{-i\beta\hbar\omega_p} = e^{-i2\pi p} = 1$ and $\bar{n}(\omega) \equiv (e^{\beta\hbar\omega} - 1)^{-1}$, equation (6.60) simplifies to

$$G_{kk'}(\omega_p) = \frac{1}{\beta\hbar} \int_{-\infty}^{+\infty} \frac{J(\omega)\,d\omega}{\omega - i\omega_p}. \qquad (6.61)$$

Thus a comparison of equations (6.61) and (6.57), for $\Omega = i(\omega_p + \varepsilon)$, gives:

$$G_R(\Omega) = \frac{\beta\hbar}{2\pi} G_{kk'}(\omega_p). \qquad (6.62)$$

This is an important relation, since the retarded Green's function measures the response of the system to an external probe. Thus the relation (6.62) enables the response to be described in terms of the thermodynamic Green's function, which in turn may be expressed in terms of the spectral function.

In the harmonic approximation (no interactions between the phonons), the Fourier coefficients of the Green's function [as given by equation (6.53d)] take a particularly simple form. Using the explicit form (6.49b) for the operators in expression (6.50), we have that

$$G_{kk'}^0(u) = \langle T\{[a_k^+(u) + a_k(u)][a_{-k'}(0) + a_{k'}^+(0)]\}\rangle \qquad (6.63a)$$

which is non-zero only if $k = k'$. Only two of these four averages are non-zero, giving

$$G_k^0(u) = \langle T\{[a_{-k}^+(u)a_{-k}(0) + a_k(u)a_k^+(0)]\}\rangle \qquad (6.63b)$$

which yields [d]

$$G_k^0(u) = \bar{n}_k\, e^{|u|\hbar\omega_k} + (\bar{n}_k + 1)\, e^{-|u|\hbar\omega_k}. \qquad (6.63c)$$

Thus, from equation (6.53d) we have

$$G_k^0(\omega_p) = \frac{1}{\beta} \int_0^\beta (\bar{n}_k\, e^{u\hbar\omega_k} + (\bar{n}_k + 1)\, e^{-u\hbar\omega_k})\, e^{-i\hbar\omega_p u}\, du$$

$$= \frac{1}{\beta\hbar} \left[\left\{ \frac{\bar{n}_k\, e^{u\hbar\omega_k}}{\omega_k - i\omega_p} + \frac{(\bar{n}_k + 1)\, e^{-u\hbar\omega_k}}{-\omega_k - i\omega_p} \right\} e^{-i\hbar\omega_p u} \right]_0^\beta. \qquad (6.64)$$

Substituting the limits, and noting that $e^{-i\beta\hbar\omega_p} = 1$,

$$\bar{n}_k(e^{\beta\hbar\omega_k} - 1) = 1 \quad \text{and} \quad (\bar{n}_k + 1)(e^{\beta\hbar\omega_k} - 1) = -1,$$

equation (6.64) becomes

$$G_k^0(\omega_p) = \frac{2\omega_k}{\beta\hbar(\omega_k^2 + \omega_p^2)} \qquad (6.65)$$

i.e. it is a pure real quantity.

6.7 Interaction representation

Result (6.65) may be used as the basis for a perturbation expansion—treating the non-harmonic parts of the Hamiltonian as the perturbation, as in Chapter 5. Thus writing

$$H = H_0 + H' \qquad (6.66)$$

where H_0 is given by equation (3.39) and H' is as in Section 5.4 but is more conveniently re-expressed in the form

$$H' = \sum_{k_1 k_2 k_3} V^{(3)}_{123} A_1 A_2 A_3 + \sum_{k_1 k_2 k_3 k_4} V^{(4)}_{1234} A_1 A_2 A_3 A_4. \qquad (6.67)$$

For convenience we have written $A_i \equiv A_{k_i j_i}$ and the coefficients $V^{(3)}_{123}$ and $V^{(4)}_{1234}$ are readily deducible from equations (5.20) and (6.49).

The development of a general perturbation expansion has been dealt with in detail by many authors, and we use the result in the form expressed by Maradudin and Fein.[1]

$$G_{kk'}(u) = \left\langle T\{\tilde{A}_k(u)\tilde{A}^*_{k'}(0)\} \sum_{n=0}^{\infty} \frac{(-1)^n}{n!} \int_0^\beta d\beta_1 \cdots \int_0^\beta d\beta_n \tilde{H}'(\beta_1) \cdots \tilde{H}'(\beta_n) \right\rangle$$
$$(6.68a)$$

where for brevity the general definition

$$\tilde{O}(\gamma) \equiv e^{\gamma H_0} O\, e^{-\gamma H_0} \qquad (6.68b)$$

i.e. an operator in the interaction representation, has been adopted. The thermal average in equation (6.68a) is over the unperturbed states and the result is the general formulation of the series developed between equations (4.43) and (4.49). The term (6.63c) comes from (6.68a) with $n = 0$. The general term in equation (6.68a) may be classified by a scheme of diagrams constructed and analysed according to the following rules, which provide an evaluation of the Fourier transform of equation (6.68a), viz equation (6.53d). For reasons that are beginning to emerge, this Fourier coefficient of the thermodynamic Green's function is often called a phonon propagator.

Rules to evaluate the contributions to the phonon propagator

(i) Represent a phonon entering a region of interaction by a line labelled kj; in the most general case a line kj' leaves the region (k is conserved in all interactions). Hence write $G_{kk'}(\omega_p) \to G_{kjj'}(\omega_p)$.

(ii) Within the region of interaction mark n interaction vertices (for nth order terms). Draw all possible distinct connected diagrams of phonon lines joining all of these vertices.

(iii) At every vertex, the sum of the k values of phonons involved (positive entering, negative leaving) must be equal to a reciprocal lattice vector (or zero). (This is the interference condition—see Section 5.4.)

(iv) At every vertex the sum of ω_ps (positive entering, negative leaving) must be zero (conservation of energy).

(v) The contribution of a given diagram to $G_{kjj'}(\omega_p)$ is obtained by the following steps:

   (a) $V^{(n)}$ are the appropriate interaction coefficients determined by the number of lines associated with the vertex.

   (b) W is a weighting factor based on the number of possible pairings of the lines in the diagram.

   (c) X is a product of terms given by equation (6.65), one for each phonon line.

   (d) Take the product $V^{(n)}WX$ and introduce the factor $(-1)^n\beta^n/n!$ (where β^n arises from the n integrations).

   (e) Sum over all intermediate $\mathbf{k}, j$ and p values.

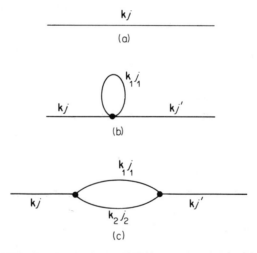

Figure 6.2

Examples for clarification

Figures 6.2(a), (b) and (c) represent cases in which $n = 0$, 1 and 2, respectively. Figure 6.2(a) represents the harmonic crystal; $\mathbf{k}j$ may represent any of the allowed non-interacting phonons.

Just as in Section 5.4 we found that only four-phonon processes contribute to first-order effects (while only cubic and quartic terms are included in H' [equation (6.67)]), so in Figure 6.2(b) we have a four-phonon vertex, being the only first-order contribution to the 'self energy'. (The significance of this name will become evident in the remaining parts of this chapter.) Since there is a four-phonon vertex and the interaction coefficient $V^{(4)}_{1234}$ is symmetrical in $\mathbf{k}_1\mathbf{k}_2\mathbf{k}_3$ and $\mathbf{k}_4$, the external phonon $\mathbf{k}j$ may be identified with any of these four, and the external phonon kj' may be identified with any of the other three, whilst the remaining two must be equal and opposite. Thus the 'pairing factor' for rule [v(b)] on p. 196 is 4×3, since all of these possibilities make an identical contribution. Thus for Figure 6.2(b) the contribution is

$$G_{kjj'}(\omega_p) = G^0_{kj}(\omega_p)S^{(1)}_p(kjj')G^0_{kj'}(\omega_p) \tag{6.69}$$

where, according to the rules, the first-order self energy is given by

$$S^{(1)}_p(kjj') = -12\beta \sum_{k_1 j_1} \sum_{p_1} V^{(4)}(-kj, kj', k_1 j_1, -k_1 j_1)G^0_{k_1 j_1}(\omega_{p_1}). \tag{6.70}$$

A phonon, such as $k_1 j_1$ in Figure 6.2(b), which is created and destroyed at the same vertex is called an 'instantaneous phonon'.

The interaction shown in Figure 6.2(c) is second order and involves two three-phonon vertices. Thus the second-order contribution to the self energy is

$$S^{(2)}_p(kjj') = 18\beta^2 \sum_{\substack{k_1 j_1 \\ k_2 j_2}} \sum_{\substack{p_1 \\ p_2}} V^{(3)}(-kj, k_1 j_1, k_2 j_2)V^{(3)}(kj', -k_1 j_1, -k_2 j_2)$$

$$\times \; G^0_{k_1 j_1}(\omega_{p_1})G^0_{k_2 j_1}(\omega_{p_2})\delta(p - p_1 - p_2). \tag{6.71}$$

The total effect of all such terms is summarized by a bubble diagram (Figure 6.3). The shaded region represents the sum of all the anharmonic self energies from diagrams that have one free phonon line entering and one leaving. This region includes diagrams with any number of vertices; the kinds of vertices (i.e. the number of phonon lines converging) present are determined by the terms retained in the Hamiltonian. Diagrams can be divided into two classes, proper and improper. The latter term is applied to diagrams that may be separated into two disconnected parts by cutting a single phonon line. Those which cannot be so separated are called proper diagrams.

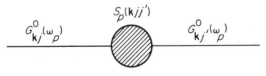

Figure 6.3

The self-energy bubbles in Figures 6.4 and 6.5 are the sums of terms evaluated using the diagram rules and for which the expressions (6.70) and

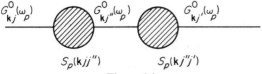

Figure 6.4

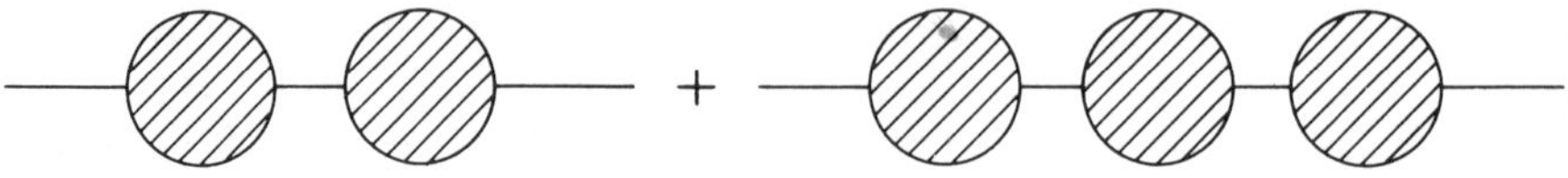

Figure 6.5

(6.71) are the lowest-order contributions. The total contribution to the Fourier transform of the Green's function from all proper diagrams is

$$G_{kjj'}(\omega_p) = G^0_{kj}(\omega_p)S_p(kjj')G^0_{kj'}(\omega_p) \tag{6.72}$$

(all schematically represented by Figure 6.3). The improper diagrams contribute a series of terms of which Figure 6.4 is the first. The sum of these may be represented schematically by Figure 6.5.

Writing the conclusions of the foregoing discussion into a single equation (not forgetting the harmonic term) we find that

$$G_{kjj'}(\omega_p) = G^0_{kj}(\omega_p)\delta_{jj'} + G^0_{kj}(\omega_p)S_p(kjj')G^0_{kj'}(\omega_p)$$
$$+ G^0_{kj}(\omega_p)\sum_{j''} S_p(kjj'')G^0_{kj''}(\omega_p)S_p(kj''j')G^0_{kj'}(\omega_p) + \cdots. \tag{6.73}$$

Equation (6.73) is an infinite series with the first few terms shown explicitly. The procedure is the same as in Section 4.4, where we used a technique that may be aptly summarized as 'picking oneself up by one's own bootlaces'. The infinite series implied in (6.73) may be written explicitly and concisely as

$$G_{kjj'}(\omega_p) = G^0_{kj}(\omega_p)\{\delta_{jj'} + \sum_{j''} S_p(kjj'')G_{kj''j'}(\omega_p)\} \tag{6.74a}$$

i.e. the infinite series is developed by feeding the equation back into itself. This is the famous Dyson equation, and may be rearranged as

$$G^0_{kj}(\omega_p)\delta_{jj'} = \sum_{j''} \{\delta_{j''j} - G^0_{kj}(\omega_p)S_p(kjj'')\}G_{kj''j'}(\omega_p). \tag{6.74b}$$

The eigenvalues of this matrix have real and imaginary parts. The real parts (Hermitian) contribute to a shift in the energy of phonons from those calculated in the harmonic approximation. The imaginary parts describe the damping, and hence predict a finite lifetime for a phonon. These effects arise from couplings between different phonons, and the corresponding normal modes are not independent. We shall consider the frequency shift and the finite lifetime in the following two sections.

6.8 Renormalized phonons

We have seen in the preceding section that there is a self energy arising from the anharmonic interactions. The Hermitian part of this contributes a real shift in the energy of the free phonon (hence the term 'self energy').

Since any experiment that measures phonon energies directly or indirectly cannot separate the anharmonic self energy from the harmonic part, it is this shifted energy that characterizes the physical phonons. If the off-diagonal elements of the anti-Hermitian parts of the matrix (6.74) are small compared with phonon energies, it is often convenient to work with a pseudoharmonic model. In this model each normal mode (phonon) is independent and has a renormalized energy and a finite lifetime. Both energy and lifetime are temperature dependent; hence the renormalized frequencies will be distinguished by a subscript T, i.e. $\omega(\mathbf{k}j)$ are the harmonic normal-mode frequencies and $\omega_T(\mathbf{k}j)$ are the corresponding renormalized modes. It is perfectly feasible that some crystals would be adequately described by a model in which the phonon energies change significantly upon renormalization even though the phonons exist for long enough to be regarded as independent. If the phonon lifetimes become so short as to be comparable with the inverse frequency, clearly a pseudoharmonic model has no value. For a pseudoharmonic model to be valid we require that

$$\omega_T(\mathbf{k}j)\tau(\mathbf{k}j) \gg 1 \tag{6.75}$$

[where $\tau(\mathbf{k}j)$ is the mean lifetime of the phonon $\mathbf{k}j$].

The pseudoharmonic approximation should not be confused with the quasiharmonic approximation as discussed in Section 4.6 and as used by Liebfried and Ludwig.[10] In the latter, the change in the frequencies with temperature takes into account only the modified interatomic forces due to the thermal expansion. This has the advantage that the new frequencies are calculated using the simpler harmonic expressions. However, since the values omit the anharmonic self-energy contributions, the quasiharmonic frequencies do not correspond to those observed. In the pseudoharmonic model the new (renormalized) frequencies represent the same quantity that is observed, and close agreement is possible. However, one must make full anharmonic calculations in order to find the self-energy parts, and this, as we have seen from the expressions, involves long computations. A particular point raised by these arguments is that caution must be exercised when establishing the parameters of a dispersion law by empirical fitting. Unless the conditions are such that self energies are negligible—or unless the self energies are properly included in the expressions—the dispersion law will not be a good representation of the physical phonons.

It is instructive to find the explicit form of the renormalized energies. Following the procedure of Cowley[3] we take part of the anharmonic Hamiltonian and include it with the harmonic Hamiltonian. The two parts are then diagonalized to yield the renormalized frequencies. We add a term of the form

$$\frac{\hbar}{2}[\omega_T(\mathbf{k}j)\omega_T(\mathbf{k}j')]^{-1/2}R_T(\mathbf{k}jj')A_T(\mathbf{k}j)A_T(\mathbf{k}j') \tag{6.76a}$$

to the harmonic part, the R_T coefficients being adjustable to affect the renormalization. Thus for every self-energy bubble in Figure 6.5 there is an additional contribution

$$\frac{\beta h}{2}\{\omega_T(\mathbf{k}j)\omega_T(\mathbf{k}j')\}^{-1/2}G^0_{\mathbf{k}j}(\omega_p)_T R_T(\mathbf{k}jj')G^0_{\mathbf{k}j'}(\omega_p)_T \qquad (6.76b)$$

but by suitable choice of $R_T(\mathbf{k}jj')$ we can eliminate the self-energy bubble. If we write

$$R_T(\mathbf{k}jj') \equiv -\frac{2}{\beta h}\{\omega_T(\mathbf{k}j)\omega_T(\mathbf{k}j')\}^{1/2}S_p(\mathbf{k}jj')_T \qquad (6.77)$$

we have taken into account the whole of the Hermitian part of the anharmonic Hamiltonian, i.e. the anharmonic self energies have been included in the frequencies of the normal modes, which are given by the eigenvalues of the new dynamical matrix

$$\omega^2(\mathbf{k}j)\delta_{jj'} + R(\mathbf{k}jj'). \qquad (6.78)$$

The corresponding eigenvectors of (6.78) are the eigenvectors of the renormalized modes. We may use these renormalized values to calculate the Green's functions, but diagrams that include a self-energy insertion in any of the phonon lines must be omitted, since they have already been taken into account.

A simpler approximation is to write the free-phonon propagators in the Dyson equation (6.74b) in explicit form using equation (6.65) and to neglect all non-diagonal terms. Making the substitution we get

$$2\omega(\mathbf{k}j)\delta_{jj'} = \beta h \sum_{j''} \{\delta_{j''j}[\omega^2(\mathbf{k}j) + \omega_p^2] - 2\omega(\mathbf{k}j)S_p(\mathbf{k}jj'')\}G_{\mathbf{k}j''j'}(\omega_p). \qquad (6.79)$$

Hence, neglecting non-diagonal terms

$$G_{\mathbf{k}jj}(\omega_p) = \frac{2\omega(\mathbf{k}j)}{\beta h\{\omega^2(\mathbf{k}j) + \omega_p^2 - 2\omega(\mathbf{k}j)S_p(\mathbf{k}jj)\}} \qquad (6.80)$$

or, defining the quantity

$$\omega^2(\mathbf{k}j) - 2\omega(\mathbf{k}j)S_p(\mathbf{k}jj') \equiv \omega_T^2(\mathbf{k}j) \qquad (6.81)$$

the anharmonic Green's function is of the same form as equation (6.65) for the harmonic approximation. The validity of equation (6.81) as a definition of the mode energies of a non-interacting system will be discussed in Chapter 7 when thermodynamical applications of the results of this chapter are discussed.

If we write the self energy as a real and imaginary part [with signs chosen to make Δ a positive contribution to the renormalized frequencies, see equation (6.81)]

$$S_p(kjj') \equiv -\Delta_p(kjj') + i\Gamma_p(kjj') \qquad (6.82)$$

we find that the cubic term (second order in the interaction representation) contributes to both Δ and Γ, while the quartic term (first order) contributes to only Δ. Thus the quartic term does not affect the lifetime of the phonons.

The lowest-order contributions to the self energy are represented by the diagrams in Figures 6.2(b) and (c). Consider first $S_p^{(1)}(kjj')$ as given by equation (6.70). The sum over the integers p_1 may be written explicitly by noting from equation (6.53c) that

$$\sum_{p=-\infty}^{+\infty} G_{kj}^0(\omega_p) = G_{kj}^0(u = 0) \qquad (6.83)$$

and consequently, from equation (6.63c) with $u = 0$:

$$\sum_{p=-\infty}^{+\infty} G_{kj}^0(\omega_p) = 2n(kj) + 1. \qquad (6.84)$$

This is a useful general result, since the term on the left-hand side of equation (6.84) occurs for every instantaneous phonon (one that is created and absorbed at the same vertex). Thus it is a useful addition to the diagram rules of Section 6.7—in particular to rule [v(c)] on p. 196—that any instantaneous phonon kj contributes a factor $2n(kj) + 1$.

Using equations (5.20c) and (6.49) we find that $V^{(4)}$, as required in equation (6.70), is given by

$$V^{(4)}(-kj, kj', k_1 j_1, -k_1 j_1) = \frac{\hbar^2}{24N} \cdot \frac{\Phi^{(4)}(-kj, kj', k_1 j_1, -k_1 j_1)}{4\omega^{1/2}(kj)\omega^{1/2}(kj')\omega(k_1 j_1)} \qquad (6.85)$$

where we have used $\omega(k_1 j_1) = \omega(-k_1 j_1)$ and where $\Phi^{(4)}$ involves the polarization vectors of the modes in argument, the exponential factors in equation (5.20c) and fourth-order force constants; its explicit form is easily deducible from the discussion of Section 5.4. Thus, from equations (6.70), (6.84) and (6.85), we see that the quartic anharmonic term in the Hamiltonian contributes to the real part of the self energy:

$$\Delta_p^{(1)}(kjj') = \frac{\hbar^2}{8N} \frac{1}{[\omega(kj)\omega(kj')]^{1/2}} \sum_{k_1 j_1} \frac{2n(k_1 j_1) + 1}{\omega(k_1 j_1)} \Phi^{(4)}(-kj, kj', k_1 j_1, -k_1 j_1). \qquad (6.86)$$

The corresponding contribution from the cubic term is more complicated. Equation (6.71) may be written explicitly as for the quartic term by making use of equations (5.20b), (6.49) and (6.65), but first consider the sums over p_1 and p_2.

From the result (6.65), and abbreviating $\omega(\mathbf{k}_i j_i) \equiv \omega_i$

$$\sum_{p_1 p_2} G^0_{\mathbf{k}_1 j_1}(\omega_{p_1}) G^0_{\mathbf{k}_2 j_2}(\omega_{p_2}) \delta(p - p_1 - p_2)$$

$$= \frac{4\omega_1 \omega_2}{\beta^2 \hbar^2} \sum_{p_1 = -\infty}^{+\infty} \frac{1}{(\omega_{p_1}^2 + \omega_1^2)} \cdot \frac{1}{(\omega_p - \omega_{p_1})^2 + \omega_2^2} \qquad (6.87)$$

where the $\delta(p - p_1 - p_2)$ has been invoked [together with equation (6.53b)] to remove the p_2 summation. Phillips[11] has shown that an expression of this form can be written in terms of a contour integration

$$\sum_{p = -\infty}^{+\infty} f(i\omega_p) = \frac{\beta \hbar}{2\pi i} \int_C f(i\omega_p) \bar{n}(i\omega_p) \, \mathrm{d}(i\omega_p) \cdot \qquad (6.88)$$

where $\bar{n}(i\omega_p) \equiv (e^{i\beta\hbar\omega_p} - 1)^{-1}$, i.e. the boson mean occupation of a mode $i\omega_p$. The contour C is taken round the singularities of the function $f(i\omega_p)$ and thus is evaluated by the usual residue theorem for simple poles:

$$\int_C f(z) \, \mathrm{d}z = 2\pi i \sum_l [(z - z_l) f(z)]_{z_l} \qquad (6.89)$$

where z_l are the simple poles of $f(z)$. (For higher-order poles see Chapter 7, Note b.)

Result (6.84) is easily verified using equations (6.88) and (6.89) by replacing $f(i\omega_p)$ with $G^0_{\mathbf{k}j}(\omega_p)$. The function (6.87) may be written

$$\frac{4\omega_1 \omega_2}{\beta^2 \hbar^2} \sum_{p_1 = -\infty}^{+\infty} \frac{1}{(\omega_1 - i\omega_{p_1})(\omega_1 + i\omega_{p_1})}$$

$$\times \frac{1}{(\omega_2 - i(\omega_p - \omega_{p_1}))(\omega_2 + i(\omega_p - \omega_{p_1}))} \qquad (6.90)$$

which has poles at

$$i\omega_{p_1} = \pm \omega_1 \qquad (6.91a)$$

and

$$i\omega_{p_1} = i\omega_p \pm \omega_2 \qquad (6.91b)$$

Thus with $f(i\omega_p)$ replaced by $G^0_{\mathbf{k}_1 j_1}(\omega_{p_1}) G^0_{\mathbf{k}_2 j_2}(\omega_p - \omega_{p_1})$ [as given by equation (6.90)] the sum of the four residues yields

$$\frac{4\omega_1 \omega_2}{\beta \hbar} \left[\frac{\bar{n}_1}{2\omega_1} \cdot \frac{1}{(\omega_2 - i\omega_p + \omega_1)} \cdot \frac{1}{(\omega_2 + i\omega_p - \omega_1)} \right.$$

$$+ \frac{\bar{n}_1 + 1}{2\omega_1} \cdot \frac{1}{(\omega_2 - i\omega_p - \omega_1)} \cdot \frac{1}{(\omega_2 + i\omega_p + \omega_1)}$$

$$+ \frac{\bar{n}_2}{(\omega_1 - i\omega_p - \omega_2)} \cdot \frac{1}{(\omega_1 + i\omega_p + \omega_2)} \cdot \frac{1}{2\omega_2}$$

$$+ \frac{\bar{n}_2 + 1}{(\omega_1 - i\omega_p + \omega_2)} \cdot \frac{1}{(\omega_1 + i\omega_p - \omega_2)} \cdot \frac{1}{2\omega_2} \Bigg] \qquad (6.92)$$

where we have used the relation

$$\bar{n}(-\omega) = -[\bar{n}(\omega) + 1] \qquad (6.93a)$$

in the second and fourth terms. In the third and fourth terms note that, since $e^{i\beta\hbar\omega_p} = 1$

$$\bar{n}(i\omega_p + \omega_2) = \bar{n}(\omega_2) \qquad (6.93b)$$

and

$$\bar{n}(i\omega_p - \omega_2) = -[\bar{n}(\omega_2) + 1]. \qquad (6.93c)$$

Result (6.92) is easily simplified by the following observation. There are only four distinct terms in the denominators

$$D_1 \equiv \omega_1 + \omega_2 - i\omega_p \qquad (6.94a)$$

$$D_2 \equiv \omega_1 - \omega_2 + i\omega_p \qquad (6.94b)$$

$$D_3 \equiv \omega_1 + \omega_2 + i\omega_p \qquad (6.94c)$$

$$D_4 \equiv \omega_1 - \omega_2 - i\omega_p. \qquad (6.94d)$$

Hence expression (6.92) becomes

$$\frac{1}{\beta\hbar} \Bigg[-\frac{2\bar{n}_1\omega_2}{D_1 D_4} - \frac{2(\bar{n}_1 + 1)\omega_2}{D_2 D_3} + \frac{2\bar{n}_2\omega_1}{D_4 D_3} + \frac{2(\bar{n}_2 + 1)\omega_1}{D_1 D_2} \Bigg] \qquad (6.95)$$

which is split easily into partial fractions to yield

$$\sum_{p_1 p_2} G^0_{k_1 j_1}(\omega_{p_1}) G^0_{k_2 j_2}(\omega_{p_2}) \delta(p - p_1 - p_2) = \frac{1}{\beta\hbar} \Bigg[\frac{\bar{n}_1 + \bar{n}_2 + 1}{D_1} + \frac{\bar{n}_2 - \bar{n}_1}{D_2}$$

$$+ \frac{\bar{n}_1 + \bar{n}_2 + 1}{D_3} + \frac{\bar{n}_2 - \bar{n}_1}{D_4} \Bigg]. \qquad (6.96)$$

Now, as before (Section 6.6), transforming to a continuous variable such that $f(\omega) = f(i\omega_p)$ when $\omega = i\omega_p$, i.e. writing $i\omega_p \to \omega + i\varepsilon$ where $\varepsilon \to +0$. For a function of this form we have

$$\lim_{\varepsilon \to +0} \frac{1}{(x \pm i\varepsilon)} = \frac{1}{(x)_p} \mp i\pi\delta(x) \qquad (6.97)$$

where the subscript $\mathbf{p}$ indicates the principal part and $\delta(x)$ is the Dirac delta function. Applying this to each of the four terms in expression (6.96) and using the result in equation (6.71), we find an expression for $\Delta_p^{(2)}(\mathbf{k}jj')$

$$\Delta_p^{(2)}(\mathbf{k}jj') = \frac{-\beta\hbar^2}{16N}\frac{1}{[\omega(\mathbf{k}j)\omega(\mathbf{k}j')]^{1/2}}$$

$$\times \sum_{\substack{\mathbf{k}_1 j_1 \\ \mathbf{k}_2 j_2}} \left\{ \frac{\Phi^{(3)}(-\mathbf{k}j, \mathbf{k}_1 j_1, \mathbf{k}_2 j_2)\Phi^{(3)}(\mathbf{k}j', -\mathbf{k}_1 j_1, -\mathbf{k}_2 j_2)}{\omega(\mathbf{k}_1 j_1)\omega(\mathbf{k}_2 j_2)} \right.$$

$$\times \Delta(\mathbf{k}_1 + \mathbf{k}_2 - \mathbf{k})\left[\frac{\bar{n}_1 + \bar{n}_2 + 1}{(\omega_1 + \omega_2 - \omega)_\mathbf{p}} + \frac{\bar{n}_2 - \bar{n}_1}{(\omega_1 - \omega_2 + \omega)_\mathbf{p}}\right.$$

$$\left.\left.+ \frac{\bar{n}_1 + \bar{n}_2 + 1}{(\omega_1 + \omega_2 + \omega)_\mathbf{p}} + \frac{\bar{n}_2 - \bar{n}_1}{(\omega_1 - \omega_2 - \omega)_\mathbf{p}}\right]\right\}. \tag{6.98}$$

There is another factor that must be taken into account when computing the renormalized frequencies—the effect of thermal expansion, which, together with the anharmonic self energy, is temperature dependent. The thermal-expansion contribution to the self energy is represented by Figure 6.6.

$$\overline{\text{k}j \qquad\qquad\qquad \bullet \qquad\qquad\qquad \text{k}j'}$$

Figure 6.6

The expansion may be treated as a strain, and is often called the 'thermal strain', the corresponding perturbation being described by a series expansion in terms of the strain parameters. If there is no other (external) source of strain we have

$$H_{\text{strain}} = \sum_{\alpha\beta}\sum_{\mathbf{k}jj'} V_{\alpha\beta}(\mathbf{k}j, -\mathbf{k}j')A(\mathbf{k}j)A(\mathbf{k}j')u_{\alpha\beta}^T + O(u_{\alpha\beta}^T u_{\alpha\beta}^T) \tag{6.99}$$

where $u_{\alpha\beta}^T$ is the thermal strain, and α and β are cartesian coordinates. This introduces an additional term to Δ

$$\Delta^S(\mathbf{k}jj') = \frac{2}{\hbar}\sum_{\alpha\beta} V_{\alpha\beta}(\mathbf{k}j, -\mathbf{k}j')u_{\alpha\beta}^T. \tag{6.100}$$

Thus to second order we have

$$\Delta_p(\mathbf{k}jj') = \Delta_p^{(1)}(\mathbf{k}jj') + \Delta_p^{(2)}(\mathbf{k}jj') + \Delta^S(\mathbf{k}jj') \tag{6.101}$$

where $\Delta_p^{(1)}$ is given by equation (6.86), $\Delta_p^{(2)}$ is given by equation (6.98) and Δ^S is given by (6.100).

Equation (6.101), together with equation (6.81), and noting equation (6.82), may be used to obtain the values of the renormalized phonon frequencies. There are, of course, problems associated with the computation of the principal parts; however, these must be dealt with in the light of specific problems. Applications of these results are discussed in Chapter 7.

6.9 Phonon lifetimes

We have seen that there is no imaginary part associated with the first-order interaction terms. However the second-order term has an imaginary part, which is found using equations (6.97), (6.71) and (6.96). We see that, to second order

$$\Gamma_p(\mathbf{k}jj') = \Gamma_p^{(1)}(\mathbf{k}jj') + \Gamma_p^{(2)}(\mathbf{k}jj') \tag{6.102}$$

where

$$\Gamma_p^{(1)}(\mathbf{k}jj') = 0$$

and

$$\Gamma_p^{(2)}(\mathbf{k}jj') = \frac{\pi\hbar}{16N[\omega(\mathbf{k}j)\omega(\mathbf{k}j')]^{1/2}}$$

$$\times \sum_{\substack{\mathbf{k}_1 j_1 \\ \mathbf{k}_1 j_2}} \left\{ \frac{\Phi^{(3)}(-\mathbf{k}j, \mathbf{k}_1 j_1, \mathbf{k}_2 j_2)\Phi^{(3)}(\mathbf{k}j', -\mathbf{k}_1 j_1, -\mathbf{k}_2 j_2)}{\omega(\mathbf{k}_1 j_1)\omega(\mathbf{k}_2 j_2)} \right.$$

$$\times \Delta(\mathbf{k}_1 + \mathbf{k}_2 - \mathbf{k})[\bar{n}_1 + \bar{n}_2 + 1)\delta(\omega_1 + \omega_2 - \omega)$$

$$- (\bar{n}_2 - \bar{n}_1)\delta(\omega_1 - \omega_2 + \omega) - (\bar{n}_1 + \bar{n}_2 + 1)\delta(\omega_1 + \omega_2 + \omega)$$

$$\left. + (\bar{n}_2 - \bar{n}_1)\delta(\omega_1 - \omega_2 - \omega)] \right\}. \tag{6.103}$$

In deriving the last equation care must be taken with the signs; with $+\omega$ (i.e. $+i\varepsilon$) in the denominator, the minus sign in equation (6.97) is applicable; with $-\omega$ (i.e. $-i\varepsilon$) the plus sign is applicable.

Now Γ represents the inverse lifetime of the phonon $\mathbf{k}j$. It is the magnitude of this quantity relative to the Hermitian part that determines the validity of a pseudoharmonic model. Equation (6.103) indicates that this cubic contribution to the phonon width is governed by the two-phonon density of states. If Γ is small (even though it is finite) compared with Δ, the model of a set of independent phonons with renormalized frequencies and each with its own finite lifetime is a good representation of the crystal for many purposes. Some of the finite-lifetime effects have been discussed in Chapter 5 and we shall look at them again in Chapter 8.

We have only considered the two lowest-order contributions to the anharmonic self energies. The diagrams of Figure 6.7 indicate some of the higher orders that arise from the cubic and quartic terms of the Hamiltonian.

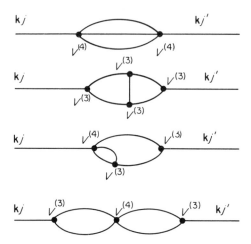

Figure 6.7   Some higher-order contributions to the phonon self energies arising from cubic and quartic anharmonicities. These are all of order α^4, where α is an order parameter (see Section 5.8), whereas Figures 6.2(b) and (c) are of order α^2

There are, of course, other scattering mechanisms that limit the lifetimes and that modify the observed mode energies. Phonons may interact with mobile electrons, with magnetic excitations, with impurities, or with other crystal excitations such as excitons. We usually aim to work under conditions such that one scattering process is dominant and all the others may be neglected. Here we have been concerned with the interactions of a phonon with other phonons.

6.10   Summary

The **response** of a system to an applied force depends on both the properties of the system and the nature of the force. A response function whose **singularities** yield the resonances or normal modes of the system can be defined. **Interaction** between the normal modes results in a **broadening** of the resonances and hence a **damping** of the modes.

Correlation functions that describe the 'effect' at one part of a system due to a 'cause' that happened at another part at an earlier time may be defined. In the language of state functions, these correlations are the **probability** of finding a system in a state $\psi(\mathbf{r}, t)$ when it was in a state $\psi(\mathbf{r}', t')$ where $t > t'$. These correlation functions may be formulated in the form of a **Green's function**, and formal relations may be developed between Green's functions that represent the **time development** of the system and those that represent the

thermodynamic properties of the system. These formal relations enable us to discuss interaction effects in terms of **thermodynamic** Green's functions. The **spectral distribution function**, which is analogous to the response function, describes the physical properties of our crystalline solid.

We invoke a similarity between the analysis of **temperature** and **imaginary time** to exploit the periodicity properties of the **one-phonon Green's function**. It is convenient to work almost entirely in the corresponding **Fourier space**. The **Fourier transform** of the one-phonon Green's function is often called the **phonon propagator**. The **free**-phonon propagator is that for a **harmonic** Hamiltonian. Higher-order terms in the Hamiltonian lead to interactions, and a general perturbation series is developed using the **interaction representation**. The terms of this infinite series may be classified and evaluated by means of a **diagram technique**. Diagrams fall into two groups: **proper** and **improper** diagrams. Improper diagrams are constructed of proper diagrams that are joined by a line representing a single phonon. The sum of all diagrams is given by **Dyson's equation**.

The interaction terms in the Hamiltonian give rise to a phonon **self energy**, so called because the Hermitian part of the contribution of a diagram modifies the energy of the phonon. This **renormalized** energy corresponds to the observed energy. The imaginary part predicts a **finite lifetime** of the phonon. A **pseudoharmonic** model, in which the anharmonic self energies are included to renormalize the modes and give each a finite lifetime, and then to regard the phonons as independent, is sometimes employed.

Finally, the effect of **thermal expansion** in modifying the phonon energies must not be omitted. We have distinguished between a **quasiharmonic** approximation in which the frequencies change **only** through the thermal expansion and a **pseudoharmonic** approximation in which the renormalization also includes the **anharmonic self energies**.

Chapter notes

[a] The method is equally applicable to fermions, but it is not our intention to present a complete account of the Green's-function method. Generality may be achieved without difficulty, but the accompanying 'ifs', 'buts', 'in the case ofs' and '$\pm$s' can only add to the reader's problems. The general references quoted in the text treat fermions and bosons. Reluctantly, but along with the spirit of the rest of this book, we must forego the interesting properties of Fermi systems.

[b] We can show that $af(v) = f(1 + v)a$ where v is the number operator a^+a, and $f(v)$ is any function that may be expressed in powers of v. Consider $f(v) = v^n$, where n is an integer,

$$av^n = av^{n-1}a^+a$$
$$= (aa^+)^na$$
$$= (1 + a^+a)^na \quad \text{[from equation (3.5)]}$$
$$= (1 + v)^na \quad \text{Q.E.D. for any integer } n.$$

In equation (6.34), $N = \sum_{r''} v(r'', t)$ and only the term $r'' = r$ does not commute with $a(r, t)$.

[c] Since $av^n = (v + 1)^n a$ where $v = a^+ a$, and H is given by equation (6.43)

$$a_k(0)\, e^{-iHt/\hbar} = e^{-i\sum_{k' \neq k}(v_{k'} + \frac{1}{2})\omega_{k'} t} \cdot e^{-i(v_k + \frac{1}{2} + 1)\omega_k t} a_k(0)$$

$$= e^{-iHt/\hbar}\, e^{-i\omega_k t} a_k(0).$$

Hence equation (6.44) follows from this result substituted into the transformation (6.42).

[d] Expression (6.63c) is obtained quite simply from equation (6.63b). Using equation (6.11) and transforming from t to u, we have

$$G_k(u) = \langle [e^{H_0 u} a^+_{-k}(0)\, e^{-H_0 u} a_{-k}(0) + e^{H_0 u} a_k(0)\, e^{-H_0 u} a_k^+(0)] \rangle$$

with

$$H_0 = \sum_k (a_k^+ a_k + \tfrac{1}{2})\hbar\omega_k = \sum_k (n_k + \tfrac{1}{2})\hbar\omega_k$$

Using note b, this becomes

$$G_k(u) = \langle [e^{n - k\hbar\omega - ku} \cdot e^{-(n - k - 1)\hbar\omega - ku} a^+_{-k}(0) a_{-k}(0) + e^{n_k \hbar\omega_k u} \cdot e^{-(n_k + 1)\hbar\omega_k u} a_k(0) a_k^+(0)] \rangle$$

$$= e^{u\hbar\omega_k} n_k + e^{-u\hbar\omega_k}(n_k + 1).$$

References

1. Maradudin, A. A., and Fein, A. E., *Phys. Rev.*, **128**, 2589–2608 (1962).
2. Alekseev, A. I., *Soviet Physics, USPEKHI*, **4**, 23–50 (1961).
3. Cowley, R. A., *Adv. in Phys.*, **12**, 421–480 (1963).
4. Kwok, P. C. K., *Solid State Physics*, **20**, 213–303 (1967).
5. Turner, R. E., and Parry, W. E., *Rep. Prog. Phys.*, **27**, 23–52 (1964).
6. Kadanoff, L. P., and Baym, G., *Quantum Statistical Mechanics*, Benjamin, New York, 1962.
7. Matsubara, T., *Progr. Theor. Phys.*, **14**, 351–378 (1955).
8. Zubarev, D. N., *Soviet Physics, USPEKHI*, **3**, 320–345 (1960).
9. Baym, G., and Mermin, N. D., *J. Math. Phys.*, **2**, 232–234 (1961).
10. Leibfried, G., and Ludwig, W., *Solid State Physics*, **12**, 275–444 (1961).
11. Phillips, E. G., *Functions of a Complex Variable*, Oliver and Boyd, London, 1956.

7

A Lattice Dynamical Treatment of . . .

7.1 Introduction

The topics included in this chapter have been chosen so as to introduce a range of phenomena that involve lattice dynamics in their interpretation. It would be rash to claim that any such list could be complete; no attempt has been made to make it complete. It is hoped that the selection is representative. Some phenomena are omitted because they belong more logically in the final chapter.

The approach adopted inevitably imposes severe limitations on the amount of detail in each section. The alternative, to select a single application of lattice dynamics and treat it more fully, merely repeats what is already available in reviews and original papers. The reader who is interested in detail in a specialist topic must ultimately look at the original reports; here we offer only a thumbnail-sketch treatment of each topic. To redress the balance, each section contains references indicating where a more complete discussion may be found.

7.2 Phonon energies and lifetimes

In Sections 6.8 and 6.9 we have derived expressions for the energies of physical phonons (as in distinction to harmonic-model phonons) and for their lifetimes. For situations when the harmonic normal-mode frequencies and a suitable representation of the principal value in equation (6.98) can be found, these new frequencies and the lifetimes may be calculated. Maradudin and Fein (Reference 1 in Chapter 6) applied the expressions of Section 6.8 and 6.9 to a face-centred cubic monatomic lattice with central-force interactions between only nearest neighbours. (Referring to Chapter 2, we see this is a model used to represent the solidified inert gases.) As a further simplification they have carried out their evaluation for two limiting cases: (a) at absolute zero (all $n_i = 0$) and (b) at high temperatures ($n_i = k_B T/\hbar \omega_i$). Maradudin and Felin used experimental parameters that were appropriate to lead (despite the inapplicability of the model) since it was the most reliable data readily available at the time. The high-temperature and absolute-zero expressions for equations (6.101) and (6.102) are easily obtained and are not quoted here. The numerical results for lead are of little interest other than their significance as an actual calculation. It was not proposed as a realistic model of lead, and no fair comparison with experiment can be made. However, in tackling the problem of explicit calculation, Maradudin and Fein dealt with some important details which serve as a guide to subsequent calculations. Leaving aside the more obvious point of the lattice dynamical model, they report helpfully on their considerations of the **k** summation involved and separate the umklapp and normal contributions; they discuss an unsuccessful, as well as a successful, representation of the principal value function; their results provide order-of-magnitude estimates of phonon widths and shifts.

The representation of the Dirac delta functions and the Cauchy principal value used by Maradudin and Fein and Zubarev[1] were

$$\delta(x) = \lim_{\varepsilon \to +0} \frac{1}{\pi} \frac{\varepsilon}{x^2 + \varepsilon^2} \tag{7.1a}$$

$$\left(\frac{1}{x}\right)_{\mathbf{p}} = \lim_{\varepsilon \to +0} \frac{x}{x^2 + \varepsilon^2} \tag{7.1b}$$

ε being a positive infinitesimal. For numerical calculations ε must be chosen to be small so that the limits in equations (7.1) are meaningfully computed, but it must be large enough to embrace several values of x. This choice becomes a compromise between the validity of the limit and the computational problems of including large numbers of points in **k** space. Generalization of the criterion for choosing a value of ε is dangerous. New calculations should aways be preceded by preliminary tests to justify a particular choice of ε. The work discussed used a value $\varepsilon = 10^{-3}$ for summation over 6912 points in the Brillouin zone. In special cases an extrapolation of results for several values of ε may be used to allow ε to approach zero.

Cowley[2] has used the same method to compute Δ and Γ for sodium iodide and potassium bromide represented by the Kellerman model (see Figure 7.1 and Appendix F).

The cubic anharmonicity contributes real and imaginary parts to the self energy, and Cowley's results are shown in Figure 7.2. The dotted curve in Figure 7.2(a) shows the results calculated by an alternative method to using the representations (7.1). The method is based on a series expansion in terms of Legendre polynomials, and would be a fast convenient method of computation once the polynomial series is known. However this requires unreasonably long calculations, since large numbers of points in **k** space must be included to achieve acceptable accuracy. There does not seem to be any development of this approach as yet.

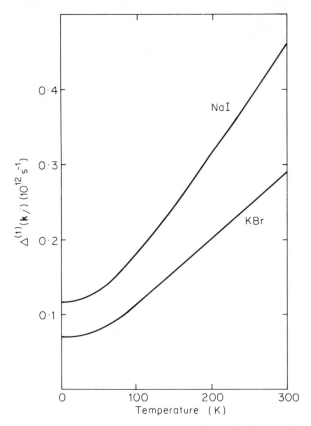

Figure 7.1   The temperature dependence of the quartic anharmonic self energy for $j = j'$ $[S_p^{(1)}(\mathbf{k}j) = \Delta^{(1)}(\mathbf{k}j)]$. Reproduced, with permission, from Cowley, R. A., *Adv. in Phys.*, **12**, 421–480 (1963)

We can see from the general expression that the first-order shifts of the frequencies due to anharmonic self-energy terms do not depend on the probe frequency ω, whereas both shift and lifetime arising from the cubic term do. In any experiment to observe lineshape and shift of the centre of the peak, ω is the frequency of the external field. We have not discussed the physical significance of ω up to this point, but it will become clear from the following sections and in Chapter 8. From Figures 7.2 we see that the shifts and lifetimes $\omega^{(2)}$ and $\Gamma^{(2)}$ are strongly dependent on ω in the two alkali halides shown. This yields a lifetime and a renormalized phonon frequency which is dependent on the probe frequency, and is demonstrated in the work by Cowley and

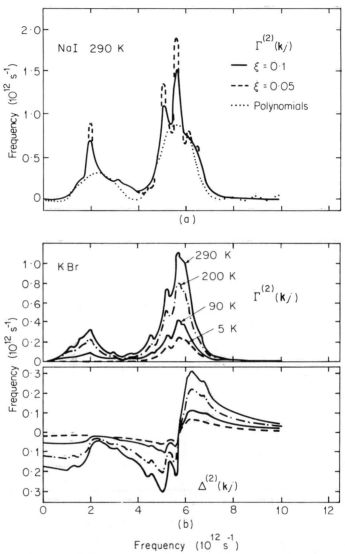

Figure 7.2 (a) The inverse lifetime $\Gamma^{(2)}(\mathbf{k}j)$ of the transverse optic mode of sodium iodide as dependent on the representation of the Dirac delta function. (b) The inverse lifetime and frequency shift $\Gamma^{(2)}(\mathbf{k}j)$ and $\Delta^{(2)}(\mathbf{k}j)$ of the transverse optic mode of potassium bromide as a function of ω with $\varepsilon = 0.1$. The results shown in these figures contain a minor computational error. This has affected the fine detail of the peaks but the overall shape is substantially correct. A revised version of part of these calculations appears in a later paper by Cowley (see p. 137 of Reference 31 of Chapter 4). (a) and (b) are reproduced, with permission, from Cowley, R. A., *Adv. in Phys.*, **12**, 421–480 (1963)

Cowley[3,4] on neutron scattering that is reproduced in Figure 7.3. Raunio[5] also has made measurements of phonon width in NaCl, KCl and RbCl. A recent review by Kwok (Reference 4 in Chapter 6) provides a comprehensive collection of the detailed expressions that we have been unable to include here.

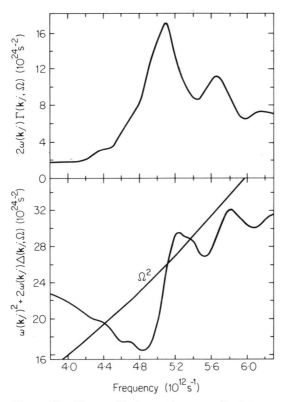

Figure 7.3   Phonon lifetime and renormalized frequency in NaI at 300 K.[3,4] (The intersections of Ω^2 and the real part of the self energy give the quasiharmonic frequencies. Arrows indicate the frequencies at which there are peaks in the spectral function.) Reproduced from Cowley, E. R., and Cowley, R. A., *Proc. Roy. Soc.*, **A287**, 259–280 (1965), by permission of the Council of The Royal Society, London

7.3   Thermodynamics

Suppose now, instead of considering the interaction of the normal modes with some probe, we consider a crystal in equilibrium and relate the results of Chapter 6 to the thermodynamical properties of the lattice. The two lowest-order diagrams, Figures 6.2(b) and (c) no longer have external lines, since each process must leave the crystal in equilibrium. Thus the phonons $\mathbf{k}j$ and $\mathbf{k}j'$ must be identical, and the corresponding line must enter and leave the vertex as in Figures 7.4.

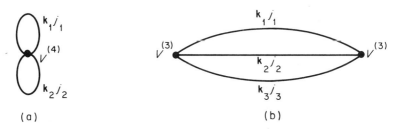

(a)   (b)

Figure 7.4   Lowest-order terms to be included when calculating the thermo-dynamic properties of an anharmonic crystal

According to the diagram rules of Section 6.7, and noting that there are two instantaneous phonons in Figure 7.4(a), we have a contribution from the quartic term of

$$-3\beta \sum_{\substack{\mathbf{k}_1 j_1 \\ \mathbf{k}_2 j_2}} V^{(4)}(\mathbf{k}_1 j_1, -\mathbf{k}_1 j_1, \mathbf{k}_2 j_2, -\mathbf{k}_2 j_2)(2n_1 + 1)(2n_2 + 1). \quad (7.2)$$

By the same arguments as in Section 4.4 [in particular equations (4.52b) and (4.50)] this contributes

$$F_4 = 3 \sum_{\substack{\mathbf{k}_1 j_1 \\ \mathbf{k}_2 j_2}} V^{(4)}(\mathbf{k}_1 j_1, -\mathbf{k}_1 j_1, \mathbf{k}_2 j_2, -\mathbf{k}_2 j_2)(2n_1 + 1)(2n_2 + 1) \quad (7.3)$$

which is identical to equation (5.24b) if we write $V^{(4)}$ explicitly. Similarly, the cubic term evaluated by applying the diagram rules to Figure 7.4(b) yields the result given explicitly by equation (5.24a). Note that the pairing factor for these thermodynamic diagrams differs from the diagrams of Chapter 6. The pairing factor here is the same as in Section 5.4.

The pseudoharmonic approximation discussed in Section 6.8 does not provide a good description of the thermodynamic quantities. These are averages of the effects of all phonons, and, if anharmonic effects are significant, it is not valid to neglect the interaction between phonons and replace the harmonic frequencies by the renormalized values at a particular temperature. A simple illustration of this is that the sum of the renormalized energies of the excited phonons is not equal to the total energy of the lattice. Use of the pseudoharmonic approximation is a procedure to include self-energy effects when observing single phonons.

Higher-order diagrams than those shown in Figure 7.4 contribute to the thermodynamic properties, especially at high temperatures. However, this is a matter of detail and their inclusion is a matter of applying the general rules that we have formulated. The diagram technique can be applied to any order process and to include all kinds of cross interactions between the phonon lines in any diagram. The complications of Section 5.8 are all included in this more elegant scheme.

When the expressions for the free energy have been derived to the required order, the thermodynamical properties such as specific heat and entropy may be obtained using the standard relations [equations (4.59) and (4.69)] as in Chapter 4. Usually analytical differentiation produces expressions that are too complex to yield to direct evaluation, and resort must be made to numerical methods. It is quite obvious from the free-energy expression that even a single evaluation of this is lengthy owing to the multiple $\mathbf{k}$ summations. Nevertheless the literature contains many reports of such calculations and (not surprisingly) many attempts to avoid the direct evaluation by approximations. Each of these appears to be limited to the conditions and to the model employed, and this is not the place to catalogue them.

7.4 Thermal expansion

In Section 4.6 we discussed the thermal expansion of a solid in a general qualitative manner. To develop an adequate analytical description we must follow the method of Born and Huang.[5] The correct procedure is to treat the thermal expansion of the crystal as any other external strain, and then to consider the normal modes of the strained lattice. This requires a Taylor-series expansion for the potential energy in terms of the displacements due to strain and those due to the vibrations.

If $u_\alpha\begin{pmatrix} l \\ \kappa \end{pmatrix}$ represents the α component of the displacement of the κth atom of the lth unit cell due to a homogeneous strain (i.e. one that does not destroy the perfect lattice structure), we can write

$$u_\alpha\begin{pmatrix} l \\ \kappa \end{pmatrix} = u_\alpha(\kappa) + \sum_\beta u_{\alpha\beta} r_\beta\begin{pmatrix} l \\ \kappa \end{pmatrix} \tag{7.4}$$

where $r_\beta\begin{pmatrix} l \\ \kappa \end{pmatrix}$ are the components of the position vector of the atom $\begin{pmatrix} l \\ \kappa \end{pmatrix}$ and $u_\alpha(\kappa)$ are the small strains within each unit cell which may differ from those given by the second term. If we are interested in only very small strains [$u_\alpha(\kappa) \ll a$ and $u_{\alpha\beta} \ll 1$] the theory of elasticity may be adequately described in terms of these parameters. However Born and Huang have shown that when higher than second-order terms are significant, it is necessary to use the more general parameters

$$\bar{u}_\alpha(\kappa) = u_\alpha(\kappa) + \sum_\beta u_{\beta\alpha} u_\beta(\kappa) \tag{7.5a}$$

and

$$\bar{u}_{\alpha\beta} = \tfrac{1}{2}(u_{\alpha\beta} + u_{\beta\alpha} + \sum_\gamma u_{\alpha\gamma} u_{\gamma\beta}). \tag{7.5b}$$

Moreover they show that these parameters provide an adequate description of **finite** strains. However these cannot be used immediately to formulate our problem, since the Hamiltonian cannot be written as a function of the $\bar{u}_{\alpha\beta}$. Initially we must expand the crystal potential energy in terms of $u_{\alpha\beta}$ and the displacements due to the normal modes. Representing the latter by the $A(\mathbf{k}j)$ of equation (6.49), we can expand the potential energy of the crystal in the form

$$\Phi = \sum_{\alpha\beta} \Phi_{\alpha\beta} u_{\alpha\beta} + \frac{1}{2} \sum_{\alpha\beta\gamma\delta} \Phi_{\alpha\beta\gamma\delta} u_{\alpha\beta} u_{\gamma\delta} + \cdots \tag{7.6a}$$

where

$$\Phi_{\alpha\beta} = \sum_{\mathbf{k}j} V^{(2)}_{\alpha\beta}(\mathbf{k}j) A(\mathbf{k}j) + \sum_{\substack{\mathbf{k}_1\mathbf{k}_2 \\ j_1 j_2}} V^{(3)}_{\alpha\beta}(\mathbf{k}_1 j_1, \mathbf{k}_2 j_2) A(\mathbf{k}_1 j_1) A(\mathbf{k}_2 j_2) + \cdots \tag{7.6b}$$

and

$$\Phi_{\alpha\beta\gamma\delta} = V^{(2)}_{\alpha\beta\gamma\delta} + \sum_{\mathbf{k}j} V^{(3)}_{\alpha\beta\gamma\delta}(\mathbf{k}j) A(\mathbf{k}j) + \cdots. \tag{7.6c}$$

Notice that the order of the coupling coefficient is given by the sum of the orders of the strain parameters $u_{\alpha\beta}$ and the normal-mode coordinates $A(\mathbf{k}j)$. The form of $V^{(n)}$ is similar to the coefficients of $q_1 q_2 \cdots q_n$ in the expansion (5.20). However the coefficients now couple static strains to the normal-mode displacements as well as the coupling between different vibrational displacements. The explicit expressions for $V^{(n)}$ are given by eliminating the $\mathbf{k}$-dependent parts of equation (5.20) where the coupling is to a static strain. The notation adopted by Born and Huang is to replace the irrelevant $\mathbf{k}j$ label by a symbol ——. Thus the coefficients in equations (7.6b) and (7.6c) are

$$V^{(2)}_{\alpha\beta}(\mathbf{k}j) = \left(\frac{N\hbar}{2\omega(0j)}\right)^{1/2} \Phi_{\alpha\beta}\begin{pmatrix} 0 \\ j \end{pmatrix} \tag{7.7a}$$

$$V^{(3)}_{\alpha\beta\gamma\delta}(\mathbf{k}j) = \left(\frac{N\hbar}{2\omega(0j)}\right)^{1/2} \Phi_{\alpha\beta\gamma\delta}\begin{pmatrix} 0 \\ j \end{pmatrix}. \tag{7.7b}$$

These describe the relative displacements of atoms within a unit cell; $\mathbf{k}$ goes to zero in the coupling parameters, since they are linear in $A(\mathbf{k}j)$ and zero $\mathbf{k}$ gives the only non-zero contribution after summation.

$$V^{(2)}_{\alpha\beta\gamma\delta} = \Phi_{\alpha\beta\gamma\delta}(\text{——}) \tag{7.7c}$$

$$V^{(3)}_{\alpha\beta}(\mathbf{k}_1 j_1, \mathbf{k}_2 j_2) = \left(\frac{\hbar^2}{4\omega(\mathbf{k}j)\omega(\mathbf{k}j')}\right)^{1/2} \Phi_{\alpha\beta}\begin{pmatrix} \mathbf{k} & -\mathbf{k} \\ j & j' \end{pmatrix}. \tag{7.7d}$$

In equation (7.7d), $\mathbf{k}_1 + \mathbf{k}_2 = 0$ yields the only non-zero contribution, since the term is second order in $A(\mathbf{k}j)$.

Following pages 326–327 of Reference 1, we can describe the response of a crystal to a deformation in terms of the density matrix [equation (4.37) with $\alpha = 0$]. Using equations (4.35) and (4.37), namely

$$\langle O \rangle = \text{Tr}\,\{O\rho\} \tag{7.8a}$$

where the density matrix ρ is

$$\rho = Z^{-1}\,e^{-\beta H} \tag{7.8b}$$

$$Z = \text{Tr}\,\{e^{-\beta H}\} \tag{7.8c}$$

and is repeated here for convenience. Now, if a perturbation, say H'_t, is introduced, the system will respond so that

$$\langle O(t) \rangle = \text{Tr}\,\{O\rho(t)\} \tag{7.9}$$

where the time development of $\rho(t)$ is described by the standard equation of motion

$$i\dot{\rho}(t) = [H + H'_t, \rho(t)]. \tag{7.10}$$

Assuming that the perturbation is small, we may write

$$\rho(t) = \rho + \Delta\rho(t) \tag{7.11}$$

and substitute this into equation (7.10). Neglecting products of small terms $[H'_t \Delta\rho(t)]$ and noting that

$$\frac{d\rho}{dt} = [H, \rho] = 0 \tag{7.12}$$

we find that

$$i\Delta\dot{\rho}(t) = [H, \Delta\rho(t)] + [H'_t, \rho] \tag{7.13}$$

subject to the boundary condition $\Delta\rho(-\infty) = 0$. Multiplying both sides of the equation by $e^{iHt/\hbar}$ from the left and by $e^{-iHt/\hbar}$ from the right we may write

$$i\Delta\dot{\rho}_H(t) = e^{iHt/\hbar}[H'_t, \rho]\,e^{-iHt/\hbar} \tag{7.14}$$

where

$$\Delta\rho_H(t) = e^{iHt/\hbar}\Delta\rho(t)\,e^{-iHt/\hbar} \tag{7.15}$$

Integration of (7.14) yields

$$i\hbar\Delta\rho_H(t) = \int_{-\infty}^{t} e^{iH\tau/\hbar}[H'_\tau, \rho]\,e^{-iH\tau/\hbar}\,d\tau \tag{7.16}$$

and hence, from equation (7.15)

$$\Delta\rho(t) = \frac{1}{i\hbar}\int_{-\infty}^{t} e^{iH(\tau-t)/\hbar}[H'_\tau, \rho]\,e^{-iH(\tau-t)/\hbar}\,d\tau. \tag{7.17}$$

Using this result, together with equation (7.11) in equation (7.9), and noting that

$$\mathrm{Tr}\,\{O(t)[H'_\tau(\tau),\rho]\} = \mathrm{Tr}\,\{[O(t),H'_\tau(\tau)]\rho\}$$
$$= \langle[O(t),H'_\tau(\tau)]\rangle \tag{7.18}$$

we get

$$\langle O(t)\rangle = \langle O\rangle + \frac{1}{i\hbar}\int_{-\infty}^{t}\langle[O(t),H'_\tau(\tau)]\rangle\,d\tau. \tag{7.19}$$

The averages are to be taken over the unperturbed states, and the operators are of the Heisenberg form, i.e.

$$O(t) \equiv e^{iHt/\hbar}O\,e^{-iHt/\hbar} \tag{7.20a}$$

$$H'_\tau(\tau) \equiv e^{iH\tau/\hbar}H'_\tau\,e^{-iH\tau/\hbar}. \tag{7.20b}$$

Now introduce the form of the perturbation. If it is periodic, we may express it as a Fourier sum which goes to zero at minus infinity:

$$H'_t = \sum_\omega e^{\varepsilon t}\,e^{-i\omega t}V_\omega \tag{7.21}$$

ε being a positive infinitesimal. Substituting this into equation (7.19) and extending the upper limit to infinity by the introduction of $\eta(t-\tau)$ as defined by equation (6.20),

$$\langle O(t)\rangle = \langle O\rangle + \frac{1}{i\hbar}\sum_\omega\int_{-\infty}^{+\infty}\eta(t-\tau)\langle[O(t),V_\omega]\rangle\,e^{(\varepsilon-i\omega)\tau}\,d\tau \tag{7.22}$$

which may be written in terms of the Fourier transform of the retarded Green's function [see equation (6.55)]

$$\langle O(t)\rangle = \langle O\rangle + \frac{2\pi}{\hbar}\sum_\omega e^{(\varepsilon-i\omega)t}G_R(OV_\omega,\omega-i\varepsilon) \tag{7.23}$$

or, using relation (6.62), this may be expressed in terms of the thermo-dynamic Green's function:

$$\langle O(t)\rangle = \langle O\rangle + \beta\sum_\omega e^{(\varepsilon-i\omega)t}G(OV_\omega,\omega-i\varepsilon). \tag{7.24}$$

This result may be used to calculate the response of the crystal to a strain. The stress $\alpha\beta$ is obtained from equation (7.6a) as

$$\frac{\partial\Phi}{\partial u_{\alpha\beta}} = \Phi_{\alpha\beta} + \sum_{\gamma\delta}\Phi_{\alpha\beta\gamma\delta}u_{\gamma\delta} + \cdots. \tag{7.25}$$

The first-order term is:

$$\langle\Phi_{\alpha\beta}\rangle \tag{7.26a}$$

and the second-order term is:

$$\sum_{\gamma\delta} \left[\langle \Phi_{\alpha\beta\gamma\delta} u_{\gamma\delta} \rangle + \beta \sum_{\omega} e^{(\varepsilon - i\omega)t} G(\Phi_{\alpha\beta}\Phi_{\gamma\delta} u_{\gamma\delta}, \omega - i\varepsilon) \right] \qquad (7.26b)$$

where the two terms in the second-order expression are consistent, the high-order term in the argument of the Green's function from the product

$$OV_{\omega} \rightarrow \frac{\partial \Phi}{\partial u_{\alpha\beta}} \cdot \Phi$$

having been rejected.

These expressions may be evaluated just as in Section 6.7, by the diagram method. The lowest-order non-zero contribution to term (7.26a) is shown in Figure 7.5; this, according to the rules, contributes:

$$\sum_{kj} V^{(3)}_{\alpha\beta}(kj, -kj)[2n(kj) + 1]. \qquad (7.27)$$

Figure 7.5

In general, any diagram with one $V^{(n)}$ vertex and any order of interaction coupling the phonons involved contributes to term (7.26a). Those of higher order than Figure 7.5 may be evaluated by the same rules. The thermal expansion may be obtained from the term (7.26a) by noting, as discussed in Section 4.6, that the total stress is zero if there are no external forces acting. Thus we may write the stress due to thermal strain ($\bar{u}^{T}_{\gamma\delta}$) is zero if

$$\langle \Phi_{\alpha\beta} \rangle = - \sum_{\gamma\delta} C_{\alpha\beta\gamma\delta} \bar{u}^{T}_{\gamma\delta} \qquad (7.28)$$

per unit volume of crystal. Hence, defining an inverse of the elastic-constant tensor

$$\bar{u}^{T}_{\alpha\beta} = - \sum_{\gamma\delta} s_{\alpha\beta\gamma\delta} \langle \Phi_{\gamma\delta} \rangle \qquad (7.29)$$

with

$$\sum_{\mu\nu} C_{\alpha\beta\mu\nu} s_{\mu\nu\gamma\delta} = \delta_{\alpha\gamma}\delta_{\beta\delta}. \qquad (7.30)$$

The coefficients of thermal expansion may be obtained to the required order by taking the temperature derivative of equation (7.29) and including the relevant diagrams. Cowley[7] has used this method to evaluate thermal-expansion coefficients for various approximate models of the alkali halides. The value of the results is whittled away by the difficulties in representing the anharmonic force constants satisfactorily.

7.5 The elastic constants

Expression describing the elastic properties of the lattice may be deduced from the second-order stress term (7.26b). The various contributions arising from this may be represented by the usual diagrams. The scheme adopted by Cowley is the clearest representation of the higher-order terms. We shall shade the region in which anharmonic interactions can occur between the normal modes involved (i.e. lines entering and leaving the shaded region must satisfy the usual rules). The real deformation coupling vertices appear outside this region, and this clarifies the classification of the various contributions. The most significant of these are shown in Figures 7.6 and 7.7.

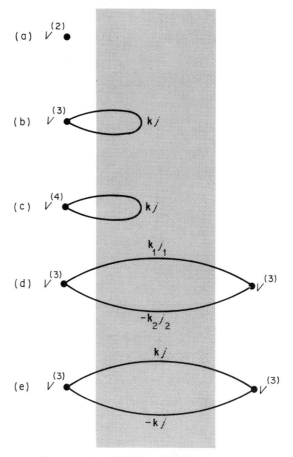

Figure 7.6 Diagrams representing contributions to the second-order stress [equation (7.26b)] in a crystal that has a centre of symmetry

The contributions corresponding to these diagrams may be evaluated using the rules of Section 6.7. Let us write the stress as the sum of the contributions by defining a convenient quantity $K_{\alpha\beta\gamma\delta}$:

$$S_{\alpha\beta} = S_{\alpha\beta}^{(a)} + S_{\alpha\beta}^{(b)} + \cdots = \sum_{\alpha\beta} K_{\alpha\beta\gamma\delta}\bar{u}_{\gamma\delta} \tag{7.31}$$

where $K_{\alpha\beta\gamma\delta} \equiv K_{\alpha\beta\gamma\delta}^{(a)} + K_{\alpha\beta\gamma\delta}^{(b)}$.

The expressions for $K_{\alpha\beta\gamma\delta}^{(a)}$, etc., are as follows:

Diagram (a): (corresponds to the harmonic approximation)

$$K_{\alpha\beta\gamma\delta}^{(a)} = V_{\alpha\beta\gamma\delta}^{(2)}. \tag{7.32a}$$

Diagram (b): [arises from the effect of the second term in equation (7.6b) when evaluating term (7.26a) and corresponds to the inclusion of the thermal strain and the use of the definitions (7.5)]

$$K_{\alpha\beta\gamma\delta}^{(b)} = -\left\{\delta_{\beta\delta}\sum_{kj} V_{\alpha\gamma}^{(3)}(kj, -kj)[2n(kj) + 1]\right\}. \tag{7.32b}$$

Diagram (c): (fourth-order vertex, two strains and two phonons, giving the simplest anharmonic part)

$$K_{\alpha\beta\gamma\delta}^{(c)} = \left\{\sum_{kj} V_{\alpha\beta\gamma\delta}^{(4)}(kj, -kj)[2n(kj) + 1]\right\}. \tag{7.32c}$$

Diagram (d): (second order in the perturbation involving two third-order vertices and any two phonons; the case $\mathbf{k}_1 j_1 = \mathbf{k}_2 j_2$ requires special treatment)

$$K_{\alpha\beta\gamma\delta}^{(d)} = -\left\{ 2\beta \sum_{\substack{k_1 k_2 \ p \\ j_1 j_2}} V_{\alpha\beta}^{(3)}(\mathbf{k}_1 j_1, \mathbf{k}_2 j_2)V_{\gamma\delta}^{(3)}(-\mathbf{k}_1 j_1, -\mathbf{k}_2 j_2) \right.$$

$$\left. \times\ G_{\mathbf{k}_1 j_1}^0(\omega_p)G_{\mathbf{k}_2 j_2}^0(\omega - i\omega_p) \right\}.$$

For the elastic constants the applied frequency $\omega \to 0$; hence summing over p yields[a]

$$K_{\alpha\beta\gamma\delta}^{(d)} = \left\{ \sum_{\substack{k_1 k_2 \\ j_1 j_2}} \frac{8}{\hbar} V_{\alpha\beta}^{(3)}(\mathbf{k}_1 j_1, \mathbf{k}_2 j_2)V_{\gamma\delta}^{(3)}(-\mathbf{k}_1 j_1, -\mathbf{k}_2 j_2)\frac{(2n_1 + 1)\omega_2}{\omega_1^2 - \omega_2^2} \right\}. \tag{7.32d}$$

Diagram (e): [the special case of diagram (d) when $\mathbf{k}_1 j_1 = \mathbf{k}_2 j_2$ must be evaluated separately, since the poles are of order two]

$$K_{\alpha\beta\gamma\delta}^{(e)} = -2\beta\left\{\sum_{kj}\sum_p V_{\alpha\beta}^{(3)}(kj, -kj)V_{\gamma\delta}^{(3)}(-kj, kj)G_{kj}^0(\omega_p)G_{kj}^0(\omega_p)\right\}.$$

The p summation may be carried out using the same procedure as for the evaluation of expression (6.87), except that the residues are as given in the chapter note that gives details of this evaluation.[b] The result is

$$K^{(e)}_{\alpha\beta\gamma\delta} = 2\beta\left\{\sum_{kj} V^{(3)}_{\alpha\beta}(kj, -kj)V^{(3)}_{\gamma\delta}(-kj, kj)\left[\frac{2n_k + 1}{\beta\hbar\omega_k} + 2n_k(n_k + 1)\right]\right\}.$$
(7.32e)

If the crystal under consideration does not have a centre of symmetry, other terms will contribute to orders comparable to those included in Figure 7.6. These extra contributions are shown in Figure 7.7 and may be evaluated as before, but with a little more complexity. We shall not consider the details of these effects.

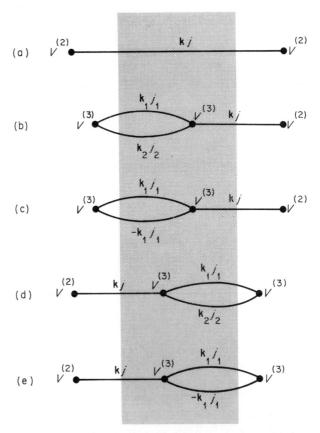

Figure 7.7   Diagrams representing the extra contribution to the stress of a crystal if there is no centre of symmetry. Terms corresponding to these diagrams vanish if there is a centre of symmetry

The elastic constants (as defined in Section 2.11) may be related to the expressions (7.32), and the corresponding ones for Figure 7.7 in the case of a non-centrosymmetric lattice) by writing the $\alpha\beta$ stress

$$S_{\alpha\beta} = \sum_{\gamma\delta} C_{\alpha\beta\gamma\delta}\bar{u}_{\gamma\delta}. \tag{7.33}$$

Equating the sum of the contributions shown in Figure 7.6 to the macroscopic result (7.33) yields the required relation. This must take into account the strain of the lattice due to the thermal expansion and ensure that the resulting elastic constants have the correct symmetry properties (see Section 2.11). Born and Huang have shown that the former point may be included by writing the deformations as matrices:

$$U \equiv \{u_{\alpha\beta}\} \tag{7.34a}$$

$$\bar{U} \equiv \{\bar{u}_{\alpha\beta}\} \tag{7.34b}$$

$$\tilde{U} \equiv \{u_{\beta\alpha}\}. \tag{7.34c}$$

With these matrices we see that equation (7.5b) becomes

$$\bar{U} = \tfrac{1}{2}(U + \tilde{U} + \tilde{U}U). \tag{7.34d}$$

The effect of thermal expansion is given by the determinant representing the volume expansion ratio:

$$|I + U| \tag{7.35}$$

I being a unit matrix. This may be expressed in terms of $\bar{U}$ by rearranging equation (7.34d) to be

$$2\bar{U} + I = (I + \tilde{U})(I + U). \tag{7.36a}$$

Taking determinants and noting that $|I + \tilde{U}| \equiv |I + U|$, we see that

$$|I + U| = |I + 2\bar{U}|^{1/2}. \tag{7.36b}$$

Hence this is the factor that is required to ensure that the extensive properties are expressed in terms of the actual unit volume, even though they are evaluated for the portion of the crystal that occupied unit volume at absolute zero. To take into account the effect of thermal strains on a tensor property we must introduce a factor $(\delta_{\alpha\alpha'} + u_{\alpha\alpha'}^{\mathrm{T}})$ for each suffix α and sum over the index α'. The expression for $C_{\alpha\beta\gamma\delta}$ has four such terms which are to be summed over, taking the form:

$$C_{\alpha\beta\gamma\delta} = |1 + 2\bar{U}^{\mathrm{T}}|^{-2} \sum_{\alpha'\beta'\gamma'\delta'} \{(\delta_{\alpha\alpha'} + u_{\alpha\alpha'}^{\mathrm{T}})(\delta_{\beta\beta'} + u_{\beta\beta'}^{\mathrm{T}})[\mathscr{S}K_{\alpha'\beta'\gamma'\delta'}]$$

$$\times (\delta_{\gamma\gamma'} + u_{\gamma\gamma'}^{\mathrm{T}})(\delta_{\delta\delta'} + u_{\delta\delta'}^{\mathrm{T}})\} \tag{7.37}$$

where $\mathscr{S}$ is a symmetrizing operator. The infinitesimal strains $u_{\alpha\alpha'}^{\mathrm{T}}$, etc., may be written in terms of $\bar{u}_{\alpha\alpha'}^{\mathrm{T}}$ through equation (7.5b), and the nett effect of this and the volume normalization factor is an external factor $|1 + \overline{U}^T|$. Thus writing the symmetry in full:

$$C_{\alpha\beta\gamma\delta} = \frac{(1 + \overline{U}^T)}{4}(K_{\alpha\beta\gamma\delta} + K_{\alpha\beta\delta\gamma} + K_{\beta\alpha\gamma\delta} + K_{\beta\alpha\delta\gamma}). \qquad (7.38)$$

In conclusion it is worth looking at some estimates of these relations. Mitskevich[8] has evaluated the expression (7.32) for a model of NaCl. His results for the temperature dependence of the elastic constants are very encouraging, even though the potential employed is probably oversimplified. These curves are redrawn in Figure 7.8.

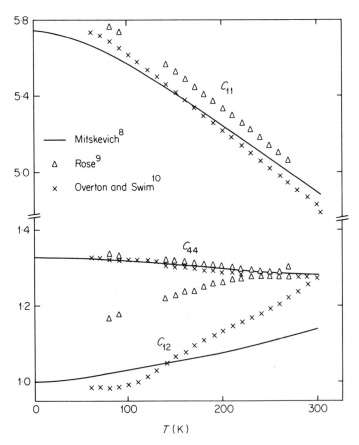

Figure 7.8   Temperature behaviour of adiabatic elastic constants of NaCl. Reproduced, with permission, from Mitskevich, V. V., *Soviet Physics—Solid State*, **3**, 2202–2217 (1962)

More recent results are shown in References 3 and 4, and further discussion along these lines, distinguishing between elastic constants for waves in the zero sound region (the frequency greater than the phonon inverse lifetimes) and the first sound region, appears in Reference 7.

7.6   Ultrasonic attenuation

We have looked in Section 5.10 at some of the qualitative features of the absorption of a sound wave in a crystal. These features are readily expressible in our Green's-function formalism and the advantages lie in the resulting similarity with other lattice dynamical problems and in the generality which permits extension to higher-order effects.

The problem is that of the response of a crystal (otherwise in equilibrium) to a periodic external driving force. This response is described by the retarded Green's function, which is a linear response function if we regard the force as coupled linearly to the nuclear displacements. We can write the amplitude of the elastic wave travelling in the z direction as

$$U_0(z) = U_0(0) \sum_{k_z} e^{ik_z z} G_R(k_z jj, \omega_s) \tag{7.39}$$

where ω_s is the elastic wave frequency. Using relation (6.62), we may rewrite equation (7.39) in terms of the thermodynamic Green's function:

$$U_0(z) = U_0(0) \frac{\beta \hbar}{2\pi} \sum_{k_z} e^{ik_z z} G_{k_z jj}(\omega_p) \tag{7.40}$$

with $i\omega_p \to \omega_s + i\varepsilon$. The summation over k_z may be carried out by expressing it as an integral and evaluating by contour integration. The Green's function in equation (7.40) is given by equation (6.80), which has poles where

$$-\omega_p^2 = \omega_{k_z j}^2 - 2\omega_{k_z j} S_p(k_z jj) = \omega_s^2 \tag{7.41a}$$

or

$$\omega_s = \omega_{k_z j} \left(1 - \frac{2S_p(k_z jj)}{\omega_{k_z j}}\right)^{1/2} \tag{7.41b}$$

$$\equiv \omega'_{k_z j} - i\omega''_{k_z j}. \tag{7.41c}$$

Provided that the self-energy parts are small, we can expand the binomial in equation (7.41b) to give

$$\omega'_{k_z j} = \omega_{k_z j} + \Delta_p(k_z jj) \tag{7.42a}$$

$$\omega''_{k_z j} = \Gamma_p(k_z jj)| \tag{7.42b}$$

where Δ_p and Γ_p are related to S_p via the definition (6.82). Thus we see that an excitation with wave vector k_z has an energy equivalent to the renormalized phonon and a damping correspondence to the lifetime. The damping is usually expressed in terms of an attenuation coefficient which is the imaginary part of k_z at the pole. Expanding ω_s as a Taylor series in the small imaginary parts:

$$\omega_s = \omega'_{k_z j} - \left(\frac{\partial \omega'}{\partial k_z}\right)_{k_z = 0} [k_z(\omega_s) - k'_z(\omega_s)] + \cdots \tag{7.43}$$

where k'_z is the real part of k_z. By comparison with equations (7.41c) and (7.42b) we get

$$k''_z(\omega_s) = \left(\frac{\partial \omega'_{k_z j}}{\partial k_z}\right)_{k_z = 0}^{-1} \Gamma_p(k_z jj') \tag{7.44}$$

where $k''_z(\omega_s)$ is the imaginary part of k_z at the pole. This corresponds directly with the attenuation coefficient $\alpha(\omega_s)$, since the imaginary part of the wave vector is a real decay factor. Thus we have (noting that $\partial \omega'_{k_z j}/\partial k_z$ = group velocity $\equiv v_{k_z j}$)

$$\alpha_j(\omega_s) = \Gamma_p(k_z jj)/v_{k_z j} \tag{7.45}$$

where $\alpha_j(\omega_s)$ is the ultrasonic attenuation coefficient of a sound wave ω_s (equal to the renormalized phonon frequency) with wave vector k_z belonging to the branch j.

We have discussed the difference in the attenuation of a longitudinal and transverse sound wave in Chapter 5. We shall not go into further details here, since the procedure should be quite clear and may be found in Reference 4 of Chapter 6. However, before leaving the subject, it is worth noting that diagrams (d) and (e) of Figure 7.6 contribute a damping term to the motion of an elastic disturbance travelling through the crystal, and hence correspond to ultrasonic attenuation. The expressions $K^{(d)}_{\alpha\beta\gamma\delta}$ and $K^{(e)}_{\alpha\beta\gamma\delta}$ have imaginary parts; the former is readily obtained by comparison with equations (6.96) and (6.103):

$$\text{imag}\,(K^{(d)}_{\alpha\beta\gamma\delta}) = \frac{2\pi}{\hbar} \sum_{\substack{k_1 j_1 \\ k_2 j_2}} V^{(3)}_{\alpha\beta}(k_1 j_1, k_2 j_2) V^{(3)}_{\gamma\delta}(-k_1 j_1, -k_2 j_2) \xi(k_1 k_2 \omega_s) \tag{7.46a}$$

where

$$\xi(k_1 k_2 \omega_s) \equiv (\bar{n}_1 + \bar{n}_2 + 1)[\delta(\omega_1 + \omega_2 - \omega_s) - \delta(\omega_1 + \omega_2 + \omega_s)]$$
$$+ (\bar{n}_2 - \bar{n}_1)[\delta(\omega_1 - \omega_2 - \omega_s) - \delta(\omega_1 - \omega_2 + \omega_s)]. \tag{7.46b}$$

For long waves ω_s is small compared with ω_1 and ω_2, and hence the terms in the $k_1 j_1$, $k_2 j_2$ summations which affect the attenuation of ω_s are those for which $\omega_1 \approx \omega_2$. Thus only the second square bracket in equation (7.46b) is significant. The corresponding term from diagram (e) is similar to equation (7.46) with $k_1 \rightarrow k$ and $k_2 \rightarrow -k$. For present purposes we need not distinguish between (d) and (e), (e) being included in (d) for finite $\omega(=\omega_s)$. Unfortunately the perturbation theory becomes, suspect for these long waves, and the expressions cannot be regarded as a good representation of the attenuation. Particular care must be taken of the relative magnitude of the phonon inverse lifetimes and the elastic wave frequency. If $\Gamma > \omega_s$, the attenuation is dominated by the effects arising from the phonons maintaining local thermodynamic equilibrium; if $\omega_s > \Gamma$ (collision-free region) the effects of phonon interactions are negligible. These are sometimes called the first sound region and zero sound regions, respectively. A correct procedure has been developed by Kananoff and Baym (Reference 6 in Chapter 6) and applied by others whose work is discussed in Section 7.7.

7.7 Thermal conductivity

In Section 5.9 we have discussed the basic features of lattice conductivity. In order to make comparisons with related properties and to provide a basis for a more complete discussion of thermal conductivity, a more flexible approach is desirable. Krumhansl[11] and his coworkers[12] discuss the problems by considering the phonon Boltzmann equation

$$D n(\mathbf{k} r t) = C n(\mathbf{k} r t) \tag{7.47}$$

where $\mathbf{D} = \partial/\partial t + \mathbf{v} \cdot \nabla$ and C is the operator that includes all the relevant scattering mechanisms. The thermal-conductivity tensor is related to the inverse of C through an expression of the form

$$\sigma_{\alpha\alpha'} = A \sum_{\mathbf{k}j} C(\mathbf{k}j) V_\alpha(\mathbf{k}j) V_{\alpha'}(\mathbf{k}j) C^{-1} \tag{7.48}$$

which reduces to equation (5.46c) in the limit that normal processes take place much more rapidly than umklapp processes. Much effort has been expended in attempts to devise a satisfactory procedure to find C^{-1}, but the direct approach is manipulatively impossible if reasonable accuracy is required. We shall not go into these details since there is no new physics, but it is worth a look at the approach of Krumhansl. The procedure is to separate the normal collision processes from the umklapp collisions and scattering from centres with time-varying density, etc. At the end of Section 5.9 we mentioned the indirect effect of the normal processes. The significance of the effect comes out very clearly in this approach. Guyer and Krumhansl[13,14] give the steady-state thermal conductivity for an isotropic, dispersionless crystal

$$\sigma = \frac{1}{3} C_V v_s^2 \left(\langle \tau_R \rangle \frac{S}{1+S} + \langle \tau_R^{-1} \rangle^{-1} \frac{1}{1+S} \right) \tag{7.49}$$

where v_s is the velocity of sound (here a constant), τ_R is a relaxation time for processes that do **not** conserve momentum (e.g. umklapp processes) and $S \equiv \tau_N / \langle \tau_R \rangle$ where τ_N is the relaxation time for processes which **do** conserve momentum.

Equation (7.49) brings out the limiting cases:

(i) $\tau_N \gg \tau_R$; hence $S(1 + S) \to 1, 1/(1 + S) \to 0$ and the second term in equation (7.49) is insignificant.

(ii) $\tau_R \gg \tau_N$; $S/(1 + S) \to 0, 1/(1 + S) \to 1$ and the first term in (7.49) is insignificant (this situation is known as the 'Ziman limit').

Hence we see that, where normal processes are much faster than umklapp processes [limit (ii)], the conductivity is characterized by the single quantity $\langle \tau_n^{-1} \rangle^{-1}$: when umklapp processes are faster, they determine the conductivity directly through $\langle \tau_R \rangle$. This distinction is clarified by the analogue suggested by Guyer and Krumhansl.

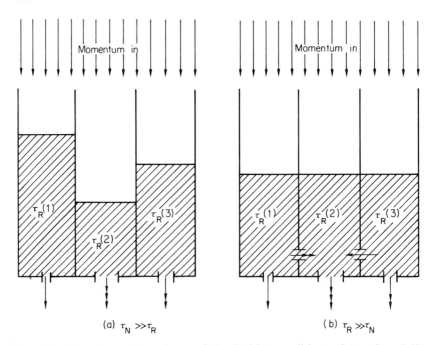

Figure 7.9 Hydrodynamic analogue of the limiting conditions of equation (7.49). Holes in the bottom represent momentum-destroying processes; holes between 'states' represent momentum-conserved coupling

Figure 7.9(a) represents a three-phonon system in which the interactions that conserve momentum are negligible. The momentum is destroyed from each mode independently and the nett effect is an average of the individual $\tau_R(\mathbf{k})$. In Figure 7.9(b) the normal processes take place much more rapidly, and modes depleted by momentum-destroying processes are replenished at the expense of those modes that decay (via non-conservation of momentum processes) with lower transition rates. This results in a uniform loss of momentum from all states, irrespectively of which states lose momentum more effectively.

If it is possible to satisfy the second limit [Figure 7.9(b)] and at the same time have a situation where the number of collisions is large we have the phenomenon of 'second sound'. This is the propagation of fluctuations in the density of harmonic phonons—first called second sound by Landau in about 1946. The analogy is with first sound propagation—particle-density fluctuations in a gas. The theory of second sound is treated as indicated in this section by Prohofsky and Krumhansl,[15] Guyer and Krumhansl[16] and Cowley.[7] From similar considerations Cowley has been able to extract an expression for the thermal conductivity. Following Prohofsky and Krumhansl, he writes the modified phonon mean occupation number as

$$n_f(\mathbf{k}j) = (e^{\beta_f \hbar \omega_f} - 1)^{-1} \qquad (7.50a)$$

where

$$\beta_f^{-1} = k_B(T + \Delta T) \qquad (7.50b)$$

and

$$\omega_f \equiv \omega(\mathbf{k}j) - \lambda \cdot \mathbf{k} - \phi \omega^2(\mathbf{k}j)\hbar + \frac{2}{\hbar}\sum_{\alpha\beta} V_{\alpha\beta}(\mathbf{k}j, -\mathbf{k}j)\eta_{\alpha\beta}. \qquad (7.50c)$$

ΔT allows for the local temperature variations, λ is determined by the resultant flow of phonons, ϕ takes account of any deviation from thermal equilibrium and the last term in expression (7.50c) arises from the effect of strain on $\omega(\mathbf{k}j)$. Expanding equation (7.50a) and considering the leading terms, we have

$$n_f(\mathbf{k}j) = n(\mathbf{k}j) + n(\mathbf{k}j)[n(\mathbf{k}j) + 1]\beta\hbar\left[\omega(\mathbf{k}j)\left(1 + \frac{\Delta T}{T}\right) - \omega_f\right]. \qquad (7.51)$$

Using the conditions that the energy, momentum and number of phonons will be conserved (locally), a set of three equations describing the thermodynamic state may be deduced which determine λ, ϕ and ΔT. From these Cowley finds

$$\sigma = \beta\frac{\hbar^2}{V}\frac{|\sum_{\mathbf{k}j} n(n + 1)\omega k_\alpha(\partial\omega/\partial k_\alpha)|^2}{\sum_{\mathbf{k}j} n(n + 1)k_\alpha^2 \Gamma_u} \qquad (7.52)$$

where for clarity $n \equiv n(\mathbf{k}j)$, $\omega \equiv \omega(\mathbf{k}j)$ and $\Gamma_u \equiv \Gamma_u(\mathbf{k}j)$, $\omega = \omega(\mathbf{k}j)$ [see, for example, expression (6.103)] is the inverse lifetime due to umklapp processes.

Cowley's numerical estimate of expression (7.52) (not intended to be a reliable computation) indicates a correct magnitude ($2 \cdot 1 \, \text{Wm}^{-1} \text{K}^{-1}$ compared with $3 \cdot 3 \, \text{Wm}^{-1} \text{K}^{-1}$ experimentally) and the approach conveniently requires only single summations over $\mathbf{k}$ space. I am indebted to Professor Cowley for his comments on an earlier approach which had been found to be invalid, and also for bringing to my notice two particularly useful papers. For a thorough treatment of the collision-free and collision-dominated effects, and for a detailed formulation of transport properties involving phonons, see Klein and Wehner[17] and Niklasson.[18] Other useful references on the phonon Boltzmann equation are the work of Kwok and Martin[19] and References 4 and 6 from Chapter 6.

7.8 Dielectric effects

What is the effect on a lattice when it is exposed to an electric field? In particular, what effect does an electromagnetic field have on the phonons? There are two aspects to be considered—the effect of the electric field on the phonon spectra and the effect of the phonons on the electromagnetic field propagating through the solid. From basic electromagnetic theory (Maxwell's equations), we can describe the field by the equations

$$\nabla \cdot [\varepsilon_0 E_{\text{L}}(\mathbf{r}) + P_{\text{L}}(\mathbf{r})] = 0 \qquad (7.53\text{a})$$

and

$$\ddot{E}_{\text{Tr}}(\mathbf{r}) + \frac{1}{\varepsilon_0} \ddot{P}_{\text{Tr}}(\mathbf{r}) = c^2 \nabla^2 E_{\text{Tr}}(\mathbf{r}) \qquad (7.53\text{b})$$

where ε_0 is the permittivity of free space, $\mathbf{E}$ and $\mathbf{P}$ are the electric field vector and the polarization, respectively, and where the subscripts L and Tr indicate longitudinal and transverse components.

The polarization involves the nuclear displacements and may be expressed in the simple form (per unit volume at $\mathbf{r}^{l0}$)

$$\mathbf{P}^{l0} = \frac{1}{v} \sum_{\kappa} z_{\kappa} \mathbf{u}^{l\kappa} \qquad (7.54)$$

where $\mathbf{r}^{l0}$ is a lattice vector, v is the volume of a unit cell and z_{κ} is the charge on the κth ion.

The electric field modifies the equation of motion (1.9) which becomes

$$m_{\kappa} \ddot{u}_{\alpha}^{l\kappa} = - \sum_{l'\kappa'} \phi_{\alpha\alpha'}^{l\kappa \atop l'\kappa'} u_{\alpha'}^{l'\kappa'} + z_{\kappa} E_{\alpha}^{l\kappa} \qquad (7.55)$$

i.e. the second term is the α component of the force on the κth ion due to the α component of the electric field at the ion site $\mathbf{r}^{l\kappa}$. If we now apply the transformation (1.14) to equation (7.55) and consider the case where the electromagnetic wavelength is much greater than the lattice spacing, we get

$$\ddot{q}(\mathbf{k}j) = -\omega_0^2(\mathbf{k}j) q(\mathbf{k}j) + F(\mathbf{k}j) \qquad (7.56\text{a})$$

with

$$F(\mathbf{k}j) \equiv N^{-1/2} \sum_{\substack{\alpha \\ l\kappa}} \frac{z_\kappa e_\alpha(\kappa, \mathbf{k}j)}{m_\kappa^{1/2}} E_\alpha^{l0} \, e^{i\mathbf{k}.\mathbf{r}^{l0}} \tag{7.56b}$$

since the field does not vary significantly over one unit cell and we write $E_\alpha^{l\kappa} \approx E_\alpha^{l0}$. Clearly $F(\mathbf{k}j)$ is zero for any acoustic mode in a centrosymmetric crystal. Thus, limiting the treatment to such crystals, we need consider only optic modes coupled to the radiation.

The polarization (7.54) may be expressed in terms of normal coordinates [using equation (1.14)] as

$$P_\alpha^{l0} = N^{-1/2} \sum_{\mathbf{k}} \sum_{\kappa} \frac{z_\kappa e_\alpha(\kappa, \mathbf{k}j)}{v m_\kappa^{1/2}} q(\mathbf{k}j) \, e^{i\mathbf{k}.\mathbf{r}^{l0}} \tag{7.57}$$

for modes belonging to the j branch. Substituting equation (7.57) into equation (7.53a) and comparing with equation (7.56b), we find that for modes that are strictly longitudinal or transverse (i.e. $e_\alpha(\kappa, \mathbf{k}j)$ is parallel or perpendicular to $\mathbf{k}$)

$$F(\mathbf{k}j) = -\Delta\omega^2(\mathbf{k}j)q(\mathbf{k}j) \tag{7.58a}$$

where

$$\Delta\omega^2(\mathbf{k}j) \equiv \sum_{\kappa} \frac{z_\kappa^2 |e_\alpha(\kappa, \mathbf{k}j)|^2}{v\varepsilon_0 m_\kappa}. \tag{7.58b}$$

Hence the longitudinal part of equation (7.56a) becomes

$$\ddot{q}(\mathbf{k}L) = -[\omega_0^2(\mathbf{k}L) + \Delta\omega^2(\mathbf{k}L)]q(\mathbf{k}L). \tag{7.59}$$

The change of frequency of the longitudinal optic phonon is determined by expression (7.58b). It is a reasonable simplification to write

$$|e_\alpha(\kappa, \mathbf{k}j)| = |e_\alpha(\kappa, \mathbf{k}L)| = |e_\alpha(\kappa, \mathbf{k}\,\mathrm{Tr})|. \tag{7.60}$$

In the absence of polarization effects, we have

$$\omega_0(\mathbf{k}L) = \omega_0(\mathbf{k}\,\mathrm{Tr}) \equiv \omega_0(\mathbf{k}) \tag{7.61}$$

(the reststrahlen frequency) but now this is lifted since

$$\omega_0^2(\mathbf{k}L) \to \omega^2(\mathbf{k}L) = \omega_0^2(\mathbf{k}L) + \Delta\omega^2(\mathbf{k}L). \tag{7.62}$$

However, if we neglect the interaction of the transverse mode with the field— that is ignoring retardation effects—$\omega_0(\mathbf{k}\,\mathrm{Tr})$ remains unchanged $[=\omega_0(\mathbf{k})]$ and hence

$$\frac{\omega^2(\mathbf{k}L)}{\omega^2(\mathbf{k}\,\mathrm{Tr})} = 1 + \frac{\Delta\omega^2(\mathbf{k}L)}{\omega_0^2(\mathbf{k})}. \tag{7.63}$$

The well known Lyddane–Sachs–Teller relation (Section 2.10) is a special case of result (7.63) with $\mathbf{k} \to 0$.

In considering the longitudinal mode, we have assumed that the coulomb interaction between ions is instantaneous, i.e. we have included only the irrotational part of $\mathbf{E}$ (i.e. $\nabla \cdot \mathbf{D} = 0$). Taking into account the finite velocity of propagation of the electrostatic interaction (the velocity of light) 'retards' the effect of this term in the equation of motion. Suppose now we include the rotational part [by including equation (7.53b)] and consider the limiting case where all ions remain in their equilibrium position (all $u_\alpha^{l\kappa} = 0$). The polarization is proportional to the field according to

$$\mathbf{P} = [\varepsilon(\infty) - 1]\varepsilon_0 \mathbf{E} \tag{7.64}$$

since the atoms are unable to follow the electromagnetic vibrations and the lattice behaves as an ordinary dielectric with relative permittivity $\varepsilon(\infty)$. This is, effectively, treating the masses as infinite, and the coupled equations having a solution corresponding to a transverse electromagnetic wave with velocity $c/\varepsilon(\infty)^{1/2}$. The irrotational part yielded the other limit where the solutions do not involve the electromagnetic radiation. Other than in these two limiting cases, the solutions contain a component of each kind of wave motion. There are regions in which the combined excitation is mainly a lattice mode and other regions in which it is mainly electromagnetic in character. In the region of crossover each has a comparable effect in determining the energy of the excitation, and the resultant is neither electromagnetic nor lattice vibrational.

If retardation effects on the transverse optic mode are neglected, the validity is limited to values of $\mathbf{k}$ greater than 1000 cm^{-1} (10^5 m^{-1}). Below this the interaction between $\mathbf{E}_{\text{Tr}}$ and $\omega_0(\mathbf{k}\,\text{Tr})$ is important. This may be included by writing equation (7.53b) in terms of $F(\mathbf{k}j)$ and $q(\mathbf{k}j)$ using equations (7.56b) and (7.57), which yields

$$\ddot{F}(\mathbf{k}\,\text{Tr}) + c^2 k^2 F(\mathbf{k}\,\text{Tr}) = -\Delta\omega^2(\mathbf{k}\,\text{Tr})\ddot{q}(\mathbf{k}\,\text{Tr}). \tag{7.65}$$

$\Delta\omega^2(\mathbf{k}\,\text{Tr})$ is numerically equal to $\Delta\omega^2(\mathbf{k}\text{L})$ in approximation (7.60). Substituting the solutions

$$q(\mathbf{k}\,\text{Tr}) = q^0(\mathbf{k}\,\text{Tr})\,e^{i\Omega t} \tag{7.66a}$$

and

$$F(\mathbf{k}\,\text{Tr}) = F^0(\mathbf{k}\,\text{Tr})\,e^{i\Omega t} \tag{7.66b}$$

into equation (7.65) and into equation (7.56a) we have the two coupled equations

$$-\Omega^2 F(\mathbf{k}\,\text{Tr}) + c^2 k^2 F(\mathbf{k}\,\text{Tr}) = \Delta\omega^2(\mathbf{k}\,\text{Tr})\Omega^2 q(\mathbf{k}\,\text{Tr}) \tag{7.67a}$$

and
$$-\Omega^2 q(\mathbf{k}\, \mathrm{Tr}) = -\omega_0^2(\mathbf{k}\, \mathrm{Tr})q(\mathbf{k}\, \mathrm{Tr}) + F(\mathbf{k}\, \mathrm{Tr}). \qquad (7.67b)$$
From these last two equations we can eliminate $q(\mathbf{k}\, \mathrm{Tr})$ and $F(\mathbf{k}\, \mathrm{Tr})$ to give a quadratic in Ω^2:
$$(\Omega^2 - c^2 k^2)[\Omega^2 - \omega_0^2(\mathbf{k}\, \mathrm{Tr})] = \Omega^2 \Delta\omega^2(\mathbf{k}\, \mathrm{Tr}). \qquad (7.68)$$
The two solutions of equation (7.68) represent the coupled phonon–photon modes which are usually called 'polaritons'. The solutions are shown as functions of $\mathbf{k}$ in Figure 7.10.

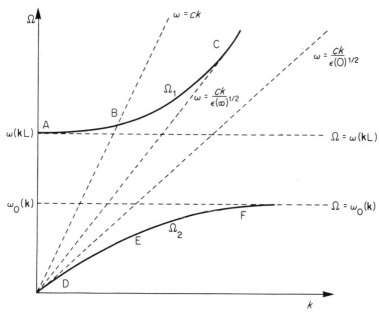

Figure 7.10   Form of the polariton frequencies given by equation (7.68). The abscissa scale is considerably magnified to illustrate clearly the composite excitation

The salient features of the polariton dispersion shown in Figure 7.10 are:

Upper branch (Ω_1):

Region A. Ω_1 approaches $\omega(\mathbf{k}\mathrm{L})$ [given by equation (7.62)] as $\mathbf{k} \to 0$. $\omega(0\mathrm{L})\varepsilon(\infty) \approx \omega(0\,\mathrm{Tr})\varepsilon(\infty)$ giving phonon-like behaviour and there is a strong retardation effect. The transverse mode disappears, since coupling introduces a strong electromagnetic component.

Region B.   There is a strong retardation effect, and $\omega_0(\mathbf{k})$ has an energy comparable to ck. Resonance effects occur between the lattice mode and the radiation.

Region C. Ω approaches $ck/[\varepsilon(\infty)]^{1/2}$, giving photon-like behaviour. The lattice behaves like a collection of infinite-mass particles.

Lower branch (Ω_2)

Region D. Ω approaches $ck/\varepsilon(0)^{1/2}$, giving photon-like behaviour with static relative permittivity.

Region E. Corresponds to Region B—strong retardation effects.

Region F. Ω approaches $\omega_0(\mathbf{k})$, i.e. behaves like a non-interacting phonon. Retardation is negligible, since $v_{\mathrm{phonon}} \ll c/\varepsilon(\infty)^{1/2}$; hence the velocity of light is effectively infinite and electrostatic interaction propagates instantaneously.

Thus at small values of $\mathbf{k}$ the lower branch behaves like a photon, while the upper branch behaves like a phonon. After the region of strong interaction, the branches have interchanged their characters. Such a crossover in a region of strong coupling is a familiar feature of interactions between different crystal excitations. We have seen also that the retardation does not affect the longitudinal modes. Basically this is because the charges see only the longitudinal vibrations, while the electromagnetic wave interacts only with the transverse vibration—hence the difference between $\omega(\mathbf{k}L)$ and $\omega(\mathbf{k}\,\mathrm{Tr})$.

The polaritons may be treated similarly to other crystal excitations and formulated in terms of 'polariton Green's functions'. The anharmonic coupling between phonons gives rise to an interaction between polaritons. The dielectric susceptibility (isotropic) $\chi(\omega\mathbf{k})$ may be deduced by this approach to be

$$\chi(\omega\mathbf{k}) = \frac{\Delta\omega^2(\mathbf{k})}{\omega_0^2(\mathbf{k}) - \Omega^2} \tag{7.69}$$

where $\varepsilon(\omega\mathbf{k}) = 1 + \chi(\omega\mathbf{k})$ and $\Delta\omega^2$ is given by expression (7.58b).

The formal treatment of a dielectric is similar to that of Section 7.4. If the applied electric field $\mathbf{E}$ is switched on at $t = -\infty$ it will interact with the electric dipole moment of the crystal $\mathbf{M}$ to produce a perturbation

$$H' = -\mathbf{M}\,.\,\mathbf{E}\,e^{-i\Omega t + \varepsilon t} \tag{7.70}$$

where $\varepsilon \to +0$. The time development of the state of the crystal following this is described by

$$\langle M(t) \rangle = \mathrm{Tr}\,(\rho(t)\mathbf{M}) \tag{7.71}$$

and the procedure following equation (7.9) is adopted. The result is

$$\chi_{\alpha\beta}(\Omega) = \beta G(M_\beta M_\alpha, \Omega + i\varepsilon) \tag{7.72}$$

where $G(M_\beta M_\alpha, \Omega + i\varepsilon)$ is the Fourier transform of the thermodynamic Green's function $G(M_\beta M_\alpha, t)$. If the dipole moment $\mathbf{M}$ is expanded in powers of the $A(\mathbf{k}j)$:

$$\mathbf{M} = \sum_j \mathbf{M}(0j)A(0j) + \sum_{\substack{\mathbf{k}_1 j_1 \\ \mathbf{k}_2 j_2}} \mathbf{M}(\mathbf{k}_1 j_1, \mathbf{k}_2 j_2)A(\mathbf{k}_1 j_1)A(\mathbf{k}_2 j_2). \quad (7.73)$$

The diagram technique used in Section 7.4 may be applied and the susceptibility computed to the desired order. The simplest of these are shown in Figure 7.11.

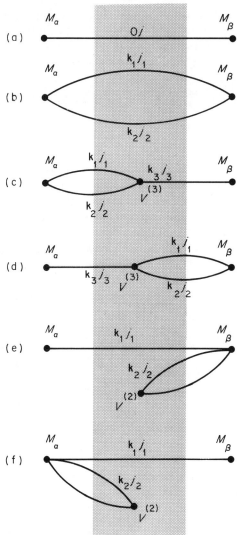

Figure 7.11   Contributions to the susceptibility
from the lattice properties of a crystal with a
centre of symmetry

Fuller details of these calculations may be found in Cowley[2] and Bilz.[20] For recent accounts of dielectric theory it is advisable to look under specific classes of crystals, e.g. ferroelectrics. References to some of these are given in the following sections.

7.9   Piezoelectric effects

A piezoelectric crystal is one in which the elastic properties are coupled to the effects produced by electric fields. A strain in the lattice produces a polarization and hence a field; an external electric field produces strains. Thus in general we must write (in the Voigt abbreviation notation defined in Section 2.11 for the suffices i and j):

$$t_i = \sum_j C_{ij}e_j - \sum_\alpha d_{\alpha i}E_\alpha \tag{7.74a}$$

$$P_\alpha = \sum_j d_{\alpha j}e_j + \sum_\beta \chi_{\alpha\beta}\varepsilon_0 E_\beta \tag{7.74b}$$

where $C_{ij}(\equiv C_{\alpha\beta\gamma\delta})$ are the elastic constants, $d_{\alpha i}(\equiv d_{\alpha,\beta\gamma})$ are the piezoelectric coefficients, $\chi_{\alpha\beta}$ is the dielectric susceptibility tensor, and P_α and E_β are the components of the polarization and electric field. (In these M.K.S. or S.I. unit equations $d_{\alpha i}$ has units of coulomb metre^{-2} (the same as polarization). Care must be taken to distinguish between this quantity $d_{\alpha j} = (\partial P_\alpha/\partial e_j)_E$ and the corresponding $(\partial P_\alpha/\partial t_j)_E$, which has units of coulomb newton^{-1}. The relations between the various parameters used to represent piezoelectric effects are discussed in Burfoot.[21])

Since elastic effects are coupled to electric effects, a purely elastic theory is not meaningful in peizoelectric crystals, and any theory of elastic properties necessarily involves both C_{ij} and $d_{\alpha i}$; similarly, the theory of dielectric effects involves $\chi_{\alpha\beta}$ and $d_{\alpha i}$. The equation of motion of an ion in such a crystal must take equations (7.74) into account, and this is discussed in the long-wave limit in pages 262–265 of Reference 6.

The strain produced by an electric field is more usually expressed in terms of the coefficients of electrostriction. Using equation (7.30) to rearrange equation (7.74a) we have, in Voigt notation:

$$e_j = \sum_i S_{ji}t_i + \sum_\alpha \left\{ \sum_i S_{ji}d_{\alpha i} \right\} E_\alpha \tag{7.75}$$

the curly brackets enclosing the moduli of electrostriction.

Using the procedure of Section 7.4 we can easily deduce that

$$d_{\alpha i} = d_{\alpha,\beta\gamma} = \beta G(M_\alpha \Phi_{\beta\gamma}, \omega = 0). \tag{7.76}$$

The diagrams for these are similar to those in Figure 7.11 with M_β replaced by $\Phi_{\beta\gamma}$; (c) and (d) do not contribute and the special case of (b) ($\mathbf{k}_1 j_1 = \mathbf{k}_2 j_2$) must be treated separately.

Reference 22 is recommended for a historical background of the development of our understanding of piezoelectricity. The books by Burfoot[21] and Jona and Shirane[23] provide further details of more recent treatments, and the subject index of *Physics Abstracts* gives sources of information about a large number of piezoelectric materials and the most recent theoretical descriptions.

7.10 Ferroelectricity

Piezoelectric crystals have no centre of symmetry and polarization occurs when the crystal is strained. Some of these crystals (there are ten crystal classes)—pyroelectrics—have a spontaneous polarization. The terminology arises since the polarization is only observable when the temperature changes (in equilibrium, surface effects tend to cancel out the volume effects). The polarization of some pyroelectric crystals can be reversed by applying an electric field—these are known as ferroelectric crystals, by analogy with ferromagnetism. Pyroelectric properties may be predicted purely from crystal symmetry considerations. However, the phenomena of ferroelectricity is only apparent when the dielectric behaviour is investigated.

The relative permittivity of a ferroelectric crystal is a function of the applied field E, since the relation between the polarization P and E is not linear. Above a critical temperature T_C, the relative permittivity of a ferroelectric satisfies a Curie–Weiss relation

$$\varepsilon = \frac{c_{el}}{T - T_C} + \varepsilon(0). \tag{7.77}$$

(Close to T_C, $\varepsilon \gg \varepsilon(0)$, and $\varepsilon(0)$ is often neglected.) Thus ferroelectricity is associated with an anomaly in the dielectric properties of the material.

In ferroelectric materials, some modes exhibit a large anharmonic behaviour and are stable only at high temperatures. Normally only a small number of modes have this strong temperature dependence, and then consideration of the behaviour of these modes provides plausible predictions of the crystal properties and phase transitions.

The dielectric behaviour is consistent with the assumption that the small k transverse optic mode has a temperature variation

$$\omega_T^2(\mathbf{k}\,\mathrm{Tr}) = K(T - T_C) \tag{7.78}$$

above T_C. At T_C, $\omega_T(\mathbf{k}j)$ approaches zero, and the instability results in a phase transition to an ordered (ferroelectric) state. At temperatures just above T_C, the self energy of the phonon is comparable to (or larger than) the harmonic phonon energy. At high temperatures equation (7.78) is similar to equation (6.81), since the anharmonic self energy is proportional to T, and we can associate $\omega^2(\mathbf{k}\,\mathrm{Tr})$ with $-KT_C$. This shows the significance of the unstable mode and its relation to the transition. Thus lattice-dynamical calculations of phonon self energies form part of this theory of ferroelectricity.

The assumption that only one mode is unstable enables the properties of some ferroelectrics to be described satisfactorily (e.g. the cubic perovskites). In others it is necessary to include two or more unstable modes to explain the observed properties. Obviously this is more complicated, since the interaction between the two (or more) unstable modes plays a significant role in determining transition temperatures.

The association of ferroelectric properties with strongly temperature-dependent modes was first proposed by Cochran.[24,25] The idea was taken up and developed primarily by Cowley[26] and Cochran.[27] General descriptions of ferroelectric behaviour may be found in Zhdanov[28] and Dekker.[29] A recent review by Zheludev[30] discusses the relation between the symmetry of the crystal structure and its ferroelectric behaviour. Another review by Smolenskii and Krainik,[31] although not a complete coverage of the subject, is useful and contains a good list of references to original papers. The books by Burfoot[21] and by Jona and Shirane[23] are probably the most helpful in the first instance.

7.11 Summary

We have attempted to introduce a range of phenomena in which the lattice dynamical properties of crystals manifest themselves. The idea of 'bare' particles (harmonic phonons) that are 'dressed' (physical phonons) by the interactions with other phonons (**self energies**) follows from the preceding chapter. We have seen how several crystal properties involve the same basic equation of motion and perturbation expansion, and that a diagram technique simplifies the classification and evaluation of the various contributions. Formally these may be extended to any order.

The equilibrium properties of a crystal (**thermodynamics**) may be deduced from the **free energy** by the standard relations. The evaluation of such quantities is very lengthy and often tedious if anharmonic effects are included; however, the results do provide the essential test of theory. These calculations must be made and if possible made in such a way that the fundamental physical interpretation is not obscured. The inclusion of the **thermal expansion** is essential to properly reflect the behaviour of a lattice, and indirectly this affects other properties. The **response** of the crystal to external and internal forces may be traced by the time-dependent **density matrix**. This leads to expressions for the **thermal expansion coefficient**, the **elastic constants** and, by analogy, to such properties as the **susceptibility** and **piezoelectricity**.

The ultrasonic attenuation may now be readily formulated in terms of the lifetimes of very long waves, and the concepts developed in Chapter 6 facilitate a straightforward theory. The analysis results in expressions very similar to the basic results of Section 6.8. The treatment of **thermal conduction** and the related phenomenon of **second sound** is through the **phonon Boltzmann** equation. The major problems in this area are, again, manipulative rather than conceptual. The lattice thermal resistance seems to be well understood, and its importance, relative to other scattering mechanisms, is properly in perspective.

The theory of **dielectrics** introduces the effect of an **electric** field into the ionic equations of motion, hence modifying the frequencies. The **transverse** and the **longitudinal optic** modes behave very differently under the influence of electric fields. The transverse mode interacts with the **photon** field (the retarded potential), while the longitudinal mode interacts with only the **irrotational** part of the field. This causes a splitting of the two modes by an amount proportional to the static **relative permittivity**. The interaction between the transverse optic phonon and the photon gives rise to a new composite crystal excitation, the **polariton**.

Crystals without a centre of symmetry exhibit **piezoelectric, pyroelectric** and **ferroelectric properties**. These all involve considerations of the lattice dynamical behaviour of the crystals.

The **ferroelectric transition** is an indication of one of the omissions from this chapter, namely the relation between the phonons of a crystal and the phase transitions experienced in the solid state.

Chapter notes

[a] To evaluate

$$\sum_p G^0_{k_1 j_1}(\omega_p) G^0_{k_2 j_2}(-\omega_p) = \frac{4\omega_1\omega_2}{\beta^2\hbar^2} \sum_p \frac{1}{\omega_1^2 + \omega_p^2} \cdot \frac{1}{\omega_2^2 + \omega_p^2}$$

we proceed as follows. The function has simple poles at $i\omega_p = \pm\omega_1, \pm\omega_2$. Hence using equations (6.88) and (6.89), the required sum becomes

$$\frac{4\omega_1\omega_2}{\beta\hbar}\left[\frac{(2n_1 + 1)}{2\omega_1(\omega_2^2 - \omega_1^2)} + \frac{(2n_2 + 1)}{2\omega_2(\omega_1^2 - \omega_2^2)}\right].$$

Noting the symmetry in k_1 and k_2 and the summation of both of them, we may write

$$\sum_p G^0_{k_1 j_1}(\omega_p) G^0_{k_2 j_2}(-\omega_p) = \frac{8}{\beta\hbar} \frac{\omega_2(2n_1 + 1)}{\omega_2^2 - \omega_1^2}$$

as is used to obtain the result (7.32d).

[b] To evaluate

$$\sum_{p=-\infty}^{\infty} G^0_k(\omega_p) G^0_k(\omega_p) = \frac{4\omega_k^2}{\beta^2\hbar^2} \sum_p \frac{1}{(\omega_k^2 + \omega_p^2)^2}$$

We proceed as follows. This may be expressed as a contour integral using equation (6.8), the integrand having two poles $i\omega_p = \pm\omega_k$ each of order two. For a pole of order

m at $z = a$, the residue of $f(z)$ is

$$\lim_{z \to a} \frac{1}{m!} \frac{d^{m-1}}{dz^{m-1}} [(z - a)^m f(z)].$$

Using this definition, the two residues are

$$\frac{4\omega_k^2}{2\pi i \beta \hbar} \lim_{i\omega_p \to \pm \omega_k} \frac{d}{d(i\omega_p)} \left[\frac{(\omega_k \mp i\omega_p)^2 (e^{i\beta\hbar\omega_p} - 1)^{-1}}{(\omega_k^2 + \omega_p^2)^2} \right]$$

and hence, carrying out the differentiation, substituting the limiting values and summing the residues according to the usual theorem we get

$$\sum_{p=-\infty}^{+\infty} G_k^0(\omega_p) G_k^0(\omega_p) = - \left[\frac{2n_k + 1}{\beta\hbar\omega_k} + 2n_k(n_k + 1) \right]$$

which is the result used in equation (7.32e).

References

1. Zubarev, D. N., *Soviet Physics, USPEKHI*, **3**, 320–345 (1960).
2. Cowley, R. A., *Adv. in Phys.*, **12**, 421–480 (1963).
3. Cowley, E. R., and Cowley, R. A., *Proc. Roy. Soc.*, **A287**, 259–280 (1965).
4. Cowley, E. R., and Cowley, R. A., *Proc. Roy. Soc.*, **A292**, 209–223 (1966).
5. Raunio, G., *Phys. Status Solidi*, **35**, 299–304 (1969).
6. Born, M., and Huang, K., *Dynamical Theory of Crystal Lattice*, Clarendon Press, Oxford, 1954, Chapts. III and VI and pp. 278–281.
7. Cowley, R. A., *Proc. Phys. Soc.*, **90**, 1127–1147 (1967).
8. Mitskevich, V. V., *Soviet Physics—Solid State*, **3**, 2202–2217 (1962).
9. Rose, F. C., *Phys. Rev.*, **49**, 50–54 (1936).
10. Overton, W. C., and Swim, R. T., *Phys. Rev.*, **84**, 758–762 (1951).
11. Krumhansl, J. A., *Proc. Phys. Soc. (London)*, **85**, 921–930 (1965).
12. Horie, C., and Krumhansl, J. A., *Phys. Rev.*, **136**, A1397–A1407 (1964).
13. Guyer, R. A., and Krumhansl, J. A., *Phys. Rev.*, **148**, 766–778, 779–788 (1966).
14. Guyer, R. A., *Phys. Rev.*, **148**, 789–797 (1966).
15. Prohofsky, E. W., and Krumhansl, J. A., *Phys. Rev.*, **133**, A1403–A1410 (1964).
16. Guyer, R. A., and Krumhansl, J. A., *Phys. Rev.*, **133**, A1411–A1417 (1964).
17. Klein, R., and Wehner, R. K., *Phys. kondens Materie*, **10**, 1–20 (1969).
18. Niklasson, G., *Ann. Physics*, **59**, 263–322 (1970).
19. Kwok, P. C., and Martin, P. C., *Phys. Rev.*, **142**, 495–504 (1966).
20. Bilz, H., 'Infra-red lattice vibration spectra of perfect crystals', in *Phonons, Scottish University Summer School, 1965* (Ed. Stevenson), Oliver and Boyd, London, 1966, pp. 208–231.
21. Burfoot, J. C., *Ferroelectrics. An Introduction to the Physical Principles*, Van Nostrand, London, 1967, Chap. 4.
22. Cady, W. G., *Piezoelectricity*, Vols. 1 and 2, Dover, New York, 1964.
23. Jona, F., and Shirane, G., *Ferroelectric Crystals*, Pergamon, New York, 1962.
24. Cochran, W., *Adv. Phys.*, **9**, 387–423 (1960).
25. Cochran, W., *Adv. Phys.*, **10**, 401–420 (1961).
26. Cowley, R. A., *Phil. Mag.*, **11**, 673–706 (1965).
27. Cochran, W., *J. Phys. Soc. Japan*, Supplement, 2nd Int. Meeting of Ferroelectrics (1969).

28. Zhdanov, G. S., *Crystal Physics*, Oliver and Boyd, London, 1965, pp. 258–296.
29. Dekker, A. J., *Solid State Physics*, Macmillan, London, 1960, Chap. 8.
30. Zheludev, I. S., *Solid State Physics*, **26**, 429–464 (1971).
31. Smolenskii, G. A., and Krainik, N. N., *Soviet Physics, USPEKHI*, **12**, 271–293 (1969) [original: *Uspekhi Fiz. Nauk. (U.S.S.R.)*, **97**, 657–696 (1969)].

8

Interaction of Phonons with Other ' 'ons'

8.1 Introduction

In Section 5.1 we gave a brief qualitative picture of the mechanism of the interaction between two phonons that are treated as waves. A similar argument indicates that a phonon may be expected to influence the properties of any excitation existing in the solid, whether it be external in origin (such as a neutron or photon) or inherently part of the solid (such as a magnon or electron). The existence of an interaction between phonons and other 'particles' is a simple idea; however the analysis of the interaction, its dependence on variable parameters such as temperature or purity, and its separation from other effects, may be exceedingly complex. In the following sections we discuss the coupling mechanism with the phonon and give indications of the methods that have been used to describe each interaction. Where relevant, applications and manifestations of the coupling are mentioned.

8.2 Photons (infrared)

We have seen in Section 7.8 the basic coupling between the retardation part of the electric field (the photon field) and the phonons. The only significant interaction is with a 'small $\mathbf{k}$' phonon belonging to the transverse optic branch. Infrared photons have energies comparable with typical phonons, and hence this is the region of the electromagnetic spectrum that is of greatest interest. However the momenta of these photons are negligible compared with the phonons, so, apart from $|\mathbf{k}| \approx 0$, the absorption of a photon with the creation of a single phonon is excluded by momentum-conservation requirements. Apart from energy and momentum conservation, there must also be a coupling mechanism before a particular process is allowed. The phonon must create an electric dipole moment parallel to the photon electric-field vector. Thus if a crystal has a centre of inversion symmetry (e.g. diamond-structure semiconductors), the displacement of two identical atoms for the optic mode at $\mathbf{k} = 0$ produces no nett polarization and hence provides no coupling. If there is not a centre of symmetry (e.g.

ZnS structures), there **is** a nett polarization and single-phonon states may couple with the photon.

In crystals such as germanium and silicon, the photon may be absorbed by a process involving two phonons. Clearly it is possible to satisfy energy and momentum conservation, but how does the coupling arise? Lax and Burstein[1] have proposed two possible mechanisms for this coupling, which are shown diagrammatically in Figure 8.1.

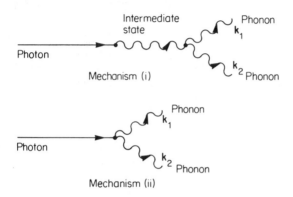

Figure 8.1   Diagrammatic representation of two possible mechanisms of coupling between photons and phonons. k_1 is created, and k_2 may be created or destroyed

Mechanism (i): The photon creates a transverse optic phonon which decays after a short life into two phonons. The intermediate state need not conserve energy, but, of course, momentum must be conserved at all stages.

Mechanism (ii): The photon couples directly with the two phonons. In a crystal such as germanium this may occur by a displaced atom distorting the charge distribution of neighbouring atoms; when they, in turn, are displaced by another phonon, a dipole moment results.

Thus the first mechanism can occur only in polar crystals, since a linear electric moment is required. In the second mechanism one phonon induces a charge and another phonon displaces it to create a second-order electric-moment term. This may occur in homopolar (covalent) crystals or in polar crystals. Where both processes are possible, their relative importance depends on the relative magnitude of the second-order electric moment and the anharmonic coupling between the transverse optic mode and the two phonons involved. The nett effect as an absorption mechanism is a difference in stimulated emission and absorption. The expressions are deduced by arguments similar to those used in Chapter 5 in the preliminary discussion of thermal conductivity and for a photon frequency ω. The absorption takes the following form.

Summation band (two phonons created):

$$K_S(\omega) = A_S \sum_{kjj'} \frac{H'(kjj')}{\omega(kj)\omega(kj')} \{1 + n(kj)n(kj')\}\delta(\omega - \omega(kj) - \omega(kj')).$$

(8.1a)

Difference band (phonon kj created, phonon kj' destroyed):

$$K_D(\omega) = A_D \sum_{kjj'} \frac{H'(kjj')}{\omega(kj)\omega(kj')} [n(kj) - n(kj')]\delta[\omega - \omega(kj) + \omega(kj')]$$

(8.1b)

where $H'(kjj')$ is the coupling coefficient for the photon–two-phonon process and $k_1 = k_2 = k$ indicates the 'equal k' [equal and opposite in equation (8.1b)] phonons, since the photon momentum is negligible. Taken as they stand these are complicated equations, since the anharmonic coupling is not known and details of the phonon spectrum are required. However Johnson[2] has made comparisons between these expressions and measured absorption curves by using some expedient assumptions. He also discusses the selection rules, the two-phonon density of states, the temperature dependence and the origin of the critical points for a number of semiconductors. Figure 8.2 reproduces his results for silicon.

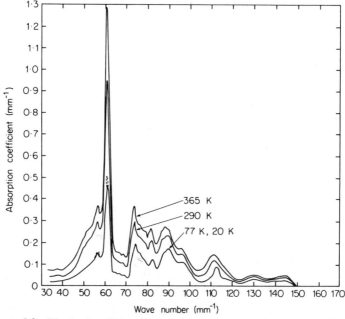

Figure 8.2   The lattice absorption coefficient in Si as a function of frequency. Reproduced from Johnson, F. A., *Progress in Semiconductors*, **9**, 181–235 (1965) by permission of Heywood and Co. Ltd., London

Extending this idea, many phonons may be involved in producing a non-zero electric moment and in satisfying the conservation laws. These multi-phonon effects will also contribute to the absorption of light, but hopefully to a smaller extent. Some general aspects of the propagation of electro-magnetic radiation through a dielectric are discussed by Loudon,[3] and some detailed discussions of infrared physics appear in Houghton and Smith.[4]

Apart from the interpretation of the absorption of infrared radiation, these considerations may be regarded as diagnostics. The observation of well defined stop bands for infrared radiation yields information about the long-wavelength optical phonons, in particular about the reststrahlen frequency. Information about the crystal and its properties is gained by radiating a crystal with photons and observing scattering and absorption. Suppose an intense source has a frequency which coincides with a strongly coupled two-phonon process. Large numbers of a well defined phonon may be created, and perhaps their relaxations observed. (For example, the 27·9 μm ($\equiv 0.044$ eV) water-vapour line is equivalent to the sum of a transverse acoustic phonon (0·010 eV) and a transverse optic phonon (0·034 eV) at the zone boundary in germanium.[5]) This has not provided significant information as yet, owing to the difficulties arising from the fast relaxation ($\sim 10^{-10}$ s even at fairly low temperatures) and the problems of large 'heating' effects at low temperatures. If these problems are overcome, direct observations on relaxation rates may be made.

8.3 Photons (optical)

The infrared photons of interest in absorption have energies comparable with those of phonons, say ~ 0.1 eV. Scattering observations on photons with energies in the region from 1 eV to 10 eV (embracing the optical range) has also provided much useful information on phonon spectra. Raman and Brillouin spectroscopy are concerned with the inelastic scattering of photons by a solid. The energy changes are accounted for by the creation or annihilation of a crystal excitation. The method may be used to probe any of the crystal excitations, but here we treat only phonons. Raman scattering involves optic-mode phonons, while Brillouin scattering involves acoustic phonons (although in second order, no clear distinction can be made if modes near the zone boundary are involved).

At first sight one might think that these scattering measurements would yield no information that could not be obtained from absorption experiments. However, crystals with a centre of inversion symmetry that are not Raman active in a particular order (e.g. NaCl, no first-order Raman effect) **are** infrared active in that order, and vice versa. Absorption experiments measure intensity variations, Raman and Brillouin scattering experiments observe frequency shifts, and X-ray scattering experiments (which we shall consider in the next section) observe scattering angles. Detailed treatments of Raman and Brillouin scattering may be found, for example, in Reference 6 of Chapter 7, in Hardy,[6] and in Loudon.[7] Here we shall look only at the general features.

The first-order Raman and Brillouin scattering conditions are:

$$\Delta_1\omega = \omega_0 - \omega_s = \pm\omega(\mathbf{k}j) \tag{8.2a}$$

$$\mathbf{Q} = \mathbf{Q}_0 - \mathbf{Q}_s = \pm\mathbf{k} \tag{8.2b}$$

where ω_0, ω_s, and $\mathbf{Q}_0$ and $\mathbf{Q}_s$ are the frequencies and wave vectors of the incident and scattered radiation; $\Delta_1\omega$ and $\mathbf{Q}$ are the frequency shift and the scattering vector. The negative frequency shift is known as the 'Stokes' component and the positive shift as the 'anti-Stokes' component which, in first order, corresponds to the creation and annihilation of a phonon, respectively. The vector diagram (with the phonon vector exaggerated) in Figure 8.3 shows that, to a good approximation, we may write

$$|\mathbf{k}| = 2|\mathbf{Q}_0|\sin(\theta/2) \tag{8.3}$$

which replaces the momentum-conservation equation (8.2b).

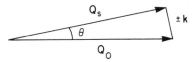

Figure 8.3 Vector diagram of first-order scattering process $\mathbf{k} \approx 0$

If the crystal is not optically dispersive at the photon frequency and we write

$$|\mathbf{Q}_0| = \omega_0\eta(\omega_0)/c \tag{8.4}$$

where $\eta(\omega_0)$ is the refractive index at frequency ω_0 and c is the velocity of light in vacuum, we may make some simple deductions from equation (8.3):

(i) For Raman scattering (optical mode, therefore $\omega(\mathbf{k}j)$ is independent of $|\mathbf{k}|$) the shift in frequency is independent of the incident photon frequency ω_0 and independent of θ.

(ii) For Brillouin scattering (acoustic modes, therefore $\omega(\mathbf{k}j)$ is proportional to $|\mathbf{k}|$ for small values) the shift in frequency is a function of ω_0 and of the scattering angle θ.

At very low temperatures the anti-Stokes component vanishes, since its intensity is proportional to $n(\mathbf{k}j)$. The intensity of the Stokes component is proportional to $1 + n(\mathbf{k}j)$, and hence at low temperatures becomes independent of temperature. At high temperatures $n(\mathbf{k}j) \approx 1 + n(\mathbf{k}j)$ and both components are comparable (varying linearly with temperature).

Whereas only some crystals have the required symmetry to give a first-order Raman effect, all crystals give a first-order Brillouin scattering. The acoustic modes produce linear terms in the electronic polarizability, irrespective of crystal symmetry; hence these can scatter photons. A Raman active material displays a shift with a Stokes and an anti-Stokes component corresponding to the transverse and the longitudinal optic modes. The Brillouin spectra have three shifts corresponding to the three acoustic modes, although along certain directions the transverse acoustic modes are degenerate and hence only two shifts are observed. In a more complete discussion of these effects the polarization of the scattered photon should be considered, since Raman and Brillouin scattering is anisotropic (even in cubic crystals).

The second-order scattering involves two phonons, and distinction between Raman and Brillouin scattering is only possible when acoustic modes for small $\mathbf{k}$ are involved (where the effect is very weak anyway). The phonons which take part may be optic or acoustic or one of each. There are six kinds of process involving two phonons $\omega(\mathbf{k}_1 j_1)(\equiv \omega_1)$ and $\omega(\mathbf{k}_2 j_2)(\equiv \omega_2)$, and in Table 8.1 $\omega_1 \geq \omega_2$.

Table 8.1 Second-order Raman processes

	Scattered frequency	Band	Component	Process responsible	
				Creation	Destruction
(i)	$\omega_0 + \omega_1 + \omega_2$	Summation	Anti-Stokes		ω_1 and ω_2
(ii)	$\omega_0 - \omega_1 - \omega_2$	Summation	Stokes	ω_1 and ω_2	
(iii)	$\omega_0 + \omega_1 - \omega_2$	Difference	Anti-Stokes	ω_2	ω_1
(iv)	$\omega_0 - \omega_1 + \omega_2$	Difference	Stokes	ω_1	ω_2
(v)	$\omega_0 + 2\omega_1$	'Overtone'	Anti-Stokes		$2\omega_1$
(vi)	$\omega_0 - 2\omega_1$	'Overtone'	Stokes	$2\omega_1$	

The energy and momentum requirements are

$$\Delta_2 \omega = \omega_s - \omega_0 = \pm\omega_1 \pm \omega_2 \tag{8.5a}$$

$$\mathbf{Q} = \mathbf{Q}_s - \mathbf{Q}_0 = \pm\mathbf{k}_1 \pm \mathbf{k}_2. \tag{8.5b}$$

By the same reasoning as in the first-order case, the second of these reduces to

$$|\pm\mathbf{k}_1 \pm \mathbf{k}_2| = \frac{2\omega_0}{c}\eta(\omega_0)\sin\theta. \tag{8.6}$$

The selection rules determining the major contributions to the second-order scattering are discussed by Birman[8] and Loudon.[7] The temperature dependence of each of these six shifts is readily obtained by including a factor $1 + n(\mathbf{k}j)$ if a phonon $\mathbf{k}j$ is created and a factor $n(\mathbf{k}j)$ if it is destroyed. These are shown, together with the corresponding processes that lead to infrared absorption, in Table 8.2.

Table 8.2 Temperature dependence of Raman processes (including a comparison with infrared)

			Temperature dependence (intensity)	
	Band	Component	Raman	Infrared
First order				
	Direct	Anti-Stokes	n_1	Independent
	Direct	Stokes	$1 + n_1$	
Second order				
(i)	Summation	Anti-Stokes	$n_1 n_2$	$1 + n_1 + n_2$
(ii)	Summation	Stokes	$(1 + n_1)(1 + n_2)$	
(iii)	Difference	Anti-Stokes	$n_1(1 + n_2)$	$n_2 - n_1$
(iv)	Difference	Stokes	$n_2(1 + n_1)$	
(v)	'Overtone'	Anti-Stokes	n_1^2	$1 + 2n_1$
(vi)	'Overtone'	Stokes	$(1 + n_1)^2$	

From Table 8.2 we see that the corresponding infrared processes have a temperature-dependent intensity that is the difference between the Stokes and anti-Stokes Raman components. This arises because in infrared absorption, the photon absorbed has exactly the same frequency as the one that is emitted by stimulation. Hence both effects occur at the same frequency and the nett effect is an algebraic sum. In the Raman effect the scattering is either side of the incident photon frequency; so the emission and absorption (of phonons) are distinct processes. A further and important difference in the characters of absorption and scattering spectra concerns its anisotropy. Scattering spectra are strongly anisotropic compared with an absorption spectra. This is particularly exhibited in cubic crystals, which have isotropic absorption spectra. The effect of the anisotropy, for example in considering polarization states of the photon, is complex in second order. We shall not discuss this and to my knowledge no complete theory yet exists. There are a number of reviews available on Raman and Brillouin scattering, e.g. Loudon[7] (Raman) and Griffin[9] (Brillouin).

8.4   Photons (X-ray)

We have discussed the interaction of phonons with photons of comparable energy (infrared) and with photons of larger energy (optical); we now consider the information available from the scattering of much higher energy photons ($\sim 10^4$ eV). These have wavelengths comparable with the crystal spacings, and the first application of X-ray scattering was the determination of structure. However, in 1941 Laval realized that X-rays could also be scattered from phonons.

Using the same notation as in the previous section, equation (8.3) is the condition for a Bragg reflection, where $\mathbf{Q}$, $\mathbf{Q}_0$ and $\mathbf{Q}_s$ now refer to an X-ray. The differential scattering cross-section (the intensity scattered into unit solid angle in direction $\mathbf{Q}_s$) is a function of the scattering vector $\mathbf{Q}$ and is of the form

$$\sigma_{\text{atoms}} = F^{(0)2} \tag{8.7a}$$

where the scattering amplitude is

$$F^{(0)} = \sum_{\kappa} \sum_{l} f_0(\kappa) \, e^{i\mathbf{Q}.(\mathbf{r}_l + \mathbf{r}_\kappa)} \tag{8.7b}$$

$f_0(\kappa)$ being an atomic scattering factor characteristic of the atom κ in the unit cell. This is often separated:

$$F^{(0)} = \left\{ \sum_{\kappa} f_0(\kappa) \, e^{i\mathbf{Q}.\mathbf{r}_\kappa} \right\} \sum_{l} e^{i\mathbf{Q}.\mathbf{r}_l} \equiv F_0(Q) \sum_{l} e^{i\mathbf{Q}.\mathbf{r}_l} \tag{8.8}$$

where for obvious reasons $F_0(Q)$ is called the structure factor. The summation over unit cells of the lattice reduces to a series of delta-function peaks where $\mathbf{Q} = \mathbf{K}$ (a reciprocal lattice vector), and this defines the zero-order Bragg reflections. However the effect of vibrations is completely neglected; the scattering from a real crystal is not from a set of stationary mathematical points. The simplest procedure to include the effects of the motions of the atoms is to introduce the Debye–Waller factor. This represents the thermal averages of the position of the atoms and effectively decreases the intensity from that of the static lattice points. The Debye–Waller factor, e^{-W} with

$$2W = \frac{1}{N} \sum_{\mathbf{k}j} w(\mathbf{k}j\mathbf{Q}) = \langle (\mathbf{Q}.\mathbf{u}) \rangle^2 \tag{8.9a}$$

where

$$w(\mathbf{k}j\mathbf{Q}) = \frac{\hbar}{m} |\mathbf{Q}.\mathbf{e}(\mathbf{k}j)|^2 \frac{n(\mathbf{k}j) + \frac{1}{2}}{\omega(\mathbf{k}j)} \tag{8.9b}$$

and $\mathbf{e}(\mathbf{k}j)$ is the polarization (eigenvector) of the phonon $\mathbf{k}j$. The thermal average may be computed for specific lattice dynamical models. It is convenient to include the factor with the atomic part and to write

$$f_0(\kappa, \mathbf{Q}) = f_0(\kappa) \, e^{-W}. \tag{8.10}$$

In order to consider scattering of these X-ray photons by phonons, the phase relations between the displacements of neighbouring atoms must be included. The scattering amplitude must now be written

$$F = \sum_\kappa \sum_l f(\kappa \mathbf{Q}) \, e^{i[\mathbf{Q}\cdot(\mathbf{r}_l + \mathbf{r}_\kappa + \mathbf{u}^{l\kappa})]}. \tag{8.11}$$

Expanding the exponential in powers of $\mathbf{u}$, the first term gives $F^{(0)}$, and second is

$$F^{(1)} = i \sum_\kappa \sum_l f(\kappa \mathbf{Q}) \, e^{i\mathbf{Q}\cdot(\mathbf{r}_l + \mathbf{r}_\kappa)} \mathbf{Q} \cdot \mathbf{u}^{l\kappa} \tag{8.12}$$

which is the first-order Bragg scattering—i.e. involving a single phonon. The next term corresponds to a second-order process involving two phonons.

The conditions on these scattering processes are summarized in Table 8.3.

Table 8.3 Conditions on scattering of X-rays with corresponding cross-sections for crystals with one atom per unit cell (volume v). f is the atomic scattering factor

Order	Momentum	Energy	σ
0	$\mathbf{Q} = \mathbf{K}$	$\lvert\mathbf{Q}_s\rvert = \lvert\mathbf{Q}_0\rvert$	$N f^2 e^{-2W} \dfrac{8\pi^3}{v} \sum_\mathbf{K} \delta(\mathbf{Q} - \mathbf{K})$
1	$\mathbf{Q} = \mathbf{K} \pm \mathbf{k}$	$\Delta\omega = \pm\omega(\mathbf{k}j)$	$f^2 e^{-2W} \sum_{\mathbf{k}j} w(\mathbf{k}j\mathbf{Q}) \dfrac{8\pi^3}{v} \sum_\mathbf{K} \delta(\mathbf{Q} + \mathbf{k} - \mathbf{K})$
2	$\mathbf{Q} = \mathbf{K} \pm \mathbf{k}_1 \pm \mathbf{k}_2$	$\Delta\omega = \pm\omega(\mathbf{k}_1 j_1) \pm \omega(\mathbf{k}_2 j_2)$	$\tfrac{1}{2} f^2 e^{-2W} \sum_{\substack{\mathbf{k}_1 j_1 \\ j_2}} w(\mathbf{k}_1 j_1 \mathbf{Q}) w(\mathbf{k}_2 j_2 \mathbf{Q})$

The first-order expression is the route from experiment to values of $\omega(\mathbf{k}j)$. Particular directions are chosen (and hence $\mathbf{Q}$ defined) such that only one mode contributes to the scattering [due to the scalar product $\mathbf{Q} \cdot \mathbf{e}(\mathbf{k}j)$] and the intensity observed. Correction should be made for second-order effects, this requires a knowledge of the whole spectrum, since the sum over $\mathbf{k}_1$ couples every mode with the one of interest. Also Compton scattering and absorption of the X-ray must be accounted for in the observed intensity of scattered radiation.

The expressions for the scattering section in crystals with more than one atom per unit cell are more complex than those in Tables 8.3 and may be found in Smith.[10] Other details may be found in Cochran[11] and Maradudin, Montroll and Weiss.[12]

8.5 Photons (γ-rays)

The highest energies of X-rays overlap with the lowest energies of γ-rays (20 keV X-rays are often employed in diffraction experiments) and so we may expect some similarity between the behaviour of X- and γ-rays. A striking aspect of this similarity was observed in Mössbauer[13] in 1958 during the course of experiments on resonance absorption using Ir^{191}, which emits a 0·129 MeV γ photon. He observed a component of γ-ray emission analogous to the elastic (Bragg) scattering of X-rays, i.e. a frequency unshifted by recoil energy. Let us consider briefly how we may associate this phenomenon, the recoilless emission of a γ photon, with the phonons of the lattice.

An unbound nucleus of mass m that emits a γ photon (energy E_γ and wavevector K_γ) will recoil with a velocity v_R given by the conservation of momentum:

$$mv_R + \hbar K_\gamma = 0. \tag{8.13}$$

Hence the recoil energy of the nucleus is

$$E_R = \tfrac{1}{2}mv_R^2 = \frac{1}{2m}\hbar^2 K_\gamma^2 = E_\gamma^2/2mc^2 \tag{8.14}$$

since $E_\gamma = \hbar c K_\gamma$.

The magnitude of v_R and E_R are significant in an understanding of the process. We can easily estimate from equations (8.13) and (8.14) that for the Ir^{191} 0·129 MeV photon $v_R \approx 228$ m s^{-1} and $E_R \approx 0·05$ eV. This is equivalent to a shift of about 10^{14} s^{-1} in the frequency, which is considerably larger than the natural (Lorentzian) line width (of the order of 10^{10} s^{-1}). Hence there is no overlap in the energy of the emission spectra and the absorption spectra for a nucleus initially at rest; consequently no resonance fluorescence occurs. In fact it would appear necessary to provide a similar nucleus with $2E_R$ before it could reabsorb the photon, since E_R is lost to the emitter and another E_R must be given as kinetic energy to the absorber in order that momentum be conserved. However this argument has neglected a larger contribution to the line broadening—the Doppler shifts of the energies of emitted photons due to the initial velocities of the nuclei.

If the nuclei are free to move the line broadening is governed by the velocity distribution law and leads to a Gaussian shape of temperature-dependent width. As the temperature is raised, one would expect the Doppler-broadened line to embrace the recoil-shifted frequency and resonance effects to be observed. At 300 K the line width is about $2E_R$, and thus resonance absorption should occur at room temperature. On cooling from this temperature, Mössbauer observed an **increase** in the resonance absorption (instead of the decrease expected from the above arguments). After further investigation he concluded that:

(i) Some γ photons were emitted without recoil.
(ii) These were **not** Doppler broadened, the only spread being the natural linewidth.

In this experiment the radioactive nuclei (of source and absorber) were part of a crystal. Two distinct components are observed in the γ-ray spectrum.

The Gaussian-shaped component with a shifted central frequency accompanies the unshifted component. The effects of temperature are summarized in Table 8.4.

Table 8.4   Effect of increase of temperature on the components of the γ-ray spectrum

Component	Width	Relative intensity (integrated)
Unshifted	Unchanged (Lorentzian)	Decrease (proportional Debye–Waller factor)
Shifted	Increases (Gaussian)	Increases

There is always a shifted component however low the temperature, and this inelastic emission is accompanied by the creation or annihilation of phonons (instead of recoil as in the case of a free atom). The occurrence of Mössbauer-effect processes relies on the transfer of the energy E_R to the lattice system, creating a crystal excitation, rather than one or two atoms taking up E_R as kinetic energy. Thus the properties of the lattice are related to the probability of the occurrence of the Mössbauer effect. Conversely, observations on the Mössbauer effect provide information about the phonons. We can see very easily how the energy E_R can be fed into the phonon system by considering the transition probability of a γ-emission process from a nucleus bound in a crystal. As in Section 5.6, the transition probability is proportional to the square of the matrix element joining the two states. The initial and final states must include the lattice and the active nuclei, and we may write

$$\Omega(n_f, n_i, \gamma) = |\langle n_f \psi(\gamma - 1)| \, e^{i\mathbf{K}_\gamma \cdot \mathbf{r}} O_\gamma |n_i \psi(\gamma)\rangle|^2 \tag{8.15}$$

for the probability that a nuclei goes from state $|\psi(\gamma)\rangle$ to state $|\psi(\gamma - 1)\rangle$ while the lattice goes from state $|n_i\rangle$ to state $|n_f\rangle$. The operator O_γ involves only the nuclear properties, and the phase factor ensures that the emission has a well-defined wave vector $\mathbf{K}_\gamma$. These may be separated:

$$\Omega(n_f, n_i, \gamma) = |\langle n_f | e^{i\mathbf{K}_\gamma \cdot \mathbf{r}} |n_i\rangle \langle \psi(\gamma - 1)|O_\gamma |\psi(\gamma)\rangle|^2 \tag{8.16}$$

the second term depending on the details of the nuclear decay. Hence the probability $\Omega(n_f n_i)$ that there is a transition from phonon state n_i to n_f is

$$\Omega(n_f n_i) = |\langle n_f | e^{i\mathbf{K}_\gamma \cdot \mathbf{r}} |n_i\rangle|^2 \tag{8.17}$$

where we are not worrying about constants of proportionality. Now the recoilless emission corresponds to no change in the phonon state, i.e. $n_f = n_i$; so the intensity of this component depends on $\Omega(n_i n_i)$. According to Lipkin[14] the energy E_R is the average energy transferred to the lattice, and this may be written

$$\sum_f \left\{ \sum_{kj} \hbar\omega(kj)[n_f(kj) - n_i(kj)]\Omega(n_f n_i) \right\} = E_R. \tag{8.18}$$

The smallest change of state is the creation of one phonon (say ω); so when we include the finite transition probabilities to larger changes we can say that

$$E_R > \hbar\omega \sum_{n_f \neq n_i} \Omega(n_f n_i) = \hbar\omega[1 - \Omega(n_i n_i)] \tag{8.19}$$

the last step utilizing the normalization

$$\sum_{n_f} \Omega(n_f n_i) = 1. \tag{8.20}$$

The inequality (8.19) may be rearranged to give

$$\Omega(n_i n_i) > 1 - E_R/\hbar\omega \tag{8.21}$$

for which modes $\hbar\omega > E_R$ clearly shows that recoilless events are an essential feature of γ emission from crystal-bound nuclei.

If we write the usual transformation to normal coordinates in equation (8.17) and use the definition (8.9b), it is not difficult to show that this probability $\Omega(n_i n_i)$ is directly proportional to the Debye–Waller factor encountered in X-ray scattering (with K_γ replacing Q).

The interpretation of the results of Mössbauer scattering experiments is somewhat complex, and in most cases the result can be obtained more directly and accurately by neutron-scattering measurements. The Mössbauer technique is particularly suited to studying impurity effects (see Section 8.11) in which the γ-active nuclei is an impurity in a host lattice. An advantage over other techniques is that the γ photon can be absorbed only by an impurity nucleus similar to the emitter, and hence the γ photons used to irradiate the lattice (plus impurities) probe only the motions of the impurities. Surface effects have also been investigated by these techniques. Further accounts may be found in Frauenfelder[15] and a more recent review by O'Connor[16] discusses the relation of the Mössbauer effect with the properties of solids. A series *Mössbauer Effect Methodology*[17] provides a running account of developments.

8.6 Neutrons

We subdivided the discussion of photons into four energy ranges. Those with lowest energy, infrared photons, have energies comparable with those of phonons, but have momenta that are negligible compared with phonon momenta ($\hbar k$). X-ray photons have momenta comparable with phonon momenta, but have energies six orders of magnitude larger. Neutrons can be collimated into beams that have both energy and momentum comparable with the corresponding phonon values. The momentum of a slow neutron $(10^{-3}–10^{-1} \text{ eV})$, given by $(2mE)^{1/2}$, is about $10^{-24}–10^{-23} \text{ kg m s}^{-1}$; a phonon in a crystal with a lattice spacing of 40 nm has $|\mathbf{k}_{max}| \approx 10^{10} \text{ m}^{-1}$, and hence $|\hbar\mathbf{k}_{max}| \approx 10^{-24} \text{ kg m s}^{-1}$. Thus, subject to the existence of a coupling mechanism, we may expect single phonons to produce significant scattering and the measurements of this to yield valuable and direct information on the phonon spectrum. This is indeed the case; neutron experiments are the most valuable source of data available on phonon energies.

The analogue of the scattering amplitude f of X-ray analysis is the neutron scattering length b. When this refers to a single nucleus without spin it is usually written b_0; in a crystal the neutron scattering amplitude for a nucleus at site $l\kappa$ is $b_{l\kappa}$. It is found that the scattered neutrons have two components: (a) coherent and (b) incoherent. These arise from the details of the nuclear structure and since, for the analysis of the lattice dynamical properties, we shall be concerned with only the coherent component, a crude picture will suffice to indicate the origin of the two parts. Suppose the scattering nucleus has a spin $\mathscr{I}$, the compound nucleus formed by interaction with the neutron has spin $\mathscr{I} \pm \frac{1}{2}$ and there is a strong interaction between the nucleus and the neutron which quickly distributes the neutron energy among all the nucleons. There will be a random time delay before the neutron 'collects' enough energy to be re-emitted, and hence it is emitted incoherently (there being no time correlation with motion of the absorbed neutron or with neutrons emitted from other nuclei). Alternatively, we may suppose that the neutron is not absorbed by a nucleus but passes through or close to it with scattering but with no discontinuity in its motion—hence it remains coherent. Thus, in general, neutron diffraction will display effects arising from both of these models of the scattering mechanism, and we would expect perfect crystals of identical atoms with zero-spin nuclei to be predominantly coherent scatterers.

The average scattering length for the coherent component may be written:

$$\bar{b} = \frac{1}{s} \sum_{\kappa=1}^{s} b_{l\kappa} \tag{8.22a}$$

and the corresponding cross-section

$$\sigma_{co} = 4\pi \bar{b}^2 \tag{8.22b}$$

since, unlike X-ray scattering, $\bar{b}$ is independent of angle and of the neutron wavelength $h/\sqrt{(2mE)}$. The incoherent scattering cross-section is given by

$$\sigma_{inco} = 4\pi(\overline{b^2} - \bar{b}^2). \tag{8.23}$$

This component of the scattered neutron intensity is of less interest in probing the fundamental crystal excitations, since it is a sum of random phase intensities from independent scattering centres, but it can be used to give information about the frequency distribution; a direct relationship exists only for monatomic cubic crystals (see Brockhouse[18]). By contrast, the coherent component is strongly correlated with the phase relationships of neighbouring atoms established by the normal modes. Fortunately the scattered neutrons from the majority of elements are predominantly coherent, the most notable exceptions being vanadium ($\sigma_{inco} > 100\sigma_{co}$) and hydrogen ($\sigma_{inco} > 40\sigma_{co}$). The cross-section from a given nucleus is obtained from experiment, since theory cannot predict meaningful values.

The energy and momentum conservation laws govern the scattering processes and both elastic (Bragg—no phonon) and inelastic (one or more phonons) scattering occurs. The cross-sections for zero-, first-, etc., order processes are analogous to those for X-rays. Observations of scattering angles lead to reliable results for the energies of the physical (renormalized) phonons. The analysis of the results and their interpretation is a geometrical problem which can be simplified by suitable construction of the experiment. The two main methods are the 'time of flight' measurements and the use of the 'triple-axis' spectrometer. A description of these, together with the background of the subject and details of the interpretation of measurements, may be found, for example, in Brockhouse, Hautecler and Stiller[19] and Bacon.[20]

Theoretically, neutron scattering has been treated by various techniques; the one most compatible with the approach in this book is that of Maradudin and Fein.[21] They deduce expressions for the coherent first-order scattering cross-section of an anharmonic crystal. The predictions are a temperature-dependent shift (from harmonic values) and width of the scattered neutrons corresponding to the renormalized phonons with finite lifetimes. These peaks with finite widths can be observed. The formula derived by Maradudin and Fein for the first-order differential scattering cross-section is (in our notation)

$$\sigma_{co}^{(1)} = \frac{N}{m} \frac{b^2}{2\pi} \frac{|Q_s|}{|Q_0|} \frac{e^{-2W}}{1 - e^{-\beta\hbar\omega}} \sum_{kj} \left\{ \frac{[Q \cdot e(kj)]^2}{\omega(kj)} F(kj, \omega) \right\} \tag{8.24a}$$

where

$$F(kj, \omega) = \frac{\Gamma(kj, \omega)}{[\omega - \omega(kj) - \Delta(kj, \omega)]^2 + \Gamma^2(kj\omega)}$$
$$+ \frac{\Gamma(kj, \omega)}{[\omega + \omega(kj) + \Delta(kj, \omega)]^2 + \Gamma^2(kj, \omega)} \tag{8.24b}$$

the lifetimes Γ and shifts Δ corresponding to those of Sections 6.8 and 6.9 by the continuation $i\omega_p \to \omega$. The Debye–Waller factor here should include anharmonic terms for consistency, $\hbar\omega$ is the energy transferred from the neutron to the lattice and Q (the neutron scattering vector) $= k + K$.

Other accounts of slow neutron scattering may be found in Marshall and Lovesey[22] and Brockhouse.[19]

8.7 Electrons

The behaviour of electrons in a crystal determines its properties more than any other factor. The interplay of electron properties and phonons may or may not be important in a particular problem, but the existence of this coupling leads to a variety of phenomena too numerous to deal with in a book of this kind. Many research monographs are devoted to detailed considerations of specific effects arising from electron–phonon interactions, and some of these are listed in the references (see the end of this section). Along with the general attitude of this chapter, we consider only the origin of an interaction and indicate some of the effects associated with it.

The general crystal Hamiltonian involves five terms:

$$H = \text{k.e. (ions)} + \text{p.e. (ions–ions)} + \text{k.e. (electrons)}$$
$$+ \text{p.e. (electrons–electrons)} + \text{p.e. (electrons–ions).} \quad (8.25)$$

We based our lattice dynamical formulation on the first two terms, but now we must look at the other terms explicitly. In the earlier parts of the book, we have used adiabatic (Born–Oppenheimer) approximation, which assumes that the atomic electrons move so easily relative to the heavier nuclei that they retain their configuration (when the nuclei move) without any time delay. The Schrödinger equation, for a crystal with the nuclei held static in positions r_i (where i runs over all the atoms) is

$$H_0(r_i)\phi(q_s, r_i) = \varepsilon(r_i)\phi(q_s, r_i) \quad (8.26)$$

where q_s is an electron coordinate, s labelling the electrons. The form of equation (8.26) reflects the approximation of ignoring the kinetic energy of the nuclei, since $H_0(r_i)$ includes the second, third, fourth and fifth terms of the Hamiltonian (8.25). If the nuclei are now allowed to move and they take up a new configuration (say $r_{i'}$), we have a corresponding eigenvalue equation for $\varepsilon(r_{i'})$. The solutions of these 'static arrangements' may be used as unperturbed eigenvectors to compute the effect of the nuclear motions. A given instantaneous configuration may be written in terms of the lattice vectors $r^{l\kappa}$ and the displacements $u^{l\kappa}$ of the nuclei from these sites. If the vector r represents any one of the arrangements such as r_i:

$$r = r^{l\kappa} + u^{l\kappa} \quad (8.27)$$

where $u^{l\kappa}$ is time dependent in general but, for equation (8.26), $u^{l\kappa}$ becomes $u_i^{l\kappa}$ (a particular static set of displacements). Employing the standard methods of perturbation theory [expanding $\psi(q_s, r)$ and $\varepsilon(r)$ in terms of $\phi(q_s, r_i)$ and $\varepsilon(r_i)$ with the expansion parameter proportional to u], we can show that the adiabatic approximation requires $r_i \to r^{l\kappa}$ (all atoms in their equilibrium positions). The wave function becomes a product

$$\psi = a(u^{l\kappa})\phi(q_s, r^{l\kappa}) \quad (8.28a)$$

and the new energies

$$E = \varepsilon(\mathbf{u}^{l\kappa} = 0) + E^{(2)} \qquad (8.28b)$$

$E^{(2)}$ is the effect of the kinetic energy of the ions together with the modification of the potential energy due to displacements. The first-order correction to the energy vanishes (for equilibrium) and the first-order correction to the wave function ϕ does not affect the energy unless we include higher orders.

Now let us consider the last term in (8.25)—the interaction between the electrons and ions—with the ions displaced. Writing the potential $\sum_{\text{el. ions}} U(\mathbf{q}_s - \mathbf{r})$ and expanding in powers of the displacements, the first term $\sum_{s,l\kappa} U(\mathbf{q}_s - \mathbf{r}^{l\kappa})$ is included above and we consider the linear term as a perturbation H'

$$H'_{e-i} = - \sum_{\substack{s \\ l\kappa}} \left(\frac{\partial U}{\partial \mathbf{u}^{l\kappa}} \right)_{\mathbf{u}=0} \mathbf{u}^{l\kappa}. \qquad (8.29)$$

Using the normal coordinate transformation (3.26a and 3.34a) this becomes

$$H'_{e-i} = - \sum_{\substack{s \\ l\kappa}} \nabla U_{\mathbf{u}=0} \sum_{\mathbf{k}j} \left\{ \left[\frac{\hbar}{2Nm_\kappa\omega(\mathbf{k}j)} \right]^{1/2} e^{i\mathbf{k}\cdot\mathbf{r}^{l\kappa}}(a^+_{-\mathbf{k}j} + a_{\mathbf{k}j})\,\mathbf{e}(\mathbf{k}j) \right\}. \qquad (8.30)$$

The effect of this term operating on the crystal state is to create or annihilate a phonon and simultaneously modify the electron state. Let $\mathbf{p}$ be the electron wave vector (corresponding to the phonon wave vector $\mathbf{k}$) and suppose the modification to the phonon state is accompanied by scattering of the electron state from $\mathbf{p}_i$ to $\mathbf{p}_f$. The transition probability for this process is

$$\Omega(\text{if}) = \frac{2\pi}{\hbar} |\langle f|H'_{e-i}|i\rangle|^2 f(p_i)[1 - f(p_f)] \qquad (8.31a)$$

where

$$\langle f|H'_{e-i}|i\rangle = \mathbf{h}_\pm(\mathbf{k}j) \cdot \mathbf{h}(\mathbf{p}) \qquad (8.31b)$$

$$\mathbf{h}_\pm(\mathbf{k}j) \equiv - \left\{ \begin{matrix} [n(\mathbf{k}j) + 1]^{1/2} \\ n(\mathbf{k}j)^{1/2} \end{matrix} \right\} \sum_{l\kappa} \left[\frac{\hbar}{2Nm_\kappa\omega(\mathbf{k}j)} \right]^{1/2} e^{-i\mathbf{k}\cdot\mathbf{r}^{l\kappa}}\,\mathbf{e}(\mathbf{k}j) \qquad (8.31c)$$

$$\mathbf{h}(\mathbf{p}) \equiv \langle \mathbf{p}_f|\nabla U|\mathbf{p}_i\rangle \qquad (8.31d)$$

and $f(\mathbf{p}_i)$ is the Fermi–Dirac function, the factor $f(p_i)(1 - f(p_f))$ ensures that there is an electron $\mathbf{p}_i$ initially and that the state $\mathbf{p}_f$ is available. The two parts of (8.31c) correspond to the creation $[n(\mathbf{k}j) + 1]$ and annihilation $[n(\mathbf{k}j)]$ of a phonon $\mathbf{k}j$.

Applying Bloch's theorem to the electron states we may write

$$\langle p_f| = e^{-i\mathbf{p}_f\cdot\mathbf{r}^{l\kappa}}\langle \psi_{p_f}(\mathbf{q})| \qquad (8.32a)$$

$$|p_i\rangle = e^{i\mathbf{p}_i\cdot\mathbf{r}^{l\kappa}}|\psi_{p_i}(\mathbf{q})\rangle. \qquad (8.32b)$$

The phase parts may be grouped with that in equation (8.31c) to give a term $e^{i(p_i - p_f - k).r^{l\kappa}}$. Thus with the sum over lattice sites, this factor is $N\Delta(\mathbf{p}_i - \mathbf{p}_f - \mathbf{k})$ where the $\Delta(\ )$ is defined by equation (3.29). Thus the explicit form of equation (8.31b) becomes (for one atom per unit cell, $m_\kappa = m$)

$$\langle f|H'_{e-i}|i\rangle = \begin{Bmatrix} [n(\mathbf{k}j) + 1]^{1/2} \\ n(\mathbf{k}j)^{1/2} \end{Bmatrix} \left[\frac{N\hbar}{2m\omega(\mathbf{k}j)} \right]^{1/2} I_{\mathbf{k}j}(p_i, p_f)\Delta(\mathbf{p}_i - \mathbf{p}_f - \mathbf{k})$$

(8.33a)

where

$$I_{\mathbf{k}j}(\mathbf{p}_i, \mathbf{p}_f) \equiv \langle \psi_{p_f}(\mathbf{q})| \, \mathbf{e}(\mathbf{k}j) \cdot \nabla U |\psi_{p_i}(\mathbf{q})\rangle$$

(8.33b)

so that the computation of the interaction between the electrons and the phonons reduces to an investigation of $I_{\mathbf{k}j}(\mathbf{p}_i, \mathbf{p}_f)$. Since this matrix representing the interaction involves details of the electron states, further development requires explicit statements of the model, e.g. representations of metals or semiconductors. Bardeen and Pines[23] discuss the basic problems in metals and, with suitable approximations, deduce an expression for the interaction. The Bohm and Pines[24–26] collective coordinates for the electron motions provide a description in terms of screening of the interionic potential due to displacements. This leads to coupled electron (plasma)–ion waves similar to longitudinal elastic waves.

The electron–phonon interaction is a fundamental part of models to explain the properties of superconductors. First suggested by Fröhlich,[27,28] taken up by Bohm, Pines, Nakajima and others, and culminating in the outstanding paper by Bardeen, Cooper and Schrieffer[29] (BCS), the electron–phonon coupling and electron–electron coupling via an intermediate phonon has become an underlying feature of theories of superconductivity. For a general reference see (for example) Rickaysen.[30]

In a semiconductor the interaction may be investigated by its effect on the transport properties.[31] An electron 'colliding' with a phonon may transfer momentum to the phonon and the charge current is modified. Phonons are considerably 'heavier' than electrons, and hence little kinetic energy will be lost by the electron, but the momentum may be significantly changed. Clearly the effect is dependent on the number of phonons, and hence leads to an increase of resistance with temperature (as shown in pure normal-state metals; in semiconductors other temperature effects, such as increase in numbers of carriers, are larger at low temperatures). The actual atoms of a perfect crystal do **not** scatter electrons—the scattering depends solely on displacements (or, of course, on any other factor, such as imperfections or impurities, marring the perfect lattice). The phonon scattering of electrons is the dominant process in high-temperature perfect crystals. Both acoustic and optic modes may produce scattering, but at normal temperatures the energies involved are such as to make the former more important. Furthermore, often we need only consider the longitudinal modes, since the coupling term involves $e(\mathbf{k}j) \cdot \nabla U$, and hence, if the modes $\mathbf{k}j$ are pure longitudinal and transverse modes, the transverse modes contribute nothing unless umklapp processes are important. On a band picture, and considering only longitudinal phonons, the mechanism of interaction is that the longitudinal density variations cause a narrowing (compression) or a widening (expansion) of the band gap. This may be described in terms of deformation parameters.

Other effects arising from electron–phonon interactions are acoustoelectric effects[32] such as phonon drag,[33] acoustic amplification[34] and intervalley scattering mechanisms,[33] and ultrasonic attenuation. General reviews on acoustoelectric effects by Einspruch,[35] Spector,[36] and more recently by Meyer and Jorgensen,[37] give many references to work on specific areas. The electron–phonon effects enter into so many aspects of physics that many are not even mentioned here—the review by Sham and Ziman[38] and books on semiconductors and superconductors should be consulted for a proper perspective. Most theoretical work is couched in the Green's-function formulation, and books dealing with these techniques usually discuss electron–phonon coupling.

Three examples of the form $I_{\mathbf{k}j}(\mathbf{p}_i, \mathbf{p}_f)$ [equation (8.33b)] are shown in Table 8.5. The first column gives some indication of the approximations involved, but for a full specification the detailed derivation should be read, the reference to which is given.

Table 8.5 Details of the electron–phonon coupling matrix for specific models

Model	Reference	$I_{\mathbf{k}j}(\mathbf{p}_i, \mathbf{p}_f)$	Definitions
Rigid ion (Wigner–Seitz method)	39	$-ie(\mathbf{k}j) \cdot (\mathbf{k} + \mathbf{K})D_0 G(\mathbf{k} \cdot \mathbf{q}_0)$	$D_0 = U(q_0) - E_0$ $U(q_0) =$ energy of electron on Wigner–Seitz cell boundary $E_0 =$ energy of electron $\mathbf{p} = 0$ (i.e. lowest) $G(\mathbf{k}, \mathbf{q}_0) = G(x)$ $\equiv 3x^{-3}(x \cos x - \sin x)$ (cf. scattering function for a square well)
Deformation potential (small k)	38	$-i\dfrac{\hbar}{4m^*}\{e(\mathbf{k}j) \cdot [\mathbf{p}_i(\mathbf{k} \cdot \mathbf{p}_i) + \mathbf{p}_f(\mathbf{k} \cdot \mathbf{p}_f)]\}$	m^* is a parameter but approximately the free-electron mass
Bardeen's method Hartree model (Fermi–Thomas screening for long waves)	40, 23	$-i\dfrac{k}{\sqrt{(Nm)}}\left[\dfrac{Ne^2}{\varepsilon_0 k^2} + \gamma D_0 G(\mathbf{k} \cdot \mathbf{q}_0)\right]$	$\varepsilon_0 =$ permittivity of free space $\gamma = \dfrac{\|\psi_0(\mathbf{q}_0)\|^2}{\langle\|\psi_0(\mathbf{q})\|^2\rangle}$ $G(x)$ and D_0 as in rigid-ion model

8.8   A generalized crystal excitation (generalon)

The periodic structure of a crystal governs the properties of any excitation mobile within it. Whatever the nature of the excitation, certain characteristic features are exhibited. With this in mind, perhaps we can extract these salient features for an unspecified " 'on'', which we shall refer to as a 'generalon'.

For clarity, we shall try this initially for a one-dimensional monatomic crystal as in Figures 8.4(a), which shows all the atoms in the same ground (lowest) state. Figure 8.4(b) shows the same lattice, but where the atom at site l is excited to a higher state. Now we shall not specify what kind of excitation this is—it could be a displacement, a vibration, an ionization, an orbital excitation, a spin excitation, etc.—or how it was put there; we postulate only that an atom l is in a different state to the others. Now if the atoms are isolated, this situation will persist—the excitation f will stay for all time at the site l, all the other atoms remaining in the ground state. However, if the coupling between neighbouring atoms involves the coordinates which also describe the excited state f, the excited state may transfer to another atom with a finite probability.

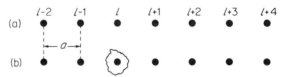

Figure 8.4   One-dimensional lattice with (a) all atoms in the lowest state $|0\rangle$ and (b) atom l in state $|f\rangle$ and others in state $|0\rangle$

The Hamiltonian for the whole linear chain of N atoms is,

$$H = \sum_{l=1}^{N} H_l + \frac{1}{2}\sum_{ll'}{}' V_{ll'} \tag{8.34}$$

where H_l is the Hamiltonian of an isolated atom and $V_{ll'}$ is the energy of interaction of the atoms at l and l' and the prime on the summation excludes the term $l = l'$. The form of $V_{ll'}$ depends on the nature of the excitation. Suppose there is only one excited atom in the chain of N atoms and this state (of the whole chain) is written $|l(f), 0\rangle$ (i.e. all atoms in state $|0\rangle$ except atom l which is in the state $|f\rangle$). Since this excited state is not localized on l, there is a finite probability that it will be found at any of the N sites. Thus the solution to the Schrödinger equation for the system

$$(H - E)\Phi^f = 0 \tag{8.35}$$

is a linear combination of $|l(f), 0\rangle$ where l may be any site:

$$\Phi^f = N^{-1/2}\sum_{l=1}^{N} b_l |l(f), 0\rangle \tag{8.36}$$

($N^{-1/2}$ is introduced as a normalizing factor), i.e.

$$P_l = (b_l)^2/N \tag{8.37a}$$

$$\sum_l P_l = 1 \tag{8.37b}$$

P_l being the probability of finding the excitation at the *l*th site. Substituting equation (8.36) and (8.34) into the Schrödinger equation (8.35) and forming the Dirac product with $\langle l'(f), 0 |$, we have

$$\sum_l \left[b_l \langle l'(f), 0 | \sum_l H_l + \frac{1}{2} \sum_{\substack{l'' \\ l'''}}' V_{l''l'''} - E | l(f), 0 \rangle \right] = 0 \tag{8.38a}$$

which becomes

$$b_{l'} \left(N E_0 + \Delta E^f + \frac{1}{2} \sum_{\substack{l'' \\ l'''}}' V_{l''l'''} - E \right) + \sum_l M_{l'l} b_l = 0 \tag{8.38b}$$

where ΔE^f = the excitation energy for an isolated atom, E_0 is the ground state energy for an isolated atom, and the third term in parentheses is the potential energy of interaction if the excited state is localized on one atom. Thus we may write

$$\sum_{l(\neq l')} M_{l'l} b_l - \varepsilon^f b_{l'} = 0 \tag{8.39a}$$

where

$$M_{l'l} \equiv \langle l(f)l'(0) | V_{ll'} | l'(f)l(0) \rangle \tag{8.39b}$$

and ε^f is the energy associated with the motion of the excited state (i.e. the energy of its transfer or, formally, the total energy minus the energy of the chain if the excitation cannot move). The matrix $M_{l'l}$ determines the transition (atom l' excited, atom l in ground state) → (l excited, l' in ground state).

The form of the solution to equation (8.39a) may be deduced by invoking the translational symmetry of the lattice. Introducing periodic boundary conditions, every atom is identical, and hence the probability of finding an atom excited is the same for all atoms. From equations (8.36) and (8.37)

$$|b_l|^2 = 1 \tag{8.40a}$$

which has the most general solution

$$b_l = e^{ikla} \tag{8.40b}$$

i.e. the probability amplitude depends only on a phase factor with a wave vector (as shown in Section 2.3)

$$k = \frac{2\pi}{Na} n \tag{8.40c}$$

where n is an integer in the range

$$-\tfrac{1}{2}N < n \le \tfrac{1}{2}N. \tag{8.40d}$$

Using equation (8.40b) in equation (8.39a), we see that ε^{f} has a set of solutions each characterized by a particular k. Hence we write

$$\varepsilon_k^f = \sum_{l(\ne l')} M_{l'l}\, e^{ika(l-l')} \tag{8.41}$$

which is a dispersion relation for our 'generalon'.

With the assumption that the excited state will transfer only to a nearest atom ($l' \pm 1$), the l summation in equation (8.41) reduces to two terms. Furthermore, if we assume that there is no preference for which direction it moves, it has equal probability of transferring to $l = l' + 1$ or to $l = l' - 1$; so $M_{l',l'+1} = M_{l',l'-1} \equiv M$. The generalon dispersion [equation (8.41)] simplifies to

$$\varepsilon_k^f = M\, e^{ika} + M\, e^{-ika} = 2M \cos ka. \tag{8.42}$$

From these simple arguments, we see that any well defined excited state f associated with an isolated atom becomes a band of N states, each state being specified by a value of $\mathbf{k}$ lying in the range (8.40d). Although we included 'displacement' as one of the examples of the localized excitations, only small-$\mathbf{k}$ optic modes may be considered in this way. These are the only modes that have energies even approximately localized at a lattice site. This is reflected in the result (8.42) which we recognize as being 'optic' **not** 'acoustic'.

The generalization to three dimensions is easily achieved; the dispersion corresponding to equation (8.42) becomes

$$\varepsilon_{\mathbf{k}}^f = \sum_{l(\ne l')} M_{l'l}\, e^{i\mathbf{k}.(\mathbf{l}-\mathbf{l}')} \tag{8.43a}$$

$$\mathbf{l} \equiv \sum_{\alpha} l_\alpha \mathbf{a}_\alpha, \qquad \alpha = 1, 2, 3 \tag{8.43b}$$

$$\mathbf{k} = \sum_{\alpha} \frac{2\pi}{N_\alpha} n_\alpha b_\alpha \tag{8.43c}$$

$$-\tfrac{1}{2}N_\alpha < n_\alpha \le \tfrac{1}{2}N_\alpha \tag{8.43d}$$

$$N = N_1 N_2 N_3 = \text{number of atoms} \tag{8.43e}$$

b_α being the reciprocal-lattice basis vectors. Hence, for nearest-neighbour-only interactions in a simple cubic lattice

$$\varepsilon_{\mathbf{k}}^f = 2M \sum_{\alpha} \cos k_\alpha a. \tag{8.44}$$

These generalons may be treated as particles (quasiparticles in some terminology) with an effective mass for small $\mathbf{k}$:

$$m^* \equiv \hbar^2 \left(\frac{\partial^2 \varepsilon_k}{\partial k^2}\right)^{-1} = \frac{\hbar^2}{2Ma^2}. \tag{8.45}$$

This is intuitively satisfactory, since larger M means a stronger interaction, implying that the excited state transfers more easily (lower effective mass); similarly the a^{-2} dependence is compatible with the motion being easier when the atoms are closer together but only after the variation of M with a is taken into account.

In this treatment we have assumed that there is only one of these generalons in the crystal. Suppose two separated atoms are in the state f. Provided that the excited states do not come close (within the distance of non-negligible interaction), the two generalons remain independent. However, if they do, the energy is modified by the difference in the interaction energy between two excited atoms and between one excited atom and one in the ground state. The possibility of the former has not been included in our Schrödinger equation. We shall see some consequences of this later. Basically then, this theory is acceptable for a small number of generalons (so that the probability of two close atoms being excited is negligible); when they become numerous, the interactions between them become important and the 'self energies' must be included. The application in Section 8.10 serves to illustrate this point.

Finally, how do we create a generalon. Let the crystal be exposed to a 'beam of energy' characterized by a wave vector $\mathbf{Q}$. The coupling between the beam and the atoms will involve a field-like parameter for the beam and a coordinate required to describe the atomic states—say $C(\mathbf{A}, \xi)$. The probability that the crystal will make the transition from the ground state Φ_0 to a state Φ_k with one generalon k is determined by the matrix

$$B_{k0} = \langle \Phi_k^f | e^{i(\mathbf{Q}.\mathbf{r} - \mathbf{k}.\mathbf{r}^l)} C(\mathbf{A}, \xi) | \Phi_0 \rangle. \tag{8.46}$$

Using the three-dimensional form of equation (8.36), it is readily found that the condition of excitation is

$$B_{k0} \neq 0 \quad \text{only if } \mathbf{Q} = \mathbf{k}. \tag{8.47}$$

The coupling is with the crystalline state involving all the atoms and **not** with an individual atom from which the excitation diffuses. Recognizing this, we can see that expression (8.47) is the condition that the exciting energy (beam) is spatially in phase with the crystal excitation to which energy is to be given. In addition, the quanta of energy of the beam must be enough to reach the threshold for a localized excitation. This threshold is ΔE^f plus the change in interaction energy ΔV for the system if one atom is excited. So if $M_{l'l}$ is positive, we would expect a sharp onset of absorption at $\Delta E^f + \Delta V$ followed by a band of absorption frequencies subject to the condition (8.47). However, this selection rule is idealized. In a real crystal, imperfections and the interactions with other generalons (of same or different kind) allow a complex range of other possibilities.

Since for all excitations of interest the interatomic coupling $V_{ll'}$ is a function of separation of the atom l and l', and since phonons cause phase-related displacements of the atoms, in principle phonons can interact with any generalon. In practice, the magnitude depends on various factors and the effects may be drowned in a sea of complications.

8.9 Excitons

The dominant long-range interaction between atoms of molecular crystals is the Van der Waals weak attractive force discussed in Section 2.6. An excited electronic state of an atom may transfer to a similar atom through this interaction. Thus, in our generalon analysis, $V_{ll'}$ is given by equation (2.31) (if we consider only the dipole–dipole Van der Waals term). Since we are dealing with a relatively weak interaction, perturbation theory should provide an adequate approximation in these crystals. Following the steps of the general arguments of the previous section, we use for the ground state (all atoms unexcited) a product of unperturbed (isolated) atomic wave functions:

$$|l(0), 0\rangle = \prod_{l=1}^{N} |0\rangle_l. \tag{8.48a}$$

For the state where only one atom l is excited

$$|l(f), 0\rangle = |f\rangle_l \prod_{l'=1}^{N}{}' |0\rangle_{l'} \tag{8.48b}$$

where the product Π' excludes $l' = l$. Thus the state of the crystal when the excitation may be on any site [equation (8.36)] becomes

$$\Phi^f = N^{-1/2} \sum_l |f\rangle_l \prod_{l'=1}^{N}{}' |0\rangle_{l'}. \tag{8.49}$$

The effect of the interactions between atoms is to modify the ground-state energy NE_0, where E_0 is the atomic ground-state energy, by an amount

$$\Delta E_0^{(1)} = \frac{1}{2} \sum_{l \neq l'}{}' \langle l'(0), 0|V_{ll'}|l'(0), 0\rangle. \tag{8.50}$$

The total change in energy due to the excitation of one atom to the state f is

$$\Delta E = \Delta E^f + \Delta V + \varepsilon^f \tag{8.51a}$$

where ΔE^f is the energy difference between the atomic ground state and the excited state; ΔV is the change in the interaction energy when one atom is excited; ε^f is the energy associated with the excited state moving. In our first-order-perturbation approximation

$$\Delta V = \sum_{l(\neq l')} [\langle l'(f)l(0)|V_{ll'}|l'(f)l(0)\rangle - \langle l'(0)l(0)|V_{ll'}|l'(0)l(0)\rangle] \qquad (8.51b)$$

ε^f is given by the solution of equation (8.39a) with

$$M_{l'l} = \langle l(f)|[\langle l'(0)|V_{ll'}|l'(f)\rangle]|l(0)\rangle \qquad (8.52)$$

i.e. using the unperturbed states (8.48b). Thus if the atomic wave functions $|0\rangle$ and $|f\rangle$ are known, the energy transfer matrix $M_{l'l}$ may be computed explicitly.

The use of perturbation theory here is effectively a 'tight-binding' approximation. This kind of generalon is a 'Frenkel exciton'.[41] The concept of an excited atomic state which has a probability $1/N$ of being associated with a particular atom and whose dynamic behaviour is governed by the lattice periodicity is valid in crystals where the atomic wave functions have only small overlap with neighbouring atoms. Molecular crystals fall into this category, since all the electronic states are strongly localized. Some ionic crystals exhibit Frenkel exciton states, but in others the overlap is such that the excited electron is only localized to a larger volume which may contain several atoms.[42,43]

Wannier[44] considered the other limit, i.e. where the overlap is large and an electron orbit may be much greater than the interatomic spacing. When the atom is excited, an electron jumps to a higher state leaving a 'hole' in the lower state. For the Frenkel state, the electron and hole exist on the same site. As their separation increases, the Coulomb attraction between them is screened by other atoms and, for separation greater than five or six atomic spacings, the effect is that of a dielectric medium decreasing the attraction by a factor ε^{-1}. Thus for crystals with a small band gap and large relative permittivity (e.g. semiconductors such as germanium and silicon), the electron–hole pairs are weakly coupled and are separated by typically 100 lattice spacings.

Since we are concerned only with non-metals (in metals the electron states are continuous) and thermal excitations are small at normal and low temperatures, the lower state of interest is in the valence band and the electron jumps to the conduction band. Now this does not provide a charge-conducting system, since the negative electron and the positive hole are bound together by their Coulomb attraction. This bound electron–hole moves through the crystal as a 'Wannier exciton' (also called a 'Mott exciton'). Since the electron and hole no longer exist at the same site, the isolated atomic wave functions are inappropriate approximations; the situation is similar to a 'nearly free electron model', and hence wave functions representing the whole crystal should be used. The electron (and hole) experiences a uniform potential due to other electrons, and the lattice is taken into account by introducing an effective mass. The theoretical analysis of the spectra resulting from this state has been given by Elliott.[45]

Some crystals will satisfy neither criterion; an electron–hole localization which extends over one or two lattice spacings is not large enough to be a Wannier exciton nor small enough to be a Frenkel exciton. Extension of the Frenkel picture into this region is discussed by Overhauser[42] and by Dexter.[43] In such crystals one may expect a considerably more complex description or in some cases elements of both models to appear (Frenkel-like and Wannier-like excitons have been observed in xenon[46]).

Excitons are of prime interest in connection with the optical properties of solids. If an electron $\mathbf{p}$ in the valence band is excited to the conduction band and there has wave vector $\mathbf{p}'$, the nett effect is

$$\mathbf{Q} = \mathbf{p}' - \mathbf{p} \tag{8.53}$$

since the hole behaves with wave vector $-\mathbf{p}$. Now if this state is to be created by the absorption of a photon, $\mathbf{p}' \approx \mathbf{p}$ and this is called a 'direct transition'. These are usually represented on an energy diagram as vertical lines joining the states, as in Figure 8.5(a).

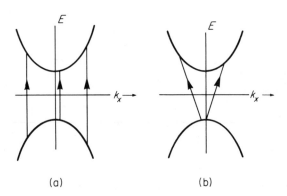

Figure 8.5 Transition between single-particle states (bands): (a) direct and (b) indirect

Other crystal excitations may be simultaneously involved in the photon absorption, and the momentum-conservation condition becomes (when one other generalon $\mathbf{k}$ is involved)

$$\mathbf{p}' - \mathbf{p} \pm \mathbf{k} \approx 0. \tag{8.54}$$

This leads to the possibility of indirect transitions, represented by non-vertical lines as in Figure 8.5(b). The most important of these are exciton–phonon states.

The various phonon branches for given **k** lead to a set of absorption edges subject to the transition being allowed by symmetry requirements. Such considerations have been discussed, for example, by McClean[47] and Elliott and Loudon.[48] At very low temperatures few phonons exist, and only processes involving the creation of a phonon [+ in equation (8.54)] are important; at high temperatures both creation and absorption of phonons contribute to the optical absorption. The details of the intensity will depend on the coupling between the photon and the electron state and (for indirect transitions) the coupling between the electron and the phonon.

The Hamiltonian including the coupling between exciton states and phonons to first order may be written

$$H = \sum_{\mathbf{f}\sigma} E_{\mathbf{f}\sigma} b_{\mathbf{f}\sigma}^+ b_{\mathbf{f}\sigma} + \sum_{\mathbf{k}j} \hbar\omega(\mathbf{k}j)(a_{\mathbf{k}j}^+ a_{\mathbf{k}j} + \tfrac{1}{2})$$

$$+ \sum_{\substack{\mathbf{f}\sigma \\ \mathbf{f}'\sigma \\ \mathbf{k}j}} \Delta(\mathbf{k} - \mathbf{f} + \mathbf{f}')D(\mathbf{k}j; \mathbf{f}\sigma, \mathbf{f}'\sigma')b_{\mathbf{f}\sigma}^+ b_{\mathbf{f}'\sigma'}(a_{-\mathbf{k}j}^+ + a_{\mathbf{k}j}) \qquad (8.55)$$

where $E_{\mathbf{f}\sigma}$ is the energy of an exciton $\mathbf{f}\sigma$, $\mathbf{f}$ being the wavevector and σ the branch (e.g. longitudinal or transverse, arising from p-state orbitals aligned parallel or perpendicular to $\mathbf{f}$); the b are the exciton second-quantization operators and D is the coupling parameter. D is dependent on the type of exciton and phonon involved, and its form varies according to the atomic and crystalline properties.[49,50] If the perturbation approximation is valid (it is often **not** valid for this coupling) the transition probabilities follow from equation (5.36) with H' given by the third term in equation (8.55) (which is really two terms—one for a phonon absorbed and one for a phonon created). These expressions lead to the absorption spectra and provide reasonable predictions for simple cases. In most cases the observed spectra are exceedingly complex, and their interpretation requires much careful analysis.

Articles reviewing the properties of excitons include Elliott[51] (semiconductors), Haken[52] (many-body approach), McClure[53] (molecular crystals), Knox[54] (general theory) and several relevant articles in a conference report on the optical properties of solids.[55] The interactions between excitons and phonons are discussed in detail in Toyazawa.[49,50]

8.10 Magnons

If the atomic excitation involves only a spin change and the electron is strongly localized at the site, the corresponding low-energy exciton is a spin wave or magnon. The spin reversal (say) may propagate through the lattice via the Heisenberg exchange interaction, which couples spins on different atoms. The magnon dispersion relations depend on the crystal structure, the nature of the magnetic ions and the strength of the exchange interaction. For a summarized version of the basic theory and properties of ferromagnetic and antiferromagnetic magnons, see Kittel.[56]

Since there is a probability $1/N$ that the excited spin state will be on a particular site, we may work in terms of spin deviations that have the same magnitude at each site but differ in phase to produce a wave. (Physically we may picture this as the magnetic dipole moment $2S$, corresponding to a spin inversion, being distributed over the N magnetic sites, the z component of each being decreased by $2S/N$. This is possible if the spin cants away from the z axis and precesses about the axis so that $S_z = S - a_l^+ a_l$ is a constant and S_x and S_y are determined by the phase; a_l^+ and a_l are the spin-deviation operators. These operators may be Fourier-transformed to magnon-creation and annihilation operators analogous to those of phonons. However, before utilizing these wave-like properties, let us look back to the atomic-energy-level picture.

If one spin inversion is created, the argument follows the general lines of Section 8.8. For clarity, let us revert to our one-dimensional lattice.

Suppose now another spin is inverted. The possibilities are indicated in Figure 8.6(b) and (c). If the second spin is outside the range of the exchange interaction with the first spin [diagram (b)], the resulting spin waves are independent. However, the interaction between two parallel spins is different from that between two antiparallel spins, so that if two close spins are inverted [diagram (c)] the Hamiltonian, and hence the energy of the spin wave, is modified. A pair of inverted spins having come together have a lower energy than when separated, so there is a tendency for them to remain together,

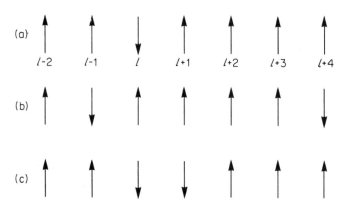

Figure 8.6   Linear chain of magnetic ions: (a) one spin inverted, (b) two separated spins inverted and (c) two adjacent spins inverted

giving rise to modified spin waves. By extension, one can conceive of multiple-spin complexes moving around in the lattice and interacting with other spin complexes. Thus the simple magnon concept is valid only at low temperatures at which the number of electronic spin states that are excited is small (i.e. $a_i^+ a_i/S \ll 1$).

The exchange interaction is strongly dependent on the interatomic separation, and this is modified by the periodic displacements due to the phonons. Clearly we may expect a coupling between magnons and phonons, subject to conservation laws. The interaction Hamiltonian is a special case of equation (8.55). Consider a phonon scattering a magnon $\mathbf{f}$ to state $\mathbf{f}'$. The amount of energy transferred from the phonon system to the magnon system is

$$\dot{U} = - \sum_{kj} \hbar\omega(\mathbf{k}j)\frac{d}{dt}\langle n(\mathbf{k}j)\rangle \tag{8.56}$$

which becomes [from the transition probability (5.38b)]

$$\dot{U} = -\frac{2\pi}{\hbar} \sum_{\substack{kj \\ f}} \hbar\omega(\mathbf{k}j)|D(\mathbf{k};\mathbf{f},\mathbf{f}')|^2$$

$$\times [n_{f'}(n_f + 1)(n(\mathbf{k}j) + 1) - n_f(n_{f'} + 1)n(\mathbf{k}j)]$$

$$\times \delta(E_{f'} - E_f + \hbar\omega(\mathbf{k}j))\Delta(\mathbf{f}' - \mathbf{f} + \mathbf{k}) \tag{8.57}$$

D being the coupling. D is determined by the dependence of the exchange energy on the relative ionic displacements $\mathbf{u}^{ll'}$; it is of the form,

$$D(\mathbf{k};\mathbf{f},\mathbf{f}') = 2S \sum_{\mathbf{r}_0^{ll'}} \mathbf{e}(\mathbf{k}j) \left[\frac{8\hbar}{mN\omega(\mathbf{k}j)}\right]^{1/2} J(\mathbf{u}^{ll'})$$

$$\times [e^{i\mathbf{f}\cdot\mathbf{r}_0^{ll'}} - e^{i\mathbf{f}'\cdot\mathbf{r}_0^{ll'}} - 1 + e^{-i\mathbf{k}\cdot\mathbf{r}_0^{ll'}}] \tag{8.58}$$

where $J(\mathbf{u}^{ll'})$ is the modified exchange integral.

Two-phonon processes will also contribute, but those in which two phonons are both created or both absorbed are much less important than the scattering corresponding to one created and one absorbed. This is a Raman-type process, in which a phonon $\mathbf{k}j$ and a magnon $\mathbf{f}\sigma$ scatter to produce a phonon $\mathbf{k}'j'$ and a magnon $\mathbf{f}'\sigma'$.

In a two sublattice antiferromagnet, there will be two interaction parameters D_1 and D_2, corresponding to coupling between parallel and antiparallel spins. Taking into account three terms [arising from interaction between (i) spins on sublattice a, (ii) spins on sublattice b and (iii) intersublattice terms] the analysis is no more difficult than for a ferromagnetic crystal.

General discussions on magnons appear in Mattis[57] and Keffer,[58] and particular reference to their interactions with phonons is made in Sinha and Upadhyaya[59,60] and in pp. 203–220 of Keffer's article. The first suggestion of such an interaction seems to be Akhiezer[61] and examples of recent treatments are Meissner[62] (including anharmonic effects) and Holden *et al.*[63] (including observations).

8.11 Excitations associated with crystal imperfections

This book has been almost entirely concerned with perfect crystals. At the end of most topics we have given indications of the next steps in the development. This section has this character; all the properties of phonons we have discussed have to be reconsidered to take into account the imperfections of real crystals. Here we give a brief summary of the way in which simple defects modify the vibrational properties of a lattice.

The smallest deviation from a perfect crystal is an impurity atom replacing an atom at a lattice site. This will cause a change in the local interatomic forces. If the impurity is an atom of the same kind differing only in mass (isotopic impurity), the force constants may be assumed to be unchanged from those in the perfect lattice. The effect of such an impurity is to introduce an additional frequency (higher than those of the perfect crystal modes) or a resonance (within the normal range). The additional frequency, a localized mode, appears if the impurity is lighter than its isotopic host (although it disappears as the masses approach the same value); the resonance is associated with a heavier impurity. Many impurities are well represented by this even if they are not isotopic with the host.

In the general case we must replace some of the masses and force constants in the equation of motion by those relevant to the impurities and to the interaction of the impurities with the host atoms. (In the case of large concentrations of impurities, the impurity–impurity interaction must also be included where appropriate. However, here we are assuming small concentrations such that each impurity atom is isolated from other impurities, its neighbours forming an otherwise perfect lattice.)

Supposing the impurity located at site l has mass M', and the interaction with host atoms is $\phi'^{ll'}_{\alpha\beta}$. The quantities

$$\Delta M \equiv M' - M \tag{8.59a}$$

$$\Delta\phi^{ll'}_{\alpha\beta} \equiv \phi'^{ll'}_{\alpha\beta} - \phi^{ll'}_{\alpha\beta} \tag{8.59b}$$

determine the deviation of the motion of the impurity atom from that of an atom identical to those forming the rest of the lattice. The equation of motion of the impurity atom may be written as in equation (1.9) (using the Einstein summation convention defined in Section 1.4);

$$M'\ddot{u}^l_\alpha + \phi'^{ll'}_{\alpha\beta}u^{l'}_\beta = 0. \tag{8.60a}$$

This may be written

$$M\ddot{u}^l_\alpha + \phi^{ll'}_{\alpha\beta}u^{l'}_\beta + \Delta M\ddot{u}^l_\alpha + \Delta\phi^{ll'}_{\alpha\beta}u^{l'}_\beta = 0 \tag{8.60b}$$

or by defining

$$C_{\alpha\beta}^{ll'} \equiv -\Delta M \omega^2 \delta_{\alpha\beta} \delta_{ll'} + \Delta\phi_{\alpha\beta}^{ll'} \tag{8.60c}$$

equation (8.60b) becomes

$$M \ddot{u}_\alpha^l + \phi_{\alpha\beta}^{ll'} u_\beta^{l'} + C_{\alpha\beta}^{ll'} u_\beta^{l'} = 0. \tag{8.61}$$

The perfect crystal in the harmonic approximation was described in terms of the Green's function G^0 (Section 6.6) and we may define Green's functions G for the imperfect lattice whose singularities yield the resonances. These functions are related through the matrix C by[64]

$$G = (1 + G^0 C)^{-1} G^0$$

$$= G^0 + G^0 C G^0 + G^0 C G^0 C G^0 + \dots . \tag{8.62}$$

Since the range of interaction is limited to the proximity of the defect, C is a finite matrix and need extend over only the affected sites. For the special case mentioned earlier, the isotopic impurity C is a diagonal matrix, since $\Delta\phi$ is zero. From the arguments of Section 1.5 [in particular from equation (1.11)] we know that the solution to equation (8.61) with $C = 0$ is

$$\omega^2 \equiv \omega_0^2(\mathbf{k}) = \sum_{l'} \frac{1}{M} \phi_{\alpha\beta}^{ll'} e^{-i\mathbf{k}.(\mathbf{r}^l - \mathbf{r}^{l'})} \tag{8.63a}$$

with the displacement of atom at $\mathbf{r}^l$ due to this mode determined by the eigenvectors

$$\xi(\mathbf{r}^l) = \xi_0 \, e^{i\mathbf{k}.\mathbf{r}^l}. \tag{8.63b}$$

If we include now the isotopic defect at $l = 0$

$$C_{\alpha\beta}^{ll'} = -\Delta M \omega^2 \delta_{\alpha\beta} \delta_{ll'} \tag{8.64}$$

equation (8.61) becomes

$$-M\omega^2 \xi(\mathbf{r}^l) + \phi_{\alpha\beta}^{ll'} \xi(\mathbf{r}^{l'}) - \Delta M \omega^2 \xi(0) \delta_{\alpha\beta} \delta_{l0} = 0. \tag{8.65}$$

Expressing $\xi(\mathbf{r}^l)$ as a Fourier sum,

$$\xi(\mathbf{r}^l) = \sum_{\mathbf{k}} \xi_{\mathbf{k}} \, e^{i\mathbf{k}.\mathbf{r}^l} \tag{8.66a}$$

or inversely

$$\xi_{\mathbf{k}} = \sum_{l} \xi(\mathbf{r}^l) e^{-i\mathbf{k}.\mathbf{r}^l} \tag{8.66b}$$

and, multiplying equation (8.65) through by $e^{-i\mathbf{k}.\mathbf{r}^l}$ and summing over all l, we see

$$-M\omega^2 \xi_{\mathbf{k}} + \phi_{\alpha\beta}^{ll'} \xi_{\mathbf{k}} e^{i\mathbf{k}.(\mathbf{r}^{l'} - \mathbf{r}^l)} - \Delta M \omega^2 \xi(0) \delta_{\alpha\beta} \delta_{l0} = 0. \tag{8.67}$$

Noting the result (8.63a), the solution of equation (8.67) is

$$\xi_k = \frac{\Delta M \omega^2 \xi(0)}{M(\omega_0^2(k) - \omega^2)} \tag{8.68}$$

which may be summed over $\mathbf{k}$ to give a relation for the frequency associated with the impurity:

$$\sum_k \frac{\Delta M \omega^2}{M[\omega_0^2(k) - \omega^2]} = 1 \tag{8.69}$$

since, from equation (8.66a), $\xi(0) = \sum_k \xi_k$.

When the substituted atom is not an isotope of the host, the effect of $\Delta \phi_{\alpha\beta}^{ll'}$ must be included. Following a similar argument to the above, we find that equation (8.69) becomes

$$\sum_k \frac{\Delta M \omega^2 [1 - f(\mathbf{k}, \omega)]}{M(\omega_0^2(k) - \omega^2)} = 1 \tag{8.70}$$

where $f(\mathbf{k}, \omega)$ is a function, dependent on the impurity—host force constant, which is zero in the isotopic case. The same approach may be made if the defect is a vacancy, but in the case of an interstitial extra terms appear in the summations.

Phonons may scatter from the point defects and the associated modes. The theory is similar to the scattering from any centre, namely the scattered wave is a plane wave modified by a spherical part whose intensity varies with r, θ, ϕ, and we look at the asymptotic solution. All distortions or defects will affect the phonons and their dynamics. Defects are classed according to their 'dimensionality'—a point defect being zero, a line dislocation being one, a stacking fault in a plane being two. Treatments of all these may be found in the literature, as may theories to take into account finite concentrations of impurities. The reviews of Lifshitz,[65] Lifshitz and Kosevich[66] and Maradudin[67,68] provide an excellent introduction to the subject and cover the basic theory. More recently there have been many papers discussing the effect of one- and two-dimensional defects on phonons, e.g. Agrawal[69] (line defects).

8.12 Summary

Since this chapter is itself a summary of the effects of phonons on other 'particles', this summary of it exemplifies Jonathan Swift's flea;[a] however we shall terminate the progression rather sooner.

The effects between **photons** and phonons have been separated into four groups. The first of these concerns **absorption**, the photons involved having **energies** comparable with phonon energies but **wavelengths** much longer

($\sim$ 20,000 lattice spacings). These **infrared** photons can give up their energy to create phonons. This causes an **attenuation** of the beam and the amount of energy absorbed by the lattice (in any frequency range) may be estimated by observing frequency dependence of the **transmitted intensity**. Clearly this may be observed as a function of **temperature** also. The effect of the temperature is to change the relative importance of the absorption processes (in which phonons are created) and the **emission** processes (in which phonons are destroyed so that a photon is emitted). At **low temperatures** only the former are important. The observed attenuation is due to the **difference** between these two fundamental processes summed over all allowed phonon combinations; it is always a **nett absorption** (unless some artificial population inversion has been established) since the **probability** for the creation of phonons is proportional to $(n + 1)$ compared with n for their destruction. We were primarily interested in the basic processes, so we did not develop the general theory of absorption of electromagnetic radiation by a solid. This may be found in most traditional textbooks and the results easily translated into the context of our discussion.

In contrast to the infrared photon, **X-ray** photons have **momenta** comparable with phonon momenta, although their energies are much greater (by a factor of about 10^5). Since the energies are so much greater, the phonon system cannot absorb an X-ray photon; here we are concerned with the **scattering** of the photon into a different momentum state. Scattering processes may result in the creation or annihilation of phonons, the number involved determining the **order** of the process; zero order corresponds to **Bragg** scattering from the crystal (modified by the **Debye–Waller** factor).

The **optical** photons are **intermediate**; their energies are larger and their momenta smaller than those of phonons. The interesting phenomena here are the **Raman** and **Brillouin** scattering; the **inelastic** scattering of photons with the creation or annihilation of phonons. These two are distinct in **first order** analyses (involving **optic** or **acoustic** phonons, respectively) but the division is blurred in higher orders. In **second-order** analyses (as in X-ray scattering) there are **summation** and **difference** bands corresponding to (a) the two phonons **existing together** (either before or after the scattering event) and (b) one replacing another (one created, another destroyed in the same process). Processes which lead to a **higher** photon energy produce the **anti-Stokes** component; those which reduce the incident photon energy give the **Stokes** component. The temperature dependence of the intensity of these scattering spectra can be predicted by elementary considerations.

Going to higher energies than the X-rays, we come to the γ-ray photons. These can be emitted from an active nucleus bound in a lattice in such a way that the **recoil energy** is taken up as a **lattice-mode** not by the nucleus. Hence, despite the vast energy differences between γ-photons and phonons there are still **coupling** effects. These are known as **Mössbauer** scattering, after the original observer. Techniques based on this effect are used as **diagnostics** of certain properties such as **defects** and **surface effects**.

If we must cast a dew over the usefulness of photons in observing phonons, surely neutrons deserve the chrism.[b] Whereas photons have either energies or momenta or both well outside the range of the corresponding phonon values, phonons and **slow neutrons** have comparable **energies** and momenta. **Neutron-scattering** measurements have provided the most **accurate** data on the **dispersion** of **crystal excitations**—in particular phonons. **Line widths** of scattered neutrons have given valuable information on the **lifetime** of the phonons observed.

The interaction between **electrons** and phonons has numerous manifestations. In **semiconductors**, electron states may often be coupled by phonon processes. This leads to scattering of electrons **between bands** and between states in the **same band**, which may be observed as an effect on the **charge transport**. An **acoustic** wave couples with the electrons in a solid and the conduction electrons absorb energy from the wave. **Acoustoelectric** effects can also produce a transfer of energy **to** the elastic wave and hence **amplify** it. The most successful theory of **superconductivity** is based on the electron–phonon interaction, two electrons being coupled via an **intermediary**—a phonon. We have merely skimmed along the surface in this area due to the multiplicity of effects and the extra background material required for many of the phenomena.

Without the electron itself moving through the lattice, an **excited electronic state** can travel with phase relationships between adjacent atoms such that it is a **crystal excitation**. This is characterized by a **dispersion** band super-imposed on the **threshold** energy required to create the excited state on one atom. These **excitons** have interests ranging from **biological** systems through **chemical** physics to **semiconductors** and **insulators**. In semiconductors, the basic excitation which leads to the exciton states is a **well separated electron–hole pair**—the **Wannier** exciton. This is in contrast to the **tightly bound pair** (within one unit cell volume) which leads to the **Frenkel** exciton. We have not considered the related excitation—the **polaron**. In this, an electron becomes **trapped** in a centre of **polarization** induced by the electron itself. The electron moves through the lattice, accompanied by the polarized region.

The **low-lying** excitons corresponding to transitions between spin states are **magnons**—quantized **spin waves**. These give rise to a **side-band** structure on exciton spectra, and they also interact with phonons via the dependence of the **exchange** interaction on interatomic separation. Finally we considered modifications to the **lattice dynamics** introduced by crystal **defects** and the new modes that appear.

Chapter notes

[a] 'So, Nat'ralists observe, A flea
Hath smaller Fleas that on him prey
And these have smaller Fleas to bite 'em
And so proceed ad infinitum.'
Jonathan Swift

[b] 'Unlike are we, unlike, O princely Heart!
Unlike our uses and our destinies.
Our ministering two angels look surprise
On one another, as they strike athwart
Their wings in passing. Thou, bethink thee, art
A guest for queens for social pageantries,
With gages from a hundred brighter eyes
Than tears even can make mine, to play thy part
Of chief musician. What hast thou to do
With looking from the lattice-lights at me—
A poor, tired, wandering singer, singing through
The dark, and leaning up a cypress tree?
The chrism is on thine head—on mine the dew—
And Death must dig the level where these agree.'
Elizabeth Barrett Browning

References

1. Lax, M., and Burstein, E., *Phys. Rev.*, **97**, 39–52 (1955).
2. Johnson, F. A., *Progress in Semiconductors*, **9**, 181–235 (1965).
3. Loudon, R., *J. Phys. A.*, **3**, 233–245 (1970).
4. Houghton, J. T., and Smith, S. D., *Infra-red Physics*, Clarendon Press, Oxford, 1966.
5. Reissland, J. A., and Ray, D., *Tr. Mezhdunar. Konf. Fiz. Nizkikh. Temp.*, *10th, 1966 (10th Int. Conf. on Low Temp. Physics)*, Vol. 1, Viniti, Moscow, 1967, pp. 267–272.
6. Hardy, J. R., 'Raman scattering by phonons', in *Phonons, Scottish Universities Summer School, 1965* (Ed. Stevenson), Oliver and Boyd, London, 1966, pp. 267–272.
7. Loudon, R., *Adv. in Phys. (G.B.)*, **13**, 423–482 (1964).
8. Birman, J. L., *Phys. Rev.*, **131**, 1489–1496 (1963).
9. Griffin, A., *Rev. Mod. Phys.*, **40**, 167–205 (1968).
10. Smith, T., 'X-ray scattering by phonons', in *Phonons, Scottish Universities Summer School, 1965* (Ed. Stevenson), Oliver and Boyd, London, 1966, pp. 166–169.
11. Cochran, W., 'X-ray scattering by phonons', in *Phonons, Scottish Universities Summer School, 1965* (Ed. Stevenson), Oliver and Boyd, London, 1966, pp. 153–168.
12. Maradudin, A. A., Montroll, E. W., and Weiss, G. H., *Solid State Physics*, **3**, 231–258 (1963) Supplement.
13. Mössbauer, R. L., *Z. Physik*, **151**, 124–143 (1958).
14. Lipkin, H. J., *Ann. Phys. (New York)*, **26**, 115–121 (1964).
15. Frauenfelder, H. (Ed.), *The Mössbauer Effect*, Benjamin, New York, 1962 (a collection of reprints).

16. O'Connor, D. A., *Contemporary Phys.* (*G.B.*), **9**, 521–535 (1968).
17. Gruverman, I. J. (Ed.), *Mössbauer Effect Methodology*, Plenum Press, New York (seven volumes up to 1971).
18. Brockhouse, B. N., in *Phonons and Phonon Interactions, Aarhus Summer School, 1963* (Ed. Bak), Benjamin, New York, 1964, pp. 221–275.
19. Brockhouse, B. N., Hautecler, S., and Stiller, H., in *The Interaction of Radiation with Solids* (Ed. Strumane, R., *et al.*), North-Holland, Amsterdam, 1964, pp. 580–642.
20. Bacon, G. E., *Neutron Diffraction*, 2nd ed., Clarendon Press, Oxford, 1962.
21. Maradudin, A. A., and Fein, A. E., *Phys. Rev.*, **128**, 2589–2608 (1962).
22. Marshall, W., and Lovesey, S. W., *Rivista Nuovo Cimento* (*Italy*), **1**, 155–173 (1969).
23. Bardeen, J., and Pines, D., *Phys. Rev.*, **99**, 1141–1150 (1955).
24. Bohm, D., and Pines, D., *Phys. Rev.*, **82**, 625–634 (1951).
25. Bohm, D., and Pines, D., *Phys. Rev.*, **85**, 338–353 (1952).
26. Bohm, D., and Pines, D., *Phys. Rev.*, **92**, 609–625 (1953).
27. Frohlich, H., *Phys. Rev.*, **79**, 845–856 (1950).
28. Frohlich, H., *Proc. Roy. Soc.*, **A215**, 291–298 (1952).
29. Bardeen, J., Cooper, L. N., and Schrieffer, J. R., *Phys. Rev.*, **108**, 1175–1204 (1957).
30. Rickaysen, G., *Theory of Superconductivity*, Wiley–Interscience, New York, 1965.
31. Reik, H. G., in *Phonons and Phonon Interactions, Aarhus Summer School, 1963* (Ed. Bak), Benjamin, New York, 1964, pp. 138–166.
32. Ridley, B. K., *Physics Bulletin* (*Inst. of Phys., London*), **22**, 461–465 (1971).
33. Weinreich, G., Sanders, M. T., and White, H. G., *Phys. Rev.*, **114**, 33–44 (1959).
34. Paige, E. G. S., 'Amplification of lattice waves', in *Phonons, Scottish Universities Summer School, 1965* (Ed. Stevenson), Oliver and Boyd, London, 1966, pp. 255–266.
35. Einspruch, N. G., *Solid State Physics*, **17**, 217–268 (1965).
36. Spector, H. N., *Solid State Physics*, **19**, 291–361 (1966).
37. Meyer, N. I., and Jorgensen, M. H., *Adv. Solid State Physics*, **10**, 21–124 (1970).
38. Sham, L. J., and Ziman, J. M., *Solid State Physics*, **15**, 221–298 (1963).
39. Mott, N. F., and Jones, H., *The Theory of the Properties of Metals and Alloys*, Clarendon Press, Oxford, 1936.
40. Bardeen, J., *Phys. Rev.*, **52**, 688–697 (1937).
41. Frenkel, J., *Phys. Rev.*, **37**, 17–44 and 1276–1294 (1931).
42. Overhauser, A. W., *Phys. Rev.*, **101**, 1702–1712 (1956).
43. Dexter, D. L., *Phys. Rev.*, **108**, 707–712 (1957).
44. Wannier, G. H., *Phys. Rev.*, **52**, 191–197 (1937).
45. Elliott, R. J., *Phys. Rev.*, **108**, 1384–1389 (1957).
46. Baldini, G., *Phys. Rev.*, **128**, 1562–1567 (1962).
47. McClean, T. P., *Progress in Semiconductors*, **5**, 53–102 (1960).
48. Elliott, R. J., and Loudon, R., *J. Phys. Chem. Solids*, **15**, 146–151 (1960).
49. Toyazawa, Y., *Prog. Theor. Phys.* (*Japan*), **20**, 53–81 (1958).
50. Toyazawa, Y., *Prog. Theor. Phys.* (*Japan*), **27**, 89–104 (1962).
51. Elliott, R. J., in *Polarons and Excitons, Scottish Universities Summer School, 1962* (Ed. Kuper and Whitfield), Oliver and Boyd, London 1963, pp. 269–293.
52. Haken, H., in *Polarons and Excitons, Scottish Universities Summer School, 1962* (Ed. Kuper and Whitfield), Oliver and Boyd, London, 1963, pp. 295–322.
53. McClure, D. S., *Solid State Physics*, **8**, 1–47 (1959).
54. Knox, R. S., 'Theory of excitons', Supplement 5, *Solid State Physics* (1963).
55. Nudelman, S., and Mitra, S. S. (Eds.), *Optical Properties of Solids*, Plenum Press, New York, 1969.

56. Kittel, C., *Quantum Theory of Solids*, Wiley, New York, 1963, Chap. 4.
57. Mattis, D. C., *The Theory of Magnetism*, Harper Row, New York, 1965.
58. Keffer, F., *Handb. der Physik*, **18**, 1–273 (1966).
59. Sinha, K. P., and Upadhyaya, U. N., *Phys. Rev.*, **127**, 432–439 (1962).
60. Sinha, K. P., and Upadhyaya, U. N., *Phys. Rev.*, **130**, 939–944 (1963).
61. Akhiezer, A. I., *J. Physics (U.S.S.R.)*, **10**, 217–230 (1946).
62. Meissner, G., *Z. Phys.*, **237**, 272–284 (1970).
63. Holden, T. M., Buyers, W. J. L., Svensson, E. C., and Cowley, R. A., *J. Phys. (C)*, **4**, 2127–2138 and 2139–2159 (1971).
64. Elliott, R. J., in *Phonons, Scottish Universities Summer School, 1965* (Ed. Stevenson), Oliver and Boyd, London, 1966, pp. 377–402.
65. Lifshitz, I. M., *Adv. Phys. (G.B.)*, **13**, 483–536 (1964).
66. Lifshitz, I. M., and Kosevich, A. M., *Rep. Prog. Phys.*, **29**, 217–254 (1966).
67. Maradudin, A. A., *Solid State Physics*, **18**, 273–420 (1966).
68. Maradudin, A. A., *Solid State Physics*, **19**, 1–134 (1966).
69. Agrawal, B. K., *Phys. Rev. (B)*, **3**, 1843–1856 (1971).

Appendix A

Fitting the Parameters of an Interatomic Potential—Example

See Sections 1.6, 4.5 and 4.6. The free energy at $T = 0$ K in the harmonic approximation is

$$F(0) = N\Phi_0 + \sum_{kj} \tfrac{1}{2}\hbar\omega(kj) \tag{A.1}$$

[see, for example, equation (4.64)]. We may write this:

$$F(0) = N\Phi_0 + \tfrac{3}{2}N\hbar\mu_1 \tag{A.2}$$

where μ_1 is the first moment of the frequency spectrum and Φ_0 is given explicitly by

$$\Phi_0 = \tfrac{1}{2}\sum_l \phi(\mathbf{r})_{\mathbf{r}=\mathbf{r}^l} \tag{A.3}$$

where $\phi(\mathbf{r})$ is the two-body interatomic potential function which we are considering. The second moment μ_2 is more readily obtained than μ_1, since it is the trace of the dynamical matrix averaged over all $\mathbf{k}$:

$$\mu_2 = \frac{1}{3sN}\sum_{\mathbf{k}} [\mathrm{Tr}\, D_{\alpha\beta}(\mathbf{k})] \tag{A.4}$$

($s = 1$ for a lattice with one atom per unit cell) which can be shown to yield

$$\mu_2 = \frac{1}{6M}\sum_l [3\mathscr{D}_r\phi(r) + r^2\mathscr{D}_r^3\phi(r)]_{\mathbf{r}=\mathbf{r}^l} \tag{A.5}$$

This expression may be evaluated directly from the interatomic potential; hence it is convenient to rewrite equation (A.2) by using the factor of Isenberg (see Reference 90 in Chapter 2) which we discussed in Section 2.12. Thus

$$F(0)/N = \Phi_0 + 1\cdot0227\hbar(2\mu_2)^{1/2}. \tag{A.6}$$

Differentiating this with respect to volume, and assuming that the internal pressure is zero (equilibrium),

$$0 = \frac{1}{3b}\Phi_1 + 1\cdot0227\hbar(2\mu_2)^{-1/2}\frac{2\,\mathrm{d}\mu_2}{\mathrm{d}V} \tag{A.7}$$

where

$$\Phi_1 \equiv \frac{1}{2}\sum_l l_i^2[\mathscr{D}_r\phi(r)]_{\mathbf{r}=\mathbf{r}^l}; \quad \mathscr{D}_r \equiv \frac{1}{r}\frac{\mathrm{d}}{\mathrm{d}r} \tag{A.8}$$

$$\frac{d\mu_2}{dV} = \frac{1}{36bM} \sum_l l_i^2 [5\mathscr{D}_r^2\phi(\mathbf{r}) + r^2\mathscr{D}_r^3\phi(r)]_{\mathbf{r}=\mathbf{r}^l} \tag{A.9}$$

and we have used $b \equiv a/2$ for convenience, since

$$\mathbf{r}^l = b(l_1, l_2, l_3); l_1 + l_2 + l_3 = \text{even integer (for f.c.c.).} \tag{A.10}$$

Now consider the potential defined by equation (2.51):

$$\phi(r) = \sum_p \frac{\sigma^p}{r^p}. \tag{A.11}$$

The required derivatives are

$$\mathscr{D}_r\phi(r) = -\sum_p \frac{p\sigma^p}{r^{p+2}} = -\sum_p \frac{p\sigma^p}{b^{p+2}} S_{p+2} \tag{A.12}$$

$$\mathscr{D}_r^2\phi(r) = \sum_p \frac{p(p+2)\sigma^p}{r^{p+4}} = \sum_p \frac{p(p+2)\sigma^p}{b^{p+4}} S_{p+4} \tag{A.13}$$

$$\mathscr{D}_r^3\phi(r) = -\sum_p \frac{p(p+2)(p+4)\sigma^p}{r^{p+6}} = -\sum_p \frac{p(p+2)(p+4)\sigma^p}{b^{p+6}} S_{p+6} \tag{A.14}$$

with

$$S_p \equiv \sum_l (l_1^2 + l_2^2 + l_3^2)^{-p/2}. \tag{A.15}$$

Hence, using these we see, from equations (A.3), (A.8), (A.5) and (A.9), respectively:

$$\Phi_0 = \frac{1}{2} \sum_p \frac{\sigma^p}{b^p} S_p \tag{A.16}$$

$$\Phi_1 = -\frac{1}{2} \sum_p \frac{p\sigma^p}{b^{p+2}} S_p \tag{A.17}$$

$$\mu_2 = \frac{1}{6M} \sum_p \frac{p(p-1)\sigma^p}{b^{p+2}} S_{p+2} \tag{A.18}$$

$$\frac{d\mu_2}{dV} = -\frac{1}{36bM} \sum_p \frac{p(p-1)(p+2)\sigma^p}{b^{p+4}} S_{p+2}. \tag{A.19}$$

So we see that the right-hand sides of equations (A.6) and (A.7) may be written explicitly in terms of the potential. Identifying $F(0)/N$ with the experimental latent heat of sublimation per atom (extrapolated to absolute zero) $-L_0$, and using a measured value of b at absolute zero, the equations to be solved for ε and σ are

$$-L_0 = \frac{1}{2}\sum_p \frac{\sigma^p}{b^p}S_p + 1.0227\hbar\left[\frac{1}{3M}\sum_p \frac{p(p-1)\sigma^p}{b^{p+2}}S_{p+2}\right]^{1/2} \tag{A.20}$$

$$0 = \frac{1}{2}\sum_p \frac{p\sigma^p}{b^{p+2}}S_p + 1.0227\hbar\left\{\frac{\sum_p [p(p-1)(p+2)\sigma^p/b^{p+4}]S_{p+2}}{[3M\sum_p [p(p-1)\sigma^p/b^{p+2}]S_{p+2}]^{1/2}}\right\}. \tag{A.21}$$

These equations may be solved without difficulty by an iterative method, and some of the results of this are tabulated below. For a two-parameter potential we put $C = 0$ and $n = 6$; for a three-parameter potential we have adopted a suitable value of C based on the Van der Waals coefficient. If desired, C also may be found empirically by adding a third equation to equations (A.20) and (A.21)—for example, by writing the elastic constant C_{11} in terms of the potential. However, measured values of C_{11} and other suitable quantities are not sufficiently accurate for this to be meaningful. The lattice sums S_p, may include as many atom sites as required for their convergence; we show results which use 'all neighbours' (A) and those which include only nearest neighbours (N). The all-neighbour sums required may be found in Appendix D.

Table A.1. Neon: $b = 2.2311 \times 10^{-10}$ m, $L_0 = 3.126 \times 10^{-21}$ J atom^{-1} (1883 J mol^{-1}), $M_{Ne} = 3.351 \times 10^{-26}$ kg

Potential m-n-6	$-C$ (10^{-78}J m^6)	$\sum_l$	$-\varepsilon$ (10^{-22} J)	σ (10^{-10} m)	μ_2 (10^{25} s^{-2})	μ_1 (10^{12} s^{-1})	Z.P.E. (J mol^{-1})
10-8-6	0.467	A	5.163	3.109	3.277	5.519	525.9
10-9-6	0.467	A	5.365	3.095	3.384	5.609	534.5
11-8-6	0.467	A	5.313	3.096	3.353	5.583	532.0
11-9-6	0.467	A	5.495	3.085	3.451	5.664	539.7
12-8-6	0.467	A	5.434	3.086	3.402	5.624	535.9
12-9-6	0.467	A	5.600	3.077	3.488	5.694	542.6
13-8-6	0.467	A	5.532	3.077	3.425	5.642	537.7
13-9-6	0.467	A	5.685	3.069	3.498	5.702	543.4
14-8-6	0.467	A	5.614	3.069	3.421	5.639	537.3
14-9-6	0.467	A	5.750	3.063	3.459	5.670	540.3
10-6	0	A	4.492	3.151	2.976	5.260	501.2
10-6	0	N	6.760	3.023	2.425	4.747	452.4
11-6	0	A	4.701	3.130	3.072	5.344	509.2
11-6	0	N	6.824	3.021	2.532	4.851	462.3
12-6	0	A	4.872	3.113	3.143	5.405	515.0
12-6	0	N	6.882	3.019	2.610	4.926	469.4
13-6	0	A	5.014	3.100	3.188	5.444	518.7
13-6	0	N	6.935	3.017	2.659	4.972	473.8
14-6	0	A	5.134	3.088	3.208	5.460	520.3
14-6	0	N	6.983	3.014	2.680	4.991	475.6

Table A.2. Argon: $b = 2.655 \times 10^{-10}$ m, $L_0 = 1.285 \times 10^{-21}$ J atom^{-1}
(7743 J mol^{-1}), $M_{Ar} = 6.628 \times 10^{-26}$ kg

Potential m-n-6	$-C$ $(10^{-78}$ J m$^6)$	$\sum_l$	$-\varepsilon$ $(10^{-22}$ J$)$	σ $(10^{-10}$ m$)$	μ_2 $(10^{25}$ s$^{-2})$	μ_1 $(10^{12}$ s$^{-1})$	Z.P.E. (J mol^{-1})
10-8-6	5·57	A	17·31	3·811	6·433	7·733	736·9
10-9-6	5·57	A	17·88	3·796	6·832	7·969	759·4
11-8-6	5·57	A	17·73	3·797	6·829	7·968	759·2
11-9-6	5·57	A	18·22	3·785	7·223	8·194	780·8
12-8-6	5·57	A	18·05	3·786	7·214	8·189	780·3
12-9-6	5·57	A	18·50	3·776	7·600	8·405	800·9
13-8-6	5·57	A	18·32	3·776	7·586	8·398	800·2
13-9-6	5·57	A	18·72	3·769	7·966	8·605	820·0
14-8-6	5·57	A	18·53	3·770	7·946	8·595	819·0
14-9-6	5·57	A	18·89	3·763	8·284	8·775	836·2
10-6	0	A	15·29	3·861	5·604	7·217	687·8
10-6	0	N	23·31	3·708	4·943	6·779	645·9
11-6	0	A	15·92	3·836	6·014	7·477	712·5
11-6	0	N	23·40	3·708	5·378	7·070	673·7
12-6	0	A	16·43	3·818	6·412	7·720	735·7
12-6	0	N	23·48	3·707	5·798	7·341	699·6
13-6	0	A	16·85	3·803	6·799	7·950	757·5
13-6	0	N	23·56	3·707	6·203	7·593	723·6
14-6	0	A	17·20	3·792	7·173	8·166	778·1
14-6	0	N	23·64	3·706	6·593	7·828	746·0
12-6	0	A*	16·54	3·834	6·929	8·025	817·7
12-9-6	5·57	A*	18·74	3·793	8·454	8·865	905·3

* Including the anharmonic free energy.

Table A.3. Krypton: $b = 2.824 \times 10^{-10}$ m, $L_0 = 1.852 \times 10^{-20}$ J atom^{-1}
(1.116×10^4 J mol^{-1}), $M_{Kr} = 1.391 \times 10^{-25}$ kg

Potential m-n-6	$-C$ $(10^{-78}$ J m$^6)$	$\sum_l$	$-\varepsilon$ $(10^{-22}$ J$)$	σ $(10^{-10}$ m$)$	μ_2 $(10^{25}$ s$^{-2})$	μ_1 $(10^{12}$ s$^{-1})$	Z.P.E. (J mol^{-1})
10-8-6	10·71	A	24·04	4·073	4·116	6·185	589·4
10-9-6	10·71	A	24·83	4·056	4·398	6·394	609·3
11-8-6	10·71	A	24·60	4·058	4·396	6·392	609·1
11-9-6	10·71	A	25·30	4·045	4·678	6·594	628·4
12-8-6	10·71	A	25·03	4·047	4·672	6·590	628·0
12-9-6	10·71	A	25·65	4·036	4·954	6·786	646·7
13-8-6	10·71	A	25·37	4·038	4·945	6·780	646·1
13-9-6	10·71	A	25·94	4·029	5·227	6·971	664·3
14-8-6	10·71	A	25·65	4·031	5·215	6·962	663·4
14-9-6	10·71	A	26·16	4·023	5·496	7·148	681·1

—continued

Potential m-n-6	$-C$ $(10^{-78}\ \mathrm{J\,m^6})$	$\sum_l$	$-\varepsilon$ $(10^{-22}\ \mathrm{J})$	σ $(10^{-10}\ \mathrm{m})$	μ_2 $(10^{25}\ \mathrm{s^{-2}})$	μ_1 $(10^{12}\ \mathrm{s^{-1}})$	Z.P.E. $(\mathrm{J\,mol^{-1}})$
10-6	0	A	21·16	4·129	3·542	5·738	546·8
10-6	0	N	32·34	3·966	3·157	5·417	516·2
11-6	0	A	22·01	4·103	3·822	5·961	568·0
11-6	0	N	32·41	3·966	3·452	5·665	539·8
12-6	0	A	22·68	4·084	4·100	6·173	588·3
12-6	0	N	32·48	3·966	3·743	5·899	562·1
13-6	0	A	23·23	4·068	4·374	6·376	607·6
13-6	0	N	32·54	3·965	4·029	6·120	583·2
14-6	0	A	23·67	4·056	4·644	6·570	626·1
14-6	0	N	32·60	3·965	4·310	6·329	603·1
12-6	0	A*	22·73	4·088	4·193	6·243	647·8
12-9-6	10·71	A*	25·75	4·041	5·106	6·889	712·0

* Including the anharmonic free energy.

Table A.4. Xenon: $b = 3\cdot063 \times 10^{-10}$ m, $L_0 = 2\cdot661 \times 10^{-20}$ J atom^{-1} $(1\cdot603 \times 10^4\ \mathrm{J\,mol^{-1}})$, $M_{\mathrm{Xe}} = 2\cdot179 \times 10^{-25}$ kg

Potential m-n-6	$-C$ $(10^{-78}\ \mathrm{J\,m^6})$	$\sum_l$	$-\varepsilon$ $(10^{-22}\ \mathrm{J})$	σ $(10^{-10}\ \mathrm{m})$	μ_2 $(10^{25}\ \mathrm{s^{-2}})$	μ_1 $(10^{12}\ \mathrm{s^{-1}})$	Z.P.E. $(\mathrm{J\,mol^{-1}})$
10-8-6	27·62	A	33·54	4·433	3·239	5·487	522·9
10-9-6	27·62	A	34·54	4·415	3·451	5·664	539·7
11-8-6	27·62	A	34·26	4·417	3·460	5·672	540·4
11-9-6	27·62	A	35·12	4·403	3·669	5·840	556·5
12-8-6	27·62	A	34·82	4·405	3·680	5·849	557·4
12-9-6	27·62	A	35·57	4·394	3·884	6·009	572·6
13-8-6	27·62	A	35·25	4·395	3·899	6·020	573·7
13-9-6	27·62	A	35·91	4·386	4·099	6·173	588·2
14-8-6	27·62	A	35·60	4·387	4·117	6·186	589·5
14-9-6	27·62	A	36·18	4·380	4·295	6·319	602·1
10-6	0	A	29·84	4·490	2·811	5·112	487·1
10-6	0	N	45·64	4·313	2·516	4·836	460·9
11-6	0	A	31·01	4·462	3·041	5·317	506·7
11-6	0	N	45·70	4·313	2·758	5·064	482·5
12-6	0	A	31·94	4·441	3·270	5·514	525·4
12-6	0	N	45·77	4·313	2·998	5·279	503·1
13-6	0	A	32·68	4·424	3·498	5·702	543·4
13-6	0	N	45·82	4·313	3·235	5·484	522·6
14-6	0	A	33·29	4·411	3·725	5·884	560·7
14-6	0	N	45·88	4·312	3·470	5·679	541·2
12-6		A*	31·96	4·443	3·296	5·535	565·3
12-9-6		A*	35·61	4·396	3·926	6·041	613·5

* Including the anharmonic free energy.

Appendix B

Ewald's Method

See Sections 2.7 and 2.10. We are interested in summing the long-range Coulomb term

$$S_k(r) \equiv \sum_{\rho_\kappa} \frac{e_{\kappa'} e_\kappa}{4\pi\varepsilon_0 |\mathbf{r} - \mathbf{r}^l_{\kappa\kappa'}|} e^{i\mathbf{k}\cdot\mathbf{r}^l_{\kappa\kappa'}}. \tag{B.1}$$

It is convenient to use an integral representation and to write formally (dropping κ labels):

$$\frac{1}{r} = \int_0^\infty f(\mathbf{r}) \, d\xi \tag{B.2}$$

with

$$f(\mathbf{r}) = \frac{2}{\sqrt{\pi}} e^{-\xi^2 r^2} \tag{B.3}$$

(see Chapter 5, note (a) for a list of this kind of integral); ξ being a dummy variable. Consider first the lattice sum

$$\tilde{S}_k(r) \equiv \sum_l f(\mathbf{r} - \mathbf{r}^l) e^{i\mathbf{k}\cdot\mathbf{r}^l} \tag{B.4}$$

$$= e^{i\mathbf{k}\cdot\mathbf{r}} \sum_l f(\mathbf{r} - \mathbf{r}^l) e^{-i\mathbf{k}\cdot(\mathbf{r} - \mathbf{r}^l)}. \tag{B.5}$$

The summation part of (B.5) is periodic and may be expanded as a Fourier sum:

$$e^{-i\mathbf{k}\cdot\mathbf{r}} \tilde{S}_k(r) = \sum_h \tilde{S}_k(h) e^{-i\mathbf{b}_h\cdot\mathbf{r}} \tag{B.6}$$

with the Fourier coefficients

$$\tilde{S}_k(h) = \frac{1}{v} \theta(\mathbf{b}_h + \mathbf{k}) \tag{B.7}$$

v being the volume per unit cell and where

$$\theta(\mathbf{b}) = \int f(\mathbf{r}) e^{-i\mathbf{b}\cdot\mathbf{r}} \, d\tau \tag{B.8}$$

$$= \frac{2\pi}{\xi^3} e^{-b^2/(4\xi^2)} \tag{B.9}$$

283

for $f(\mathbf{r})$ given by equation (B.3). Thus we may write

$$\tilde{S}_{\mathbf{k}}(r) = \frac{2}{\sqrt{\pi}} \sum_{l} e^{-\xi^2(\mathbf{r}-\mathbf{r}^l)^2 + i\mathbf{k}.\mathbf{r}^l} = \frac{2\pi}{v} \sum_{h} \frac{1}{\xi^3} e^{-(\mathbf{b}_h+\mathbf{k})^2/(4\xi^2) + i(\mathbf{b}_h+\mathbf{k}).\mathbf{r}}. \tag{B.10}$$

The sum over l is rapidly convergent if ξ is large, while the sum over h is rapidly convergent if ξ is small. Now to find the summation $S_k(r)$ we must integrate $\tilde{S}_k(r)$ since we have summed only the integrand of the representation (B.2) so far. The trick is to use the l summation expression for $\tilde{S}_k(r)$ for large ξ and the h summation expression for small values of ξ. Thus we divide the integration in equation (B.2) into two ranges. Let the division be at

$$\xi = \frac{2\varepsilon}{a} \tag{B.11}$$

where $a/2$ is the nearest ion separation and ε is now dimensionless. We write, from equation (B.10),

$$\int_0^\infty \tilde{S}_k(r) \, d\xi = \int_0^{2\varepsilon/a} \sum_h (\cdots) \, d\xi + \int_{2\varepsilon/a}^\infty \sum_l (\cdots) \, d\xi. \tag{B.12}$$

These integrations are readily performed to give

$$S_k(r) = \frac{e_\kappa e_{\kappa'}}{4\pi\varepsilon_0 v} \sum_h \frac{1}{|\mathbf{b}_h + \mathbf{k}|^2} e^{-(\mathbf{b}_h+\mathbf{k})^2 a^2/(16\varepsilon^2) + i(\mathbf{b}_h+\mathbf{k}).\mathbf{r}}$$

$$+ \sum_l \frac{\{1 - G[(2\varepsilon/a)(\mathbf{r} - \mathbf{r}^l)]\}}{|\mathbf{r} - \mathbf{r}^l|} e^{i\mathbf{k}.\mathbf{r}^l} \tag{B.13}$$

where $G(y)$ is the Gauss function

$$G(y) \equiv \frac{2}{\sqrt{\pi}} \int_0^y e^{-x^2} \, dx \tag{B.14}$$

which approaches unity for large y. This form of $S_k(\mathbf{r})$ converges well if ε is carefully chosen as a compromise between the number of terms required in each summation. ε is usually of order unity, but it is always advisable to carry out test cases to ensure optimum convergence.

Appendix C

Metals

See Section 2.9. The contribution of the lattice potential to the electron energies may be written in terms of a pseudopotential. This is not localized at the ion sites as in the other classes of crystals we have discussed; however it is small, and may be treated as a perturbation. Approximations which effectively localize the potential are often valid. Here we shall introduce the form of the pseudopotential and indicate the localization approximation; considerations of electron–phonon effects, non-localized theory, details of the electron state, scattering, dispersion, plasma oscillations, Kohn anomalies, etc., require too much of a diversion into the properties of electrons in metals for our objectives.

The electron states may be separated into two groups; those which are closely associated with an ion site—arising from the nucleus and its tightly bound electrons—and those of the conduction band. If the spatial extent of the 'core' states is small, it will be reasonable to use the wave functions of the isolated ion, and represent them by the functions $|i\rangle$. The conduction band states are characterized by a wave vector $\mathbf{p}$, and we write them $|\mathbf{p}\rangle$.

Using an expansion in terms of orthogonalized plane waves (orthogonalized in this case to $|i\rangle$) we have for a conduction-band state

$$\psi = (1 + \mathscr{P})\phi \tag{C.1}$$

where $\mathscr{P}$ is the projection operator to the states $|i\rangle$, ϕ is the pseudowave function,

$$\phi = \sum_{\mathbf{p}} a_{\mathbf{p}}|\mathbf{p}\rangle \tag{C.2}$$

where $|\mathbf{p}\rangle$ is a plane wave and $a_{\mathbf{p}}$ are the expansion coefficients. We may work in terms of ϕ rather than ψ (the real wave function) and, writing this in the one-electron Schrödinger equation,

$$H\psi = -\frac{\hbar^2}{2m_e}\nabla^2\psi + V(\mathbf{r})\psi = E\psi \tag{C.3}$$

we see that

$$-\frac{\hbar^2}{2m_e}\nabla^2\phi + W\phi = E\phi \tag{C.4}$$

285

where

$$W \equiv \{V(\mathbf{r}) + (E - H)\mathscr{P}\}\phi. \tag{C.5}$$

$\mathscr{P}$ may be expressed in terms of $|i\rangle$; hence

$$\mathscr{P}\phi = \frac{1}{(Nv)^{1/2}} \sum_i |i\rangle \langle i| \sum_{\mathbf{p}} a_{\mathbf{p}}|\mathbf{p}\rangle \tag{C.6}$$

[(v being the volume per ion). Hence the pseudopotential (so called from the form of equation (C.4))] is

$$W = V(\mathbf{r})\phi + \frac{1}{(Nv)^{1/2}} \sum_i (E - E_i)|i\rangle \langle i| \sum_{\mathbf{p}} a_{\mathbf{p}}|\mathbf{p}\rangle. \tag{C.7}$$

There are contributions to this from the mobile electrons, the free-ion field and a repulsive part due to overlap. The second and third of these may be expressed as a contribution from each lattice site, and the effect of the conduction electrons also may be written as a sum of charges associated with each site. Thus we can express W as a superposition

$$W(\mathbf{r}) = \sum_l w(\mathbf{r} - \mathbf{r}^l). \tag{C.8}$$

Allowing this to operate on a plane wave $|\mathbf{p}\rangle$, we find

$$\langle \mathbf{p}'|W(\mathbf{r})|\mathbf{p}\rangle = S(\mathbf{k} \cdot \mathbf{r}^l)w(\mathbf{k}) \tag{C.9}$$

where

$$S(\mathbf{k} \cdot \mathbf{r}^l) = \frac{1}{N} \sum_l e^{-i\mathbf{k}\cdot\mathbf{r}^l} \tag{C.10}$$

$$\mathbf{k} = \mathbf{p}' - \mathbf{p} \tag{C.11}$$

and $w(\mathbf{k})$ is the Fourier transform of $w(\mathbf{r} - \mathbf{r}^l)$, often called the 'form factor'. [The structure of equation (C.9) is familiar in scattering theory; see, for example, Section 8.4.] So we have replaced the Schrödinger equation (C.3) by a pseudopotential equation (C.4), treated W as small and replaced it by a sum over potentials centred at the lattice sites, and arrived at the concept of the normal mode $\mathbf{k}$.

Finally, let us look at an example of $w(\mathbf{k})$; the effect of the conduction electrons is to screen the localized pseudopotential and reduce it by a factor which is the relative permittivity corresponding to $\mathbf{k}$. In this approximation we can show that

$$w(\mathbf{k}) = \frac{1}{v\varepsilon(\mathbf{k})} \left[\beta(k^2\alpha^2 + 1)^{-2} - \frac{Ze^2}{\varepsilon_0 k^2} \right] \tag{C.12}$$

where Z is the nett charge on the ion and α and β are parameters determined by the decay of overlap between ions. These parameters may be found phenomenologically for specific cases and the energies of the associated modes deduced. The details may be found in References 33 and 34 in Chapter 2; another review, by S. K. Joshi and A. K. Rajagopal, appears in *Solid State Physics*, **22**, 159–312 (1968).

Appendix D

Lattice Sums—Face-centred-cubic Crystal

See Section 2.10 and Appendix A. In Appendix A we have used lattice sums of the type

$$S_p = \sum_l (l_1^2 + l_2^2 + l_3^2)^{-p/2} = \sum_l l^{-p} \tag{D.1}$$

where for face-centred-cubic lattice $l_1 + l_2 + l_3 =$ an even integer. Other related sums which appear frequently are

$$S_{p+2}(l_1^2) \equiv \sum_l (l_1^2 l^{-(p+2)}) \tag{D.2}$$

$$S_{p+4}(l_1^4) \equiv \sum_l (l_1^4 l^{-(p+4)}) \tag{D.3}$$

$$S_{p+4}(l_1^2 l_2^2) = \sum_l (l_1^2 l_2^2 l^{-(p+4)}) \tag{D.4}$$

$$S_{p+6}(l_1^6) = \sum_l (l_1^6 l^{-(p+6)}) \tag{D.5}$$

$$S_{p+6}(l_1^2 l_2^4) \equiv \sum_l (l_1^2 l_2^4 l^{-(p+6)}) \tag{D.6}$$

$$S_{p+6}(l_1^2 l_2^2 l_3^2) \equiv \sum_l (l_1^2 l_2^2 l_3^2) l^{-(p+6)} \tag{D.7}$$

Examples of these sums are tabulated below, the l summation being taken over as many neighbours necessary to achieve convergence to the accuracy quoted. The corresponding summations for nearest neighbour only are easily evaluated and have not been included here.

Lattice sums like those of equation (2.64), *viz*

$$X_m^{n_1 n_2 n_3}(\mathbf{k}) \equiv \sum_l \frac{l_1^{m_1} l_2^{m_2} l_3^{m_3}}{l^m} (1 - \cos \mathbf{k} \cdot \mathbf{r}^l) \tag{D.8}$$

appear in the dynamical matrix (for the model described in Section 2.10) for three sets of $(n_1 n_2 n_3)$. The three kinds of sum which arise are (i) $n_1 = n_2 = n_3 = 0$; $m = p + 2$, (ii) $n_1 = 2$, $n_2 = n_3 = 0$; $m = p + 4$, (iii) $n_1 = 0$, $n_2 = n_3 = 1$; $m = p + 4$ (p is the power involved in the potential). Examples of these sums are given for three directions [100] [110] and [111] with four points along each up to the Brillouin-zone boundary.

Table D.1. All-neighbour lattice sums

p	S_p	$S_{p+2}(l_1^2)$	$S_{p+4}(l_1^4)$	$S_{p+4}(l_1^2 l_2^2)$	$S_{p+6}(l_1^6)$	$S_{p+6}(l_1^4 l_2^2)$	$S_{p+6}(l_1^2 l_2^2 l_3^2)$
2	44·236	14·745	8·4070	3·1692	5·6575	1·3748	0·4197
4	4·5334	1·8445	1·0324	0·4061	0·6512	0·1906	0·0249
5	2·8923	0·9641	0·5233	0·2204	0·3102	0·1065	0·0073
6	1·8022	0·6007	0·3195	0·1406	0·1815	0·0690	0·0027
							10^{-4}
7	1·1804	0·3935	0·2055	0·0940	0·1126	0·0465	9·9368
8	0·7998	0·2666	0·1375	0·0646	0·0733	0·0321	3·8052
9	0·5521	0·1840	0·0940	0·0450	0·0492	0·0224	1·4993
10	0·3847	0·1282	0·0651	0·0316	0·0336	0·0157	0·5981
	10^{-2}	10^{-2}	10^{-2}	10^{-2}	10^{-2}	10^{-2}	10^{-5}
11	26·960	8·9868	4·5430	2·2219	2·3236	1·1097	2·4051
12	18·956	6·3187	3·1840	1·5673	1·6176	0·7832	0·9722
13	13·355	4·4517	2·2381	1·1068	1·1318	0·5532	0·3943
14	9·4211	3·1404	1·5763	0·7820	0·7944	0·3909	0·1603
	10^{-3}	10^{-3}	10^{-3}	10^{-3}	10^{-3}	10^{-3}	10^{-7}
15	66·512	22·171	11·116	5·5274	5·5892	2·7634	6·5227
16	46·982	15·661	7·8456	3·9075	3·9383	1·9536	2·6575
17	33·198	11·066	5·5406	2·7626	2·7780	1·3813	1·0835
18	23·463	7·8210	3·9143	1·9533	1·9610	0·9766	0·4419
	10^{-3}	10^{-3}	10^{-3}	10^{-3}	10^{-3}	10^{-4}	10^{-8}
19	16·585	5·5284	2·7661	1·3812	1·3850	6·9057	1·8029
20	11·725	3·9083	1·9551	0·9766	0·9785	4·8829	0·7357
21	8·2894	2·7631	1·3820	0·6906	0·6915	3·4527	0·3003
22	5·8609	1·9536	0·9771	0·4883	0·4888	2·4414	0·1226
	10^{-3}	10^{-4}	10^{-4}	10^{-4}	10^{-4}	10^{-4}	10^{-10}
23	4·1439	13·813	6·9078	3·4527	3·4551	1·7263	5·0028
24	2·9301	9·7669	4·8840	2·4414	2·4426	1·2207	2·0422
25	2·0718	6·9060	3·4533	1·7263	1·7269	0·8632	0·8337
26	1·4649	4·8831	2·4417	1·2207	1·2210	0·6104	0·3403

Table D.2. [100] direction; all-neighbour X sums

	m	n_1	n_2	n_3	$X(\frac{1}{4})$	$X(\frac{1}{2})$	$X(\frac{3}{4})$	$X(k_{max})$
$p = 6$								
	8	0	0	0	0·16573	0·53696	0·88284	1·03008
	10	2	0	0	0·08690	0·27372	0·43876	0·50637
	10	0	1	1	0·03941	0·13162	0·22204	0·26185
$p = 8$								
	10	0	0	0	0·07519	0·25287	0·42757	0·50433
	12	2	0	0	0·03856	0·12802	0·21478	0·25078
	12	0	1	1	0·01831	0·06242	0·10690	0·12678
$p = 9$								
	11	0	0	0	0·05207	0·17644	0·30031	0·35518
	13	2	0	0	0·02651	0·08905	0·15026	0·17703
	13	0	1	1	0·01278	0·04369	0·07503	0·08908
$p = 10$								
	12	0	0	0	0·03636	0·12376	0·21150	0·25059
	14	2	0	0	0·01842	0·06231	0·10585	0·12506
	14	0	1	1	0·00897	0·03072	0·05283	0·06276

— continued

Table D.2—cont.

	m	n_1	n_2	n_3	$X(\frac{1}{4})$	$X(\frac{1}{2})$	$X(\frac{3}{4})$	$X(k_{\max})$
$p = 11$								
	13	0	0	0	0·02551	0·08707	0·14920	0·17697
	15	2	0	0	0·01287	0·04376	0·07466	0·08839
	15	0	1	1	0·00632	0·02166	0·03727	0·04429
$p = 12$								
	14	0	0	0	0·01795	0·06137	0·10534	0·12505
	16	2	0	0	0·00903	0·03080	0·05271	0·06249
	16	0	1	1	0·00446	0·01529	0·02632	0·03128
$p = 13$								
	15	0	0	0	0·01265	0·04331	0·07442	0·08839
	17	2	0	0	0·00636	0·02171	0·03723	0·04418
	17	0	1	1	0·00315	0·01080	0·01859	0·02210

Table D.3. [110] direction; all-neighbour X sums

	m	n_1	n_2	n_3	$X(\frac{1}{4})$	$X(\frac{1}{2})$	$X(\frac{3}{4})$	$X(k_{\max})$
$p = 6$								
	8	0	0	0	0·16452	0·52249	0·84106	0·99935
	10	0	0	2	0·04026	0·14415	0·27702	0·40231
	10	2	0	0	0·06213	0·18917	0·28202	0·29852
	10	1	1	0	0·03696	0·10278	0·12459	0·08124
$p = 8$								
	10	0	0	0	0·07448	0·24439	0·40341	0·48620
	12	0	0	2	0·01875	0·06889	0·13510	0·19836
	12	2	0	0	0·02786	0·08775	0·13416	0·14392
	12	1	1	0	0·01736	0·05000	0·06225	0·04124
$p = 9$								
	11	0	0	0	0·05155	0·17015	0·28244	0·34168
	13	0	0	2	0·01309	0·04830	0·09509	0·13992
	13	2	0	0	0·01923	0·06092	0·09368	0·10088
	13	1	1	0	0·01213	0·03515	0·04400	0·02926
$p = 10$								
	12	0	0	0	0·03597	0·11914	0·19845	0·24067
	14	0	0	2	0·00919	0·03400	0·06707	0·09881
	14	2	0	0	0·01339	0·04257	0·06569	0·07093
	14	1	1	0	0·00852	0·02477	0·03111	0·02074
$p = 11$								
	13	0	0	0	0·02523	0·08372	0·13974	0·16976
	15	0	0	2	0·00648	0·02398	0·04736	0·06982
	15	2	0	0	0·00938	0·02987	0·04619	0·04997
	15	1	1	0	0·00600	0·01748	0·02199	0·01468
$p = 12$								
	14	0	0	0	0·01775	0·05996	0·09854	0·19845
	16	0	0	2	0·00457	0·01693	0·03346	0·04935
	16	2	0	0	0·00659	0·02101	0·03254	0·03525
	16	1	1	0	0·00424	0·01235	0·01555	0·01039
$p = 13$								
	15	0	0	0	0,01251	0·04158	0·06955	0·08465
	17	0	0	2	0·00323	0·01196	0·02365	0·03489
	17	2	0	0	0·00464	0·01481	0·02295	0·02488
	17	1	1	0	0·00299	0·00873	0·01100	0·00735

Table D.4. [111] direction; all-neighbour X sums

m	n_1	n_2	n_3	$X(\frac{1}{4})$	$X(\frac{1}{2})$	$X(\frac{3}{4})$	$X(k_{max})$
$p = 6$							
8	0	0	0	0·16406	0·51289	0·78066	0·78587
10	2	0	0	0·05469	0·17096	0·26022	0·26196
10	0	1	1	0·02537	0·07819	0·11791	0·11867
$p = 8$							
10	0	0	0	0·07421	0·23893	0·37019	0·37278
12	2	0	0	0·02474	0·07964	0·12340	0·12426
12	0	1	1	0·01195	0·03830	0·05914	0·05955
$p = 9$							
11	0	0	0	0·05134	0·16613	0·25828	0·26011
13	2	0	0	0·01711	0·05538	0·08609	0·08670
13	0	1	1	0·00836	0·02697	0·04184	0·04214
$p = 10$							
12	0	0	0	0·03583	0·11622	0·18103	0·18231
14	2	0	0	0·01942	0·03874	0·06034	0·06077
14	0	1	1	0·00587	0·01902	0·02960	0·02981
$p = 11$							
13	0	0	0	0·02512	0·08161	0·12725	0·12815
15	2	0	0	0·00837	0·02720	0·04242	0·04272
15	0	1	1	0·00414	0·01343	0·02093	0·02108
$p = 12$							
14	0	0	0	0·01767	0·05744	0·08962	0·09026
16	2	0	0	0·00589	0·01915	0·02987	0·03009
16	0	1	1	0·00292	0·00949	0·01480	0·01491
$p = 13$							
15	0	0	0	0·01245	0·04050	0·06320	0·06365
17	2	0	0	0·00415	0·01350	0·02107	0·02122
17	0	1	1	0·00206	0·00671	0·01047	0·01054

Appendix E

Sample Calculation of Normal-mode Frequencies

See Section 2.10. For a cubic crystal with one atom per unit cell, the secular equation is

$$\begin{vmatrix} A - \omega^2 & B & C \\ B & D - \omega^2 & E \\ C & E & F - \omega^2 \end{vmatrix} = 0 \tag{E.1}$$

where $A = D_{xx}$, $B = D_{xy}$, etc. For the six directions in which this factorizes into a quadratic and a linear equation, this simplifies:

$$\text{For } [100]: B = C = E = 0, F = D \tag{E.2}$$

$$\text{For } [110]: C = E = 0, D = A \tag{E.3}$$

$$\text{For } [111]: B = C = E, D = F = A \tag{E.4}$$

$$\text{For } [210]: C = E = 0 \tag{E.5}$$

$$\text{For } [211]: B = C, F = D \tag{E.6}$$

$$\text{For } [221]: C = E, D = A. \tag{E.7}$$

As an example, let us consider the [100] and [111] directions where the two transverse modes are degenerate. In these cases the secular equation has roots

$$\omega_{100}^2(|\mathbf{k}|, j = 1) = A_{[100]} \tag{E.8}$$

$$\omega_{100}^2(|\mathbf{k}|, j = 2) = \omega_{100}^2(|\mathbf{k}|, j = 3) = D_{[100]} \tag{E.9}$$

$$\omega_{111}^2(|\mathbf{k}|, j = 1) = A_{[111]} + 2B_{[111]} \tag{E.10}$$

$$\omega_{111}^2(|\mathbf{k}|, j = 2) = \omega_{111}^2(|\mathbf{k}|, j = 3) = A_{[111]} - B_{[111]} \tag{E.11}$$

Using the definition of the dynamical matrix [equation (1.12)], the potential [equation (2.51)] and the lattice sums defined in Appendix D [equation (D.8)], we find

$$A_{\mathbf{k}} = \frac{1}{M} \sum_p \left\{ -\frac{p\sigma^p}{b^{p+2}} X_{p+2}^{000}(\mathbf{k}) + \frac{p(p + 2)\sigma^p}{b^{p+4}} X_{p+4}^{200} \right\} \tag{E.12}$$

292

$$B_k = \frac{1}{M} \sum_p \frac{p(p+2)\sigma^p}{b^{p+2}} X_{p+4}^{110} \tag{E.13}$$

$$D_k = \frac{1}{M} \sum_p \left\{ -\frac{p\sigma^p}{b^{p+2}} X_{p+2}^{000}(k) + \frac{p(p+2)\sigma^p}{b^{p+4}} X_{p+4}^{020}(k) \right\}. \tag{E.14}$$

(The elements C, E and F are easily deduced from these by varying the superscripts on the X sums.)

Thus the procedure to find $\omega^2(k)$ is: (i) select a potential and read its parameters (from the tables in Appendix A), (ii) select a point in k space along one of these directions and read the values of the relevant X sums (from the tables in Appendix D), (iii) evaluate the A_k, B_k, etc., involved [noting, of course, the significance of the $\sum_p$ defined below equation (2.51)].

Some results of this procedure are tabulated below. Table E.1 shows the normal-mode frequencies for a harmonic crystal at $T = 0$ K and (in parentheses) those corresponding to $T = 40$ K. This includes only the effects due to thermal expansion. Table E.2 shows the same quantities for a different potential; in this case the values in parentheses give the corresponding frequencies for a lattice of heavier atoms. The potential used (12-6 and 12-9-6) are **not** chosen because they are the best representations of the interatomic interactions—they are purely examples.

Table E.1. Argon, 12-6, all-neighbours (see Table A.2 for parameters)

k	$\omega_L(10^{13}\,s^{-1})$		$\omega_{T_1}(10^{13}\,s^{-1})$		$\omega_{T_2}(10^{13}\,s^{-1})$	
	$T = 0$ K	$(T = 40$ K$)$	$T = 0$ K	$(T = 40$ K$)$	$T = 0$ K	$(T = 40$ K$)$
[100]						
$(\pi/b)(\frac{1}{4}, 0, 0)$	0·400	(0·345)	0·301	(0·267)	ω_{T_1}	
$(\pi/b)(\frac{1}{2}, 0, 0)$	0·777	(0·676)	0·578	(0·494)	ω_{T_1}	
$(\pi/b)(\frac{3}{4}, 0, 0)$	1·052	(0·921)	0·731	(0·648)	ω_{T_1}	
$(\pi/b)(1, 0, 0)$	1·160	(1·018)	0·797	(0·706)	ω_{T_1}	
[110]						
$\frac{3}{4}(\pi/b)(\frac{1}{4}, \frac{1}{4}, 0)$	0·455	(0·394)	0·306	(0·271)	0·191	(0·171)
$\frac{3}{4}(\pi/b)(\frac{1}{2}, \frac{1}{2}, 0)$	0·819	(0·713)	0·594	(0·525)	0·378	(0·337)
$\frac{3}{4}(\pi/b)(\frac{3}{4}, \frac{3}{4}, 0)$	0·998	(0·873)	0·841	(0·742)	0·551	(0·490)
$\frac{3}{4}(\pi/b)(1, 1, 0)$	0·976	(0·857)	1·028	(0·904)	0·691	(0·613)
[111]						
$\frac{1}{2}(\pi/b)(\frac{1}{4}, \frac{1}{4}, \frac{1}{4})$	0·480	(0·416)	0·229	(0·204)	ω_{T_1}	
$\frac{1}{2}(\pi/b)(\frac{1}{2}, \frac{1}{2}, \frac{1}{2})$	0·887	(0·772)	0·413	(0·368)	ω_{T_1}	
$\frac{1}{2}(\pi/b)(\frac{3}{4}, \frac{3}{4}, \frac{3}{4})$	1·124	(0·981)	0·517	(0·460)	ω_{T_1}	
$\frac{1}{2}(\pi/b)(1, 1, 1)$	1·128	(0·984)	0·518	(0·462)	ω_{T_1}	

Table E.2. 12-9-6, all-neighbours (see Table A.2 for parameters)

	$\omega_L(10^{13}\ \text{s}^{-1})$		$\omega_{T_1}(10^{13}\ \text{s}^{-1})$		$\omega_{T_2}(10^{13}\ \text{s}^{-1})$	
	Argon	(Xenon)	Argon	(Xenon)	Argon	(Xenon)
[100]						
$(\pi/b)(\frac{1}{4}, 0, 0)$	0·441	(2·176)	0·330	(1·434)	ω_{T_1}	
$(\pi/b)(\frac{1}{2}, 0, 0)$	0·845	(4·037)	0·611	(2·657)	ω_{T_1}	
$(\pi/b)(\frac{3}{4}, 0, 0)$	1·139	(5·305)	0·801	(3·487)	ω_{T_1}	
$(\pi/b)(1, 0, 0)$	1·255	(5·787)	0·873	(3·802)	ω_{T_1}	
[110]						
$\frac{3}{4}(\pi/b)(\frac{1}{4}, \frac{1}{4}, 0)$	0·498	(2·421)	0·335	(1·461)	0·215	(0·864)
$\frac{3}{4}(\pi/b)(\frac{1}{2}, \frac{1}{2}, 0)$	0·889	(4·240)	0·648	(2·857)	0·423	(1·736)
$\frac{3}{4}(\pi/b)(\frac{3}{4}, \frac{3}{4}, 0)$	1·081	(5·052)	0·915	(4·098)	0·611	(2·570)
$\frac{3}{4}(\pi/b)(1, 1, 0)$	1·059	(4·830)	1·114	(5·068)	0·761	(3·264)
[111]						
$\frac{1}{2}(\pi/b)(\frac{1}{4}, \frac{1}{4}, \frac{1}{4})$	0·524	(2·536)	0·255	(1·066)	ω_{T_1}	
$\frac{1}{2}(\pi/b)(\frac{1}{2}, \frac{1}{2}, \frac{1}{2})$	0·960	(4·580)	0·459	(1·923)	ω_{T_1}	
$\frac{1}{2}(\pi/b)(\frac{3}{4}, \frac{3}{4}, \frac{3}{4})$	1·212	(5·728)	0·573	(2·403)	ω_{T_1}	
$\frac{1}{2}(\pi/b)(1, 1, 1)$	1·217	(5·748)	0·575	(2·411)	ω_{T_1}	

Appendix F

Kellerman's Rigid Ion Model

See Section 2.10. The dynamical matrix may be separated into two parts—the long-range Coulomb part and the short-range repulsive part:

$$D_{\alpha\beta} = D_{\alpha\beta}^C + D_{\alpha\beta}^R \tag{F.1}$$

where, for the general case,

$$D_{\alpha\beta}(\kappa\kappa') = (m_\kappa m_{\kappa'})^{-1/2} \sum_l \phi_{\alpha\beta}^l(\kappa\kappa') \, e^{i\mathbf{k}\cdot\mathbf{r}_{\kappa\kappa'}^l} \tag{F.2}$$

$$\mathbf{r}_{\kappa\kappa'}^l \equiv \mathbf{r}^l + \mathbf{r}_{\kappa\kappa'}. \tag{F.3}$$

In NaCl the structure is such that

$$e^{i\mathbf{k}\cdot\mathbf{r}_{\kappa\kappa'}^l} \to \cos(\mathbf{k}\cdot\mathbf{r}_{\kappa\kappa'}^l). \tag{F.4}$$

From lattice symmetry properties we know that

$$D_{\alpha\beta}(\kappa\kappa') = D_{\alpha\beta}(\kappa'\kappa) = D_{\beta\alpha}(\kappa\kappa'). \tag{F.5}$$

In order to understand the expressions we shall deduce, it is essential to be clear about the description of the lattice. The sodium ions and the chlorine ions form a f.c.c. structure; the basis vectors of one of these are

$$\mathbf{a}_1 = \frac{a}{2}(0, 1, 1) \qquad \mathbf{a}_2 = \frac{a}{2}(1, 0, 1) \qquad \mathbf{a}_3 = \frac{a}{2}(1, 1, 0) \tag{F.6}$$

and the vector joining ions $\kappa = 1$ and $\kappa = 2$ is

$$\mathbf{r}_{12} = \frac{a}{2}(1, 1, 1) \tag{F.7}$$

the corresponding volume of a unit cell is $v = a^3/4$. Thus the lattice vectors are

$$\mathbf{r}^l = \frac{a}{2}(l_1, l_2, l_3) \tag{F.8}$$

and the position vectors of the other atom in the unit cell are

$$\mathbf{r}_{12}^l = \frac{a}{2}(l_1 + 1, l_2 + 1, l_3 + 1) \equiv \frac{a}{2}(m_1, m_2, m_3) \tag{F.9}$$

with the f.c.c. values

$$l_1 + l_2 + l_3 = \text{even integer}; \, l^2 = l_1^2 + l_2^2 + l_3^2 \tag{F.10}$$

$$m_1 + m_2 + m_3 = \text{odd integer}; \, m^2 = m_1^2 + m_2^2 + m_3^2. \tag{F.11}$$

The reciprocal lattice vectors are

$$\mathbf{b}_h = \frac{2\pi}{a}\mathbf{h}; \, \mathbf{h} = (h_x, h_y, h_z) \tag{F.12}$$

h_x, h_y and h_z being all even or all odd integers.

A wave vector $\mathbf{k}$ in the Brillouin zone will be written

$$\mathbf{k} = \frac{2\pi}{a}\mathbf{q}; \qquad \mathbf{q} = (q_x, q_y, q_z). \tag{F.13}$$

Taking these definitions of the structure, and using the results of Appendix B, the Coulomb part of the dynamical matrix is seen to be: For $\kappa = \kappa'$:

$$D_{\alpha\beta}^C(\kappa\kappa) = \frac{e^2}{4\pi\varepsilon_0 v}\left[\sum_h G_{\alpha\beta}^{\kappa\kappa}(h) + \sum_l H_{\alpha\beta}(l) + \frac{8\varepsilon^3}{3\sqrt{\pi}}\delta_{\alpha\beta}\right]. \tag{F.14}$$

For $\kappa \neq \kappa'$

$$D_{\alpha\beta}^C(\kappa\kappa') = -\frac{e^2}{4\pi\varepsilon_0 v}\left[\sum_h^l G_{\alpha\beta}^{\kappa\kappa'}(h) + \sum_m H_{\alpha\beta}(m)\right] \tag{F.15}$$

where G and H are defined by

$$G_{\alpha\beta}^{\kappa\kappa}(h) = G_{\alpha\beta}^{11}(h) = -\frac{4\pi(h_\alpha + q_\alpha)(h_\beta + q_\beta)}{|\mathbf{h} + \mathbf{q}|^2}e^{-(\pi^2/4\varepsilon^2)(\mathbf{h}+\mathbf{q})^2} \tag{F.16}$$

$$G_{\alpha\beta}^{\kappa\kappa'}(h) = G_{\alpha\beta}^{12}(h) = G_{\alpha\beta}^{11}\cos\pi(h_x + h_y + h_z) \tag{F.17}$$

$$H_{\alpha\beta}(l) = 2\left[\frac{l_\alpha l_\beta}{l^2}g(l) - f(l)\delta_{\alpha\beta}\right]\cos\pi\mathbf{q}.\mathbf{l} \tag{F.18}$$

with

$$f(l) = \frac{2}{\sqrt{\pi}}\frac{\varepsilon}{l^2}e^{-\varepsilon^2 l^2} + \frac{1}{l^3}[1 - G(\varepsilon l)] \tag{F.19}$$

$$g(l) = \frac{4}{\sqrt{\pi}}\varepsilon^3 e^{-\varepsilon^2 l^2} + 3f(l) \tag{F.20}$$

$G(\varepsilon l)$ being defined by equation (B.12). The term $H_{\alpha\beta}(m)$ follows from (F.18) by replacing l by m.

The repulsive part of the dynamical matrix may be found as in the text, leading to equation (2.64). We find for all κ, κ'

$$D^R_{\alpha\beta}(\kappa\kappa') = D^R_{\alpha\beta}(\kappa\kappa')\delta_{\alpha\beta}. \tag{F.21}$$

For $\kappa = \kappa'$

$$D^R_{\alpha\beta}(\kappa\kappa) = -\frac{e^2}{4\pi\varepsilon_0 v}(A + 2B). \tag{F.22}$$

For $\kappa \neq \kappa'$

$$D^R_{xx}(\kappa\kappa') = A \cos \pi q_x + B(\cos \pi q_y + \cos \pi q_z) \tag{F.23}$$

with corresponding expressions for $D^R_{yy}(\kappa\kappa')$ and $D^R_{zz}(\kappa\kappa')$ obtained from equation (F.23) by cyclically moving the suffices.

The six eigenvalues for a given $\mathbf{k}$, $\omega^2(\mathbf{k}j)$, are found by adding equations (F.12), (F.13), (F.19) and (F.20) to obtain the full dynamical matrix (F.1) and then diagonalizing. This procedure may be carried out for any value of $\mathbf{k}$ (except $\mathbf{k} = 0$, where some terms in $D^C_{\alpha\beta} = \infty$) and hence we may find the whole phonon spectrum (six branches) corresponding to this approximation. If this model is applied to diamond structures, equations (F.17) and (F.18) must have the sine part replaced, i.e. in equation (F.17)

$$\cos \pi(h_x + h_y + h_z) \rightarrow e^{i\pi'(h_x + h_y + h_z)/2} \tag{F.24}$$

and in equation (F.18)

$$\cos \pi(\mathbf{q} \cdot \mathbf{l}) \rightarrow e^{i\pi \mathbf{q} \cdot \mathbf{l}} \tag{F.25}$$

the factor of $\frac{1}{2}$ appearing in substitution (F.24), since, in diamond

$$\mathbf{r}_{12} = \frac{a}{4}(1, 1, 1).$$

Appendix G

Shell Model

See Sections 2.7 and 2.10. Applying this model to germanium [structure as in Figure 2.8(a)] we can separate the Coulomb part and the 'bonding' part of the dynamical matrix:

$$D_{\alpha\beta}(\kappa\kappa') = D_{\alpha\beta}^{C}(\kappa\kappa') + D_{\alpha\beta}^{B}(\kappa\kappa') \tag{G.1}$$

where $D_{\alpha\beta}^{B}(\kappa\kappa')$ includes the forces shown in Figure 2.14 between only nearest neighbour atoms; $D_{\alpha\beta}^{C}(\kappa\kappa')$ extends over the whole lattice. The Coulombic part may be evaluated as in the Kellerman method (see Appendix F). To evaluate the bonding part, the components of the unit cell are labelled $\kappa = 1$ (core 1), $\kappa = 2$ (core 2), $\kappa = 3$ (shell 1) and $\kappa = 4$ (shell 2). For our cubic symmetry we expect that this interaction is fully specified by six independent quantities $\phi_{\alpha\beta}^{B}(12)$, $\phi_{\alpha\beta}^{B}(14)$ and $\phi_{\alpha\beta}^{B}(34)$ for $\alpha = \beta$ and $\alpha \neq \beta$. In addition the shell and core of each atom are coupled by a restoring force constant $-\alpha [= B_{\alpha\alpha}(13) = B_{\alpha\alpha}(24)]$.

The wave-vector dependence of $D_{\alpha\beta}^{B}(\kappa\kappa')$ may be deduced from the general form of the dynamical matrix [e.g. equation (1.12)]; for example, consider $D_{\alpha\alpha}^{B}(12)$. There are four atoms to be included in the interaction with atom 1 at $(0, 0, 0)$, namely those at $(a/4)(1, 1, 1)$, $(a/4)(-1, 1, 1)$, $(a/4)(1, -1, 1)$ and $(a/4)(1, 1, -1)$. Writing these into $e^{i\mathbf{k}\cdot\mathbf{r}_{\kappa\kappa'}}$ for a general value of $\mathbf{k} \equiv (k_x, k_y, k_z)$ we find that

$$D_{\alpha\alpha}^{B}(12) = \frac{4}{m_\kappa}\phi_{\alpha\alpha}^{B}(12)(\cos k_x a \cos k_y a \cos k_z a + i \sin k_x a \sin k_y a \sin k_z a) \tag{G.2}$$

all the terms involving mixtures of cos and sin cancelling. If we restrict our interest to values of (k_x, k_y, k_z) which lie in the symmetry directions [100] and [111], the 12×12 dynamical matrix factorizes into three 4×4 matrices. For these directions we write

$$\omega^2 \mathbf{U}(\kappa) = \sum_{\kappa'=1}^{4} D(\kappa\kappa')\mathbf{U}(\kappa') \tag{G.3}$$

where

$$D(\kappa\kappa') = \sum_{\alpha\beta} D_{\alpha\beta}(\kappa\kappa'). \tag{G.4}$$

For example, a longitudinal mode in the [111] direction is described by the displacement vector $U(\kappa') = (1/\sqrt{3})(u, u, u)$ and hence $D(\kappa\kappa') = D_{xx}(\kappa\kappa') + D_{yy}(\kappa\kappa') + D_{zz}(\kappa\kappa')$; a longitudinal wave in the [100] direction is $U(\kappa') = (u, 0, 0)$ and hence $D(\kappa\kappa') = D_{xx}(\kappa\kappa')$. For the transverse mode in [100] direction we may take $U(\kappa') = (1/\sqrt{2})(0, u, u)$ (this is not unique) and we find $D(\kappa\kappa') = D_{yy}(\kappa\kappa') + D_{yz}(\kappa\kappa')$.

We solve the dynamical problem to find $\omega^2(\mathbf{k})$ by writing equation (G.3) explicitly as four equations in $U(1)$, $U(2)$, $U(3)$ and $U(4)$. The coefficients in this are the Coulomb and bonding terms. By putting the shell masses (m_3 and m_4) to zero and requiring that $U(1)$ and $U(2)$ are non-trivial, the expression for $\omega^2(\mathbf{k})$ is of the form

$$\omega^2(\mathbf{k}) = F_0(\mathbf{k}) \pm |F(\mathbf{k})| \qquad (G.5)$$

where $F_0(\mathbf{k})$ and $F(\mathbf{k})$ may be expressed apart from the $\mathbf{k}$ dependence in terms of eight parameters $\phi^B_{xx}(12)$, $\phi^B_{xx}(14)$, $\phi^B_{xx}(34)$, $\phi^B_{xy}(12)$, $\phi^B_{xy}(14)$, $\phi^B_{xy}(34)$, α and Z (Z is a parameter determining the amount of charge in the shell). These eight reduce to seven since the ratios ϕ^B_{xx}/ϕ^B_{xy} have a common factor. The seven independent parameters may be fitted by experimental data, but usually further assumptions are made to reduce the number. The results for germanium shown in Figure 2.8(c) are based on a shell model which uses an experimental value of the relative permittivity and only two other parameters.

Appendix H

Polynomials with Symmetries of Interest

See Section 2.12. For group theoretical notation (and a reprint of the paper from which these were taken), see R. S. Knox and A. Gold, *Symmetry in the Solid State*, Benjamin, 1964. The following data have been reproduced, with permission, from Bell, D. G., *Rev. Mod. Phys.*, **26**, 315–317 (1954).

Cubic symmetries

1 An O_h group

A_s s 1

$\quad g$ $(525/16)^{\frac{1}{2}}[x^4 + y^4 + z^4 - 3/5]$

$\quad i$ $(693693/32)^{\frac{1}{2}}[x^2 y^2 z^2 + (g)/22 - 1/105]$

A_i i $(15015/32)^{\frac{1}{2}}[x^4(y^2 - z^2) + y^4(z^2 - x^2) + z^4(x^2 - y^2)]$

A_d (doubly degenerate)

$$A_d(1)\begin{cases} d & (5/4)^{\frac{1}{2}}[2x^2 - y^2 - z^2] \\ g & (735/16)^{\frac{1}{2}}[2x^4 - y^4 - z^4 - 6(d)/7] \\ i & (11011/32)^{\frac{1}{2}}[2x^6 - y^6 - z^6 - 15(g)/11 - 5(d)/7] \end{cases}$$

$$A_d(2)\begin{cases} d & (15/4)^{\frac{1}{2}}[y^2 - z^2] \\ g & (2205/16)^{\frac{1}{2}}[y^4 - z^4 - 6(d)/7] \\ i & (33033/32)^{\frac{1}{2}}[y^6 - z^6 - 15(g)/11 - 5(d)/7] \end{cases}$$

$A_{d'}$ (triply degenerate)

$$A_{d'}(x)\begin{cases} d & (15)^{\frac{1}{2}}yz \\ g & (2205/4)^{\frac{1}{2}}[x^2 yz - (d)/7] \\ i_1 & (1486485/128)^{\frac{1}{2}}[x^4 yz - 6(g)/11 - (d)/21] \\ i_2 & (27027/128)^{\frac{1}{2}}[y^4 + z^4 - 10y^2 z^2/3]yz \end{cases}$$

A_g (triply degenerate)

$$A_g(x)\begin{cases} g & (315/4)^{\frac{1}{2}}[y^2 - z^2]yz \\ i & (99099/16)^{\frac{1}{2}}[x^2 yz(y^2 - z^2) - (g)/11] \end{cases}$$

A_l No representation of order less than nine

A_f f $(105)^{\frac{1}{2}}xyz$

A_h (doubly degenerate)

$\quad A_h(1)$ h $(1155/4)^{\frac{1}{2}}[2x^2 - y^2 - z^2]xyz$

$\quad A_h(2)$ h $(3465/4)^{\frac{1}{2}}[y^2 - z^2]xyz$

$A_{f'}$ (triply degenerate)

$$A_{f'}(x)\begin{cases} f & (105/4)^{\frac{1}{2}}[y^2 - z^2]x \\ h & (10395/16)^{\frac{1}{2}}[(y^2 - z^2)x^3 - (f)/3] \end{cases}$$

A_p (triply degenerate)

$$A_p(x)\begin{cases} p & 3^{\frac{1}{2}}x \\ f & (175/4)^{\frac{1}{2}}[x^3 - 3(p)/5] \\ h_1 & (43659/64)^{\frac{1}{2}}[x^5 - 10(f)/9 - 3(p)/7] \\ h_2 & (3465/64)^{\frac{1}{2}}[y^4 + z^4 - 6y^2z^2]x \end{cases}$$

2   A T_d group

B_s A_s and A_f
B_i A_i and A_l
B_d (doubly degenerate) A_d and A_h
B_p (triply degenerate) A_p and $A_{d'}$
B_f (triply degenerate) $A_{f'}$ and A_g

3   A D_{4h} group

C_s A_s and $A_d(1)$
C_g $A_g(x)$
$C_{d'}$ $A_d(2)$ and A_i
C_d $A_{d'}(x)$
$C_{d''}$ (doubly degenerate)

$$C_{d''}(1)\begin{cases} A_{d'}(y) \\ A_g(y) \end{cases}$$

$$C_{d''}(2)\begin{cases} A_{d'}(z) \\ -A_g(z) \end{cases}$$

C_h $A_h(2)$ and A_l
C_p $A_p(x)$
$C_{f'}$ A_f and $A_h(1)$
C_f $A_{f'}(x)$
$C_{p'}$ (doubly degenerate)

$$C_{p'}(1)\begin{cases} A_p(y) \\ A_{f'}(y) \end{cases}$$

$$C_{p'}(2)\begin{cases} A_p(z) \\ -A_{f'}(z) \end{cases}$$

4   A D_{3d} group

D_s A_s and $(1/3)^{\frac{1}{2}}[A_{d'}(x) + A_{d'}(y) + A_{d'}(z)]$
D_g A_i and $(1/3)^{\frac{1}{2}}[A_g(x) + A_g(y) + A_g(z)]$
D_d (doubly degenerate)

$$D_d(1)\begin{cases} A_d(1) \\ (1/6)^{\frac{1}{2}}[2A_{d'}(x) - A_{d'}(y) - A_{d'}(z)] \\ (1/2)^{\frac{1}{2}}[A_g(z) - A_g(y)] \end{cases}$$

$$D_d(2) \begin{cases} A_d(2) \\ (1/2)^{\frac{1}{2}}[A_{d'}(y) - A_{d'}(z)] \\ (1/6)^{\frac{1}{2}}[2A_g(x) - A_g(y) - A_g(z)] \end{cases}$$

$D_f \quad A_l$ and $(1/3)^{\frac{1}{2}}[A_{f'}(x) + A_{f'}(y) + A_{f'}(z)]$

$D_p \quad A_f$ and $(1/3)^{\frac{1}{2}}[A_p(x) + A_p(y) + A_p(z)]$

$D_{p'} \quad$ (doubly degenerate)

$$D_{p'}(1) \begin{cases} A_h(1) \\ (1/6)^{\frac{1}{2}}[2A_p(x) - A_p(y) - A_p(z)] \\ (1/2)^{\frac{1}{2}}[A_{f'}(z) - A_{f'}(y)] \end{cases}$$

$$D_{p'}(2) \begin{cases} A_h(2) \\ (1/2)^{\frac{1}{2}}[A_p(y) - A_p(z)] \\ (1/6)^{\frac{1}{2}}[2A_{f'}(x) - A_{f'}(y) - A_{f'}(z)] \end{cases}$$

5   A C_{4v} group

$E_s \quad C_s$ and C_p

$E_g \quad C_g$ and C_h

$E_{d'} \quad C_{d'}$ and C_f

$E_d \quad C_d$ and $C_{f'}$

$E_p \quad$ (doubly degenerate)

$$E_p(1) \begin{cases} C_{p'}(1) \\ C_{d''}(2) \end{cases}$$

$$E_p(2) \begin{cases} C_{p'}(2) \\ C_{d''}(1) \end{cases}$$

6   A D_{2d} group

$F_s \quad C_s$ and C_f

$F_f \quad C_{f'}$ and C_g

$F_d \quad C_d$ and C_h

$F_p \quad C_p$ and $C_{d'}$

$F_{p'} \quad$ (doubly degenerate)

$$F_{p'}(1) \begin{cases} C_{p'}(1) \\ C_{d''}(2) \end{cases}$$

$$F_{p'}(2) \begin{cases} C_{p'}(2) \\ -C_{d''}(1) \end{cases}$$

7   A D_{2h} group

$G_s \quad C_s$ and C_d

$G_d \quad C_{d'}$ and C_g

$G_{d'} \quad (1/2)^{\frac{1}{2}}[C_{d''}(1) - C_{d''}(2)]$

$G_{d''} \quad (1/2)^{\frac{1}{2}}[C_{d''}(1) + C_{d''}(2)]$

G_f C_f and C_h

G_p C_p and $C_{f'}$

$G_{p'}$ $(1/2)^{\frac{1}{2}}[C_{p'}(1) + C_{p'}(2)]$

$G_{p''}$ $(1/2)^{\frac{1}{2}}[C_{p'}(1) - C_{p'}(2)]$

8   A D_{2d} group

H_s C_s and $C_{f'}$

H_f C_f and C_g

H_d $C_{d'}$ and C_h

H_p C_p and C_d

$H_{p'}$ (doubly degenerate)

$$H_{p'}(1)\begin{cases}C_{p'}(1)\\C_{d''}(1)\end{cases}$$

$$H_{p'}(2)\begin{cases}C_{p'}(2)\\C_{d''}(2)\end{cases}$$

9   A C_{3v} group

I_s D_s and D_p

I_f D_f and D_g

I_p (doubly degenerate)

$$I_p(1)\begin{cases}D_{p'}(1)\\D_d(1)\end{cases}$$

$$I_p(2)\begin{cases}D_{p'}(2)\\D_d(2)\end{cases}$$

10   A C_3 group

K_s B_s and $(1/3)^{\frac{1}{2}}[B_p(x) - B_p(y) - B_p(z)]$

K_f B_{i} and $(1/3)^{\frac{1}{2}}[B_f(x) - B_f(y) - B_f(z)]$

K_p (doubly degenerate)

$$K_p(1)\begin{cases}(1/6)^{\frac{1}{2}}[2B_p(x) + B_p(y) + B_p(z)]\\B_d(1)\\(1/2)^{\frac{1}{2}}[B_f(y) - B_f(z)]\end{cases}$$

$$K_p(2)\begin{cases}(1/2)^{\frac{1}{2}}[B_p(z) - B_p(y)]\\B_d(2)\\(1/6)^{\frac{1}{2}}[2B_f(x) + B_f(y) + B_f(z)]\end{cases}$$

11   A C_{2v} group

L_s G_s and $G_{p'}$

$L_{p'}$ G_p and $G_{d''}$

L_d $G_{d'}$ and G_f

L_p $G_{p''}$ and G_d

12   A C_{2v} group

M_s G_s and $G_{p''}$
$M_{p'}$ G_p and $G_{d'}$
M_d $G_{d''}$ and G_f
M_p $G_{p'}$ and G_d

13   A C_{2v} group

N_s F_s and F_p
$N_{p'}$ $F_{p'}(1)$
N_d F_d and F_f
N_p $F_{p'}(2)$

14   A C_{2v} group

O_s G_s and G_p
$O_{p'}$ $G_{p'}$ and $G_{d''}$
O_d G_d and G_f
O_p $G_{p''}$ and $G_{d'}$

15   An S_4 group

P_s F_s and F_f
P_p F_p and F_d
$P_{p'}$ $(1/2)^{\frac{1}{2}}[F_{p'}(1) + iF_{p'}(2)]$
$P_{p''}$ $(1/2)^{\frac{1}{2}}[F_{p'}(2) + iF_{p'}(1)]$

16   A C_{1h} group

Q_s M_s and M_p
Q_p $M_{p'}$ and M_d

17   A C_{1h} group

R_s L_s and $L_{p'}$
R_p L_p and L_d

18   A C_{1h} group

S_s M_s and $M_{p'}$
S_p M_p and M_d

19   A C_2 group

T_s M_s and M_d
T_p M_p and $M_{p'}$

20   A C_2 group

U_s N_s and N_d
U_p N_p and $N_{p'}$

21   A C_1 group

V_s U_s and U_p

Close-packed hexagonal symmetries

(i)   A D_{3h} group

a_s s 1
  d $(45/4)^{\frac{1}{2}}[x^2 - 1/3]$
  f $(35/8)^{\frac{1}{2}}[3y^2 - z^2]z$
  g $(11025/64)^{\frac{1}{2}}[x^4 - 6(d)/7 - 1/5]$
  h $(31185/128)^{\frac{1}{2}}[(3y^2 - z^2)zx^2 - (f)/9]$
  i_1 $(693693/256)^{\frac{1}{2}}[x^6 - 15(g)/11 - 5(d)/7 - 1/7]$
  i_2 $(3003/1024)^{\frac{1}{2}}[y^6 - 15y^4z^2 + 15y^2z^4 - z^6]$

a_f f $(35/8)^{\frac{1}{2}}[y^2 - 3z^2]y$
  h $(31185/128)^{\frac{1}{2}}[(y^2 - 3z^2)x^2y - (f)/9]$
  i $(27027/128)^{\frac{1}{2}}[y^4 + z^4 - 10y^2z^2/3]yz$

a_g g $(315/8)^{\frac{1}{2}}[y^2 - 3z^2]xy$
  i $(165165/128)^{\frac{1}{2}}[x^3y(y^2 - 3z^2) - 3(g)/11]$

a_p p $(3)^{\frac{1}{2}}x$
  f $(175/4)^{\frac{1}{2}}[x^3 - 3(p)/5]$
  g $(315/8)^{\frac{1}{2}}[3y^2 - z^2]zx$
  h $(43659/64)^{\frac{1}{2}}[x^5 - 10(f)/9 - 3(p)/7]$
  i $(165165/128)^{\frac{1}{2}}[zx^3(3y^2 - z^2) - 3(g)/11]$

$a_{p'}$ (doubly degenerate)

$$
a_{p'}(1)
\begin{cases}
p & (3)^{\frac{1}{2}}y \\
d & (15)^{\frac{1}{2}}yz \\
f & (525/8)^{\frac{1}{2}}[x^2y - (p)/5] \\
g_1 & (2205/4)^{\frac{1}{2}}[x^2yz - (d)/7] \\
g_2 & (315/4)^{\frac{1}{2}}[z^2 - y^2]yz \\
h_1 & (72765/64)^{\frac{1}{2}}[x^4y - 2(f)/3 - 3(p)/35] \\
h_2 & (693/128)^{\frac{1}{2}}[y^4 - 10y^2z^2 + 5z^4]y \\
i_1 & (1486485/128)^{\frac{1}{2}}[x^4y^2 - 6(g_1)/11 - (d)/21] \\
i_2 & (99099/16)^{\frac{1}{2}}[x^2yz(z^2 - y^2) - (g_2)/11]
\end{cases}
$$

$$a_{p'}(2) \begin{cases} p & (3)^{\frac{1}{2}}z \\ d & (15/4)^{\frac{1}{2}}[y^2 - z^2] \\ f & (525/8)^{\frac{1}{2}}[zx^2 - (p)/5] \\ g_1 & (2205/16)^{\frac{1}{2}}[x^2(y^2 - z^2) - (d)/7] \\ g_2 & (315/64)^{\frac{1}{2}}[y^4 - 6y^2z^2 + z^4] \\ h_1 & (72765/64)^{\frac{1}{2}}[zx^4 - 2(f)/3 - 3(p)/35] \\ h_2 & (693/128)^{\frac{1}{2}}[-5y^4 + 10y^2z^2 - z^4]z \\ i_1 & (1486485/512)^{\frac{1}{2}}[x^4(y^2 - z^2) - 6(g_1)/11 - (d)/21] \\ i_2 & (99099/256)^{\frac{1}{2}}[x^2(y^4 - 6y^2z^2 + z^4) - (g_2)/11] \end{cases}$$

a_d (doubly degenerate)

$$a_d(1) \begin{cases} d & (15)^{\frac{1}{2}}xy \\ f & (105)^{\frac{1}{2}}xyz \\ g & (2205/8)^{\frac{1}{2}}[x^3y - 3(d)/7] \\ h_1 & (10395/4)^{\frac{1}{2}}[x^3yz - (f)/3] \\ h_2 & (3465/4)^{\frac{1}{2}}[y^2 - z^2]xyz \\ i_1 & (297297/64)^{\frac{1}{2}}[x^5y - 10(g)/11 - 5(d)/21] \\ i_2 & (9009/128)^{\frac{1}{2}}[y^4 - 10y^2z^2 + 5z^4]xy \end{cases}$$

$$a_d(2) \begin{cases} d & (15)^{\frac{1}{2}}zx \\ f & (105/4)^{\frac{1}{2}}[y^2 - z^2]x \\ g & (2205/8)^{\frac{1}{2}}[zx^3 - 3(d)/7] \\ h_1 & (10395/16)^{\frac{1}{2}}[(y^2 - z^2)x^3 - (f)/3] \\ h_2 & (3465/64)^{\frac{1}{2}}[-y^4 + 6y^2z^2 - z^4]x \\ i_1 & (297297/64)^{\frac{1}{2}}[zx^5 - 10(g)/11 - 5(d)/21] \\ i_2 & (9009/128)^{\frac{1}{2}}[5y^4 - 10y^2z^2 + z^4]zx \end{cases}$$

(ii) A C_{3h} group

b_s a_s and a_f
b_p $1/\sqrt{2}[a_{p'}(1) - ia_{p'}(2)]$
$b_{p'}$ $1/\sqrt{2}[a_{p'}(2) - ia_{p'}(1)]$
$b_{p''}$ a_p and a_g
b_d $1/\sqrt{2}[a_d(1) - ia_d(2)]$
$b_{d'}$ $1/\sqrt{2}[a_d(2) - ia_d(1)]$

(iii) A C_{3v} group

c_s a_s and a_p
c_f a_f and a_g
c_p (doubly degenerate)

$$c_p(1) \begin{cases} a_{p'}(1) \\ a_d(1) \end{cases}$$

$$c_p(2) \begin{cases} a_{p'}(2) \\ a_d(2) \end{cases}$$

(iv) A C_{2v} group

d_s a_s and $a_{p'}(2)$
d_d a_g and $a_d(1)$
d_p a_p and $a_d(2)$
$d_{p'}$ a_f and $a_{p'}(1)$

(v) A C_3 group

e_s b_s and $b_{p''}$
e_p b_p and b_d
$e_{p'}$ $b_{p'}$ and $b_{d'}$

(vi)   A C_{1h} group

m_s d_s and $d_{p'}$
m_p d_p and d_d

(vii)   A C_{1h} group

g_s d_s and d_p
g_p $d_{p'}$ and d_d

(viii)   A C_1 group

h_s g_s and g_p

Appendix J

Third- and Fourth-order Force Constants

See Section 5.4. For atoms which interact with a central two-body force we may write

$$\Phi = \frac{1}{2}\sum_{ll'}\left\{\sum_{\alpha}\phi_{\alpha}u_{\alpha}^{ll'} + \frac{1}{2}\sum_{\alpha\beta}\phi_{\alpha\beta}u_{\alpha}^{ll'}u_{\beta}^{ll'}\right.$$
$$\left. + \frac{1}{6}\sum_{\alpha\beta\gamma}\phi_{\alpha\beta\gamma}u_{\alpha}^{ll'}u_{\beta}^{ll'}u_{\gamma}^{ll'} + \frac{1}{24}\sum_{\alpha\beta\gamma\delta}\phi_{\alpha\beta\gamma\delta}u_{\alpha}^{ll'}u_{\beta}^{ll'}u_{\gamma}^{ll'}u_{\delta}^{ll'}\right\} \tag{J.1}$$

with

$$\phi_{\alpha} \equiv \frac{\partial}{\partial\alpha}\phi(r) = \frac{\partial r}{\partial\alpha}\frac{\partial}{\partial r} = \frac{\alpha}{r}\frac{\partial}{\partial r} \tag{J.2}$$

where α, β, γ and δ are cartesian components of $\mathbf{r}$. Therefore

$$\phi_{\alpha\beta\gamma} = \frac{\partial^2}{\partial\alpha\,\partial\beta}[\gamma\phi'(r)]$$
$$= \alpha\delta_{\beta\gamma}\phi''(r) + \beta\delta_{\alpha\gamma}\phi''(r) + \gamma\delta_{\alpha\beta}\phi''(r) + \alpha\beta\gamma\phi'''(r) \tag{J.3}$$

where $\phi'(r) \equiv (1/r)(\partial/\partial r)\phi$ (see Appendix A).

Now the α component of $\mathbf{r}$ is bl_{α}; hence we see that

$$\phi_{\alpha\beta\gamma} = b^3 l_{\alpha}l_{\beta}l_{\gamma}\phi'''(r) + b(l_{\alpha}\delta_{\beta\gamma} + l_{\beta}\delta_{\alpha\gamma} + l_{\gamma}\delta_{\alpha\beta})\phi''(r) \tag{J.4}$$

and

$$\phi_{\alpha\beta\gamma\delta} = b^4 l_{\alpha}l_{\beta}l_{\gamma}l_{\delta}\phi''''(r) + b^2\mathscr{P}(l_{\alpha}l_{\beta}\delta_{\gamma\delta})\phi'''(r) + (\delta_{\alpha\beta}\delta_{\gamma\delta} + \delta_{\beta\gamma}\delta_{\alpha\delta} + \delta_{\alpha\gamma}\delta_{\beta\delta})\phi''(r) \tag{J.5}$$

with

$$\mathscr{P}(l_{\alpha}l_{\beta}\delta_{\gamma\delta}) = l_{\alpha}l_{\beta}\delta_{\gamma\delta} + l_{\alpha}l_{\gamma}\delta_{\beta\delta} + l_{\alpha}l_{\delta}\delta_{\beta\gamma} + l_{\beta}l_{\gamma}\delta_{\alpha\delta} + l_{\beta}l_{\delta}\delta_{\alpha\gamma} + l_{\gamma}l_{\delta}\delta_{\alpha\beta}. \tag{J.6}$$

Author Index

This is an alphabetical index to those names appearing in the reference lists. Names of laws and effects appear in the subject index.

Numbers in italics give the reference and are followed by the page numbers on which it may be found; where there are several references to a particular author on one page—the page numbers are given after all those reference numbers.

Subject Index

The most significant page numbers for a particular topic are shown in italics.

313